THE

HISTORY AND DIRECTORY

OF THE

BOROUGH OF DERBY,

INTENDED AS A

GUIDE TO STRANGERS VISITING THE TOWN.

BY STEPHEN GLOVER,

AUTHOR AND PUBLISHER OF THE HISTORY OF DERBYSHIRE; THE PEAK GUIDE;
THE DIRECTORY OF DERBYSHIRE; THE HISTORY OF BELVOIR CASTLE; &c.

DERBY:
PRINTED AND PUBLISHED FOR S. GLOVER AND SON,
BY HENRY MOZLEY AND SONS.
1843.

Facsimile edition first published in Great Britain by
The Breedon Books Publishing Company Limited
44 Friar Gate, Derby DE1 1DA
1992

ISBN 1 873626 28 2

Printed and bound by The Bath Press Limited, Bath and London.
Jacket printed by BDC Printing Services Ltd of Derby.

PREFACE.

In presenting this Volume to his Friends and the Public, the Compiler assures them that it has been his most anxious desire to form a useful book of reference for all purposes. It contains a list of a great portion of the Householders residing in the Borough, of the Freeholders entitled to Vote for the Southern Division of the County, of the Electors for the Borough Members, and of the Municipal Electors. Also a list of Noblemen's and Gentlemen's Seats, a description of the Public Buildings and Manufactories, and a variety of other information, valuable both to the Inhabitant and the Stranger. That errors will be discovered in it he is ready to acknowledge, since it would be impossible to avoid them; but he hopes that a due consideration will be given to the rapid changes that take place, even daily, in a town of this magnitude; and that these will be admitted as a sufficient apology for such errors as may be found to occur.

S. Glover begs to announce to his numerous Subscribers for the County Directory, and for the Railway Guide, that it is his determination to proceed with all possible despatch to bring them before the Public. In returning thanks to his numerous supporters, he has only to observe, that should his humble endeavours give satisfacton to his Friends, it will be gratifying to his feelings, and prove a stimulus to further exertion.

CONTENTS.

HISTORY.

	Page
DERBY, Situation	1
Scenery, Soil, Air, Water	2
Mr. Wolley's account of Derby, in 1712	3
Manor and Corporation	4
Court of Requests	7
Improvement Act	7
New Streets built	8
Fairs, Markets, Provisions	9
New Market	10
St. Alkmund's, Michael's and All Saints' parishes	11
St. Werburgh's, and St. Peter's parishes	12
Population, increase in thirty-five years	13
General observations	14
Police of the Borough	15
Churches and Chapels	16
All Saints' Church	16
Cavendish Vault	20
Countess of Shrewsbury's Monumental inscription and charities	20
St. Alkmund's Church	21
Bullock's Monument and Charities	22
St. Michael's Church and Charities	23
St. Werburgh's Church and Charities	24
St. John's Church	25
St. Peter's Church	26
Ditto, Charities	27
Trinity Church and Christ Church	27
The Catholic Church of St. Marie	28
The Unitarian Chapel	29
The Friends' Meeting House	29
The Independent Chapel	30
The Congregational Chapel	30
The General Baptist Chapel	31
The Particular Baptist Chapel	32
The Wesleyan Methodist Chapel	32
The Methodist New Connexion	33
The Primitive Methodists	33
The Jerusalem Church	33
CHARITABLE INSTITUTIONS.	
The Infirmary	34
The Dispensary	36
Ladies' Charity	37
Large's Hospital	37
Society for the Relief of Families of Distressed Clergymen	39
Countess of Shrewsbury's Almshouses	39
Wilmot's Almshouses	40
Linacre's Charity	40
Liversage's Charity	40
————— Almshouses	41
Schools	42
Free Grammar School	42
St. Peter's National, Infants', and Sunday Schools	42
St. Alkmund's Sunday Schools	42
St. Werburgh's ditto	42
All Saints' ditto	43
St. Michael's ditto	43
St. John's ditto	43
Trinity Church ditto	43
Christ Church ditto	43
St. Marie's Catholic Church Sunday Schools	43
National School	43
Diocesan School	43
Lancastrian School	44
British Girls' School	44
Infant's School, Mill Street	44
Wesleyan Methodist Sunday Schools	44
——————— Day School	44
The New Connexion of General Baptist Sunday Schools	45
Independent Church Sunday Schools	45
Methodist New Connexion School	45
	Page
The Particular Baptist Sunday Schools	45
Unitarian Chapel Sunday Schools	45
Primitive Methodist Chapel Sunday Schools	45
Town Hall	46
County Hall	49
County Jail	50
New Assembly Room	55
Theatre	55
Newspapers	55
Philosophical Society	55
Athenæum, Royal Hotel, Post Office, and Derby and Derbyshire Bank	56
Town and County Museum	58
News' Room	58
Town and County Library and News' Room	58
Mechanics' Institution and Hall	59
The Arboretum	61
The Gallery of Paintings, Sculpture, &c., in the Residence of Joseph Strutt, Esq.	64
The Derby Football, Bowling-greens, &c.	67
St. Mary's Chapel	68
The Castle	68
Babington Hall, and Mr. Beardsley's House	69
Exeter House	70
Mr. Jessopp's House	70
St. Helen's House	71
Abbot's Hill, the Friary, Houses in Friar gate, the Wardwick, Iron gate, &c.	71
Trades and Manufactures	72
Dyeing Cloth, Wool, &c.	72
Brewing Ale	72
Hosiery	73
Bobbin-net Lace	75
The Silk Mill	76
Weaving of Piece-goods, Ferrets, Galloons, Doubles, &c.	78
Tape and Smallwares	78
Porcelain	79
Spar Ornaments	79
Lead Mills	80
Iron Foundries	80
Ironmongers, Engine Boiler Manufacturers, Engineers, Clock and Watch Manufacturers, and Jewellers	81
Roman Cement and Plaster Manufacturers, Printing Establishments, Circular Saw Mills, Coach and Harness Manufactory	82
Builders	82
The Division of the Borough into Wards	83
Contested Elections, Mayors of the Borough, Remarkable Floods	84
Derby Station	86
Railway Distance Tables	88

DIRECTORY.

	Page
Alphabetical List of the Inhabitants	1 to 96
Additions and Alterations	96
Classification of Trades	102
Members of Parliament, Magistrates, and Councilmen of the Borough	137
Officers of the Borough	138
Derby Poor Law Union	138
Parish Officers	139
Places of Worship	139
Public Buildings, &c.	141
Post Office Regulations	141
Lord Lieutenant, Members of Parliament, High Sheriff, Coroners, and Magistrates for the County	142
Noblemen and Gentlemen's Seats	144
Carriers by water and land	152
Distance Table	161
Additional Burgesses	162
Country Butchers	168

HISTORY OF DERBY.

DERBY, the capital of a rich and interesting county, is a corporate and borough
Deoraby, town, with a constituency of about 1800 electors, freemen, and bur-
Darbie. gesses, sending two representatives to parliament, and consisting of
five parishes, with their dependent chapelries and townships, in the hundred of
Morleston and Litchurch, in the diocess of Lichfield and Coventry, in the midland
circuit, in the southern division of the county, and a polling place, for forty-
three parishes and townships. Derby is advantageously situate towards the upper
extremity of a fertile plain, amidst scenery varied, luxuriant, and beautiful, upon
the banks of the Derwent, which, after its romantic course through the Peak, flows
in a considerable stream through the town, dividing it into two unequal portions, of
which the greater one is situated on the western bank of the river, upon ground of
different heights, and is surrounded with gentle and pleasant eminences, from which
flow the Markeaton and other brooks.   It is in longitude 1° 25′ W., latitude 52° 58′
N., 126 m. N. N. W. from London, 178 m. from Brighton, 28 m. from Leicester, 17 m.
from Loughborough ; 16 m. W. from Nottingham, 54 m. from Lincoln and Gainsborough, 66 m. from Boston, 103 m. from Hull ; 264 m. S. from Edinburgh, 90
m. from York, 36 m. from Sheffield, 24 m. from Chesterfield, 23 m. from Mansfield, 13 m. from Alfreton ; 91 m. S. E. from Liverpool, 109 m. from Lancaster,
73 m. from Chester, 62 m. from Manchester, 38 m. from Buxton, 27 m. from
Bakewell, 17 m. from Matlock Bath, 16 m. from Cromford, 13 m. from Wirksworth, 8 m. from Belper ; 128 m. N. E. from Bath and Bristol, 40 m. from
Birmingham, 23 m. from Lichfield, 11 m. from Burton-upon-Trent, 42 m. from
Coventry, 14 m. from Ashby-de-la-Zouch ; 19 m. S. E. from Uttoxeter, and
13 m. from Ashbourn.

There have been various conjectures concerning the name of the town ; but the
most probable is its derivation from the British appellation of the river on which
it is situate.   *Derwent* is the name applied to swift streams in different parts of
England.   The Roman station called *Castrum Parvum* or Little Chester, took the
name of *Derventio*, from its proximity to the British town.   In the chronicle of
the princely Ethelward, the learned son of Alfred, we are told that the Saxon
name of this town was *Northworthige*, and that the Danes called it *Deoraby*.
We may suppose that the casual appellation of *Northworthige*, or the northern-
market, had reference to its position with respect to *Repton* or *Repandum*, the

b

capital of Mercia, situate at about the distance of eight miles, on the southern bank of the Trent. That it was known to the Saxons, as well as the Danes, by the appellation of *Deoraby*, appears from the general Saxon Chronicles, where it is mentioned by no other name, and from coins struck in this town, during the reigns of Athelstan and Edgar. The word *Deoraby* is a corruption of the old British name, or perhaps an adaptation of it to the Saxon idiom; the syllable *aby* being the origin of our word *abode*. From *Deoraby* the more modern appellation *Derby* is easily deduced. Some persons have imagined that the name is compounded of *Deer*, a wild or swift animal, and *by* or *aby*, an abode; and they point to the arms of the town as authority for their supposition. Mr. Pilkington thinks this conjecture is rendered probable by two circumstances. " One is," says that ingenious topographer, " that the arms of the town are, a buck couchant in a park; and the other, that one of the lanes adjoining the town is called Lodge lane." To this it has been replied that the arms are derived from the name, for the name was used long before the introduction of armorial bearings into England. They are allusive or hieroglyphic arms, the *buck* expressing the syllable *Deer* or *Der*, and the *park*, the syllable *by* or *abode*. As to Lodge lane, it was probably the approach to a monastic lodge belonging to St. Helen's. There are others (as the Rev. Robert Simpson remarks,) among whom are Bishop Gibson, who have supposed that the name *Derby* is derived from *Bi*, by, and *Dur*, water; but this differs little from the derivation already given.

The town of Derby is situate on the western bank of the Derwent, about forty-five miles from the source of that river, and nearly ten from its junction with the Trent. As the river approaches the town from Darley, it is less confined by the great ridge of limestone and granite hills that embank its eastern side until it has passed the village of Duffield. The valley then opening to a considerable extent in that direction, the waters expand and frequently overflow the more level ground, and consequently the stream rolls on with a wider and less rapid course. Opposite to the town of Derby, it embraces several insulated knowls or holmes, and the land stretches in meadows and marshes. The western bank, on which the town is built, rises with a bold but not abrupt sweep, in several undulated heights from the water's edge. These heights are indented by a valley, through which flows a strong brook from Markeaton. This brook is known by various names: it was anciently called the Odde-brook. The part of it without the town, and, until it becomes united with a small stream, named the Foulbrook drainage, from Little-over, is called the Markeaton brook, and the remainder, to its junction with the Derwent, is denominated the Morledge Creek.

The vicinity of Derby presents a pleasing variety of scenery, enriched by verdant meadows, woods, and water. The best views to be obtained of the town are on the east, from Chaddesden-hill, or the meadows; on the west, from a field at the top of the hill going along a lane, from the Uttoxeter road, or from the top of the County prison; on the south-west, from a field on the Burton road, a little beyond the Firs, the residence of the Rev. E. H. Abney. In every view, the tower of All Saints' forms an important feature. The greater part of the town being in an open valley, cannot be seen from a distance of more than ten or twelve miles any way. It is most open to the south.

The soil in the neighbourhood of the town is chiefly red marl, with a substrata of quartz and gravel, which often lies a great depth. It is rich and very productive. On the borders of the borough, much of it is laid out in garden ground, and let in small patches, at the average rate of £10. per acre. The pasture lands let from £4. to £7. per acre. In the immediate vicinity of Derby there is but little arable land. Clay is abundant, and bricks are made near the Uttoxeter and Burton roads, of a good colour and consistency.

The air of the surrounding hills is particularly pure, and that of the town itself cannot be charged with any defect of salubrity. Though placed in a valley, watered by a large river and a wide rivulet, it is not subjected to the mephitic fogs of stagnate waters. Many persons, in proportion to the population, have attained to old age, and even outlived a hundred years, in Derby, as in other places, and the general health of the inhabitants is good.

The town is abundantly supplied with excellent water from Becket's well and other springs, and by the Water Company; and the spring water used for beverage and culinary purposes is clear and wholesome. The floods, occasioned by the swollen waters of the Derwent and the Markeaton brook, are injurious at periods when heavy rain on the Peak hills have caused the Derwent or the brook to overflow their banks. Latterly a culvert has been constructed to relieve the lower parts of the town from this inconvenience, and the brook-course has been arched over, and a great improvement made in Victoria street, formerly called the Brookside.

The general supply of water for culinary use is raised from the Derwent by an engine at the bottom of St. Michael's lane, and conveyed through a pipe into a reservoir at the top of St. Michael's church, about the distance of one hundred yards, and the height of twelve. From thence, as from a grand artery, the stream is conveyed by tubes, under the pavement, into many of the streets and courts. Exclusive of this ample supply from the river, springs are common: the water, which is very hard, lies within a few feet of the surface, and is raised by pumps. The Market-place pump is supplied from Becket's well, which is excellent water.

We have a very particular and interesting account of the population of Derby, at the beginning of the eighteenth century, by Mr. William Woolley, who resided here in the reign of queen Anne, and wrote his manuscript (preserved in the College of Arms) about the year 1712. He describes it to be in his time, a very large, populous, rich, and well frequented borough-town; few inland towns in the kingdom equalling it. It had above seven hundred free burgesses, and the number of inhabitants were estimated at four thousand. Though not very regularly built, yet it had a great many very good houses, especially on all parts of the outside of the town, mostly of brick, of which there are (he says) as good made in this town, and as cheap, as almost in any part of England. Many of the residents were persons of quality, and many coaches were kept in it. The religious house called St. Helen's had been converted into dwelling houses, with good orchards, and there was an alley or footway in the middle of the street called St. Helen's. Mr. Woolley was decidedly of opinion that the tower of All Saints' church was built in the time of Henry VII. He describes the market-place as a square with good buildings about it: on the *east* side is a handsome large pile of building, called the court, which helps to grace it much, as does the cross, under which there is a conduit of good water, brought (he says) out of the Newlands. There is also the guild-hall at the south-west corner of the place, where the Corporation meets, under which is the town gaol, but it is at present a very tattered, ill-contrived, ill-looking building. Over against it stands a good handsome hall, erected by Mr. Crompton, part on the butchery on the *west* side of the place, and part on pillars, where the market people that sell butter, eggs, and poultry, stand; and behind it is part of the Rotten-row. It is said (adds Mr. Woolley) he built this hall with a design to make an exchange with the corporation for theirs; at present it is only used by some button makers, that work in it. The mill beside the Markeaton brook, at the bottom of St. Mary's-gate, belonged to Mr. Osborne, and over the pool stood the Ducking-stool. The site of the old nunnery, with some adjacent meadows, were in the possession of Simon Degge, esq. (Sir Simon Degge, recorder of the borough,) but the green belonged to the free burgesses, and was made use of by bakers to lay stacks of gorse, carpenters to lay their timber, and brickmakers. In the middle of it stood the kennel for the town hounds; for the site of which the gentlemen of the hunt used to present to the mayor a brace of hares, dressed, towards his dinner, on Michaelmas day. The town pinfold also stood upon Nun's-green. Below the Morledge creek, over against the lower weir that turned the stream of the Derwent down to the Holmes mills, stood the residence of Mrs. Musters, an heiress of the Mundy family: the mills belonged to her husband. The Holmes was planted round with trees, and was the pleasantest walk about the town. It was a common pasture belonging to the burgesses, and used by them for bleaching cloth. To the westward of the mill stood a good house, on the side of Cockpit-hill, built by Mr. Beardsley, which was pulled down so lately as 1819. On the south side of the Osmaston road, where it branches off from the London road, stood a few poor houses, called Knock-a-down. On the hill westward, were the remains of St. Leonards', a religious lazar-house. The gallows stood till within a few years past, a small distance farther to the west, on the Normanton road. The house near Babington lane (late belonging to the Sitwell family) was then in the possession of Sir Simon Degge. It was built by the Mellors. At the bridge over the brook at the bottom of the corn-market, stood the county gaol, described by Mr. Woolley as a convenient brick and stone building, with an entrance to the Corn-market, under a large handsome stone arch. The Thorn Tree alehouse, on the south side of the brook, is said to have been, at that time, long famous for the best ale in the town. A good house adjoined it, built by Mr. Burton, but then recently purchased by Mr. Wagstaffe. This house has been enlarged, modernized, and almost re-built, by Joseph Strutt, esq., the present possessor. On the Brook-side stood a good house, built by Mr. Green: in 1712 it belonged to Mr. Barnes; it was probably that next the Independent chapel, recently occupied by Mr. Charles Callow, and now by Henry Mozley, jun., esq. In the Wardwick stood several houses belonging to Mr. Mundy, Mr. Gisborne, and Mr. Roberts. The Friary, in the Friar-gate, had been converted into a good house, belonging to Mr. Dalton. This house was re-built by Samuel Crompton, esq., and is now the property of Henry Mozley, esq. The Presbyterian meeting-house, in the Friar-gate, was then the only dissenting place of worship in the town. The cattle and horse fairs were kept at the upper end of the Friar-gate, as they continue to be. Large's hospital for clergymen's widows was then designed, but not completed. It may be surmised from this account of Mr. Woolley's, that the town had not increased in extent, as in density of population and in the buildings of some of the principal inhabitants, during the preceding century.

Derby is rapidly increasing in population and improvement. The principal streets have been improved upon M'Adam's plan, and the footpaths are paved with stone or bricks. The houses are mostly built with red bricks, which are made in the vicinity of the town. The public buildings are generally built of durable stone, procured in the county. Many new streets have been laid out during the last quarter of a century; they are uniformly built, some on elevated and others on eligible sites, on the south, west, north, and east of the town. The parishes that have most increased are St. Peter's, St. Werburgh's, and St. Alkmund's. The old town was built in an irregular manner, upon a peninsula formed by the junction of the Derwent and the Markeaton brook. From each stream the land rises to the centre and forms a ridge, upon which the churches of All Saints, St. Michael, St. Alkmund, and the beautiful Catholic church of St. Mary are built. The land rises considerably to the south beyond the Markeaton brook, upon which St. Peter's, Trinity, and Christ churches are erected. On the south-west bank of the same brook, St. Werburgh's and St. John's churches are built on low sites. There are but few of the ancient houses now remaining: these are in Friar-street, St. Peter's-street, Amen-alley, Iron-gate, Sadler-gate, Wardwick, St. Mary's gate, &c. The most ancient thoroughfares or streets are called gates, as Friar-gate, Bridge-gate, St. Mary's-gate, Iron-gate, and Sadler-gate; the word gate implying, in many old authors, not so much the door-way or portal of any building, as the road or pathway leading to it. The principal streets or thoroughfares are the Friar-gate (in many parts twenty-four yards wide), Ashbourn road, Uttoxeter road, Bridge-street, Brook-street, Ford-street, St. Helen's street, Willow-row, Bold-lane, St. Mary's-gate, Sadler-gate, Curzon-street, Wardwick, Victoria-street, Green-lane, St. Peter's-street, Babington-lane, Burton road, Normanton road, Osmaston road, London-street, Castle-street, Traffic-street, Liversage-street, Canal-street, Park-street, Hope-street, North Midland-terrace, John-street, Station-street, Siddal's-lane, Morledge, Tenant-street, Market-place, Derwent-street, Full-street, Corn-market, Rotten-row, Iron-gate, Queen-street,

King-street, Duffield road, Kedleston road, Bridge-gate, Chester road, Nottingham road, Exeter-street, and Erasmus-street. The whole of the streets in each parish will be found alphabetically arranged in the lists. The various approaches to the town have undergone considerable improvements within the last fifteen years, and those from London, Birmingham, Uttoxeter, and the north, are much enlarged. Derby has now on every side excellent roads and entrances.

The manor or lordship of Derby is of considerable extent. It is bounded on the north by Little Chester, Darley Abbey, and Allestree; on the west, by Markeaton; on the south-west, by Mickleover and Littleover; on the south, by Normanton and Osmaston; on the south-east, by Alvaston and Boulton; and on the east by Chaddesden. It is nearly circular, the diameter being about two miles, and the land, according to the survey of Mr. Swanwick, is 1840 acres. The ground occupied by streets, or what is particularly understood by the town, occupies about 400 acres in the centre of this circle. At the time when Mr. Hutton wrote (1790) its extent was not more than a third part of its present acreage. The Corporation are the lords of the manor.

CORPORATION.

Derby has been a corporate town by charter, from the earliest times, under the government of Bailiffs. According to the charter of James I. it was incorporated by the name and style of mayor and burgesses. By the last charter granted by Charles II. 1680, the corporation was to consist of a mayor, nine aldermen, fourteen brothers, fourteen capital burgesses, and the common burgesses.

The mayor for the ensuing year, was elected from the aldermen, every Michaelmas day, by the then mayor and aldermen. Any vacancy among the aldermen was filled up from the brothers, by the mayor and aldermen—among the brothers, by the mayor and brothers from the capital burgesses—among the capital burgesses by the mayor—aldermen, brothers, and capital burgesses, from the burgesses at large. The mayor, aldermen, brothers, and capital burgesses, formed the common council for the general affairs of the town. The Corporation as thus formed, continued the governing power in the town till the passing of the Municipal Reform act in 1832, when the exclusive right of the burgesses was done away, and the corporation was chosen from the inhabitants at large; it now consists of a mayor, twelve aldermen, and thirty-six councillors, chosen from the six wards into which the town was then divided. The officers of the borough are the Recorder, Town Clerk, Chamberlain, High Constable, and two Sergeants at mace.* The Duke of Devonshire is the High Steward.

The mayor is also escheator and clerk of the market, and by the said charter he is empowered to take such reasonable toll for beasts, cattle and other things in the fairs and markets sold and bought, as they have heretofore lawfully had and received. The mayor and burgesses of the borough are exempt from being empanelled on juries at the assizes. They are also empowered to keep two courts leet, and six yearly fairs, and to take toll, but pay none through the whole kingdom, remitting one half to the duchy of Lancaster.

The corporation is empowered to hold courts of record, and quarterly and petty sessions: the former are regularly advertised, and the latter are held by the magistrates acting for the borough, every Monday and Friday, at the town hall. John Balguy, esq. is the chairman of the quarter sessions.

There is no account of any territorial possessions held by the corporation, in the name of the burgesses, until the reign of queen Mary, the grant of whose ample gift is inserted in the Appendix to volume I. of the History of Derbyshire.

* See page 138.

The corporation estate was granted in 1553, by queen Mary, who, in consideration of £266. assigned to the corporation fifty-four separate estates, which had
belonged to the abbey of Darley, to the college of All Saints', the guild of the
Holy Trinity, the chantry of St. Mary in All Saints' college, and the free chapel
of St. James. These estates consisted of about eighty-six houses, chiefly in Derby,
and about 216 acres of land in and near the town ; divers tithes of hay, corn, wool,
lamb, &c. ; St. Mary's mill, three fulling mills, and one water mill, called the Derwent mills ; the free chapel of St. James, with all the lands, the advowson of the
churches of All Saints', St. Michael's, and St. Alkmund's, in Derby, and the
manor and advowson of Heath : all which said messuages, lands, tenements,
tithes, &c. were of the clear yearly value of £77. 2s. 7d. Out of the issues of
these estates the corporation were to pay, every Michaelmas, into the exchequer,
the fee-farm rent of £41. 14s. 11d. ; and the further sums of 1s. yearly to
Thomas Warde and his heirs ; 10d. to the chamberlains ; 1s. to the churchwardens of All Saints' ; £13. 6s. 8d. to two priests for performing duty in All Saints' ;
£6. 13s. 4d. to the minister of St. Alkmund's ; and the sum of £1. 13s. 4d. to the
bailiffs for collecting the rents. The grant ordains that a free school for ever shall
be maintained by the said corporation ; to the master and usher £13. 6s. 8d. to
be paid quarterly by equal portions every year.

The advowsons of the livings of All Saints' and St. Alkmund's have been disposed of since the passing of the Municipal Reform Act, agreeably to the provisions
of that act.

The corporation lands are enjoyed by the burgesses in common, under particular regulations. They are the Siddals and the Old Meadows, of which the
hay-grass is let on a long lease to Messrs. Cox, who are obliged to clear the land
by the 25th of June ; after which any burgess has a right to turn in his cattle,
until the ensuing Lady-day : in the Holmes, the Chequer closes, Cowsley field
and the new Pasture, the burgesses have the right of pasture throughout the year,
on the payment of 26s. for each cow or horse. All these lie eastward of the town.
Bradshaw Hayes, containing about 14 acres, to the south, was sold by the corporation about thirty-three years ago, to the Governors of the Infirmary, for £200.
per acre. The Castle fields were undoubtedly among the lands bestowed by Queen
Mary's grant upon the corporation, and it is not very clear whether that land came
into the possession of the Borough family by purchase or otherwise, during the
period that Isaac Borough, esq. was recorder of the town, early in the reign of
George II. It was sold in 1822 by the late Thomas Borough, esq. of Chetwynd
Park, Shropshire, for the sum of £22,000. to Mr. Copeland of Lincoln, who has
resold it in lots, and several streets are built thereon.

The corporation estate has been continually wasting, and, as Mr. Hutton justly
observes, it would be difficult for the most penetrating eye to find out the fifty-
seven estates. For what trust, adds Mr. Hutton, can withstand fifty-seven temp-
tations ! In 1791, Mr. Hutton estimated the corporation estates at £2000. a year.
Since his time much valuable land and premises have been disposed of ; viz. the
Cowsley field, about 20 acres, the Bradshaw Hayes, about 14 acres, at £200.
per acre, and much land for building purposes ; the proceeds of which is probably
invested in the funds. The rental of the corporation estate in 1806, was £1436.

Within the last thirty-six years the income of the Corporation is doubled, notwithstanding property to the amount of several thousand pounds has been
disposed of.

All such whose fathers were burgesses when they were born, or who have served
an apprenticeship to a burgess, have a right to demand their burgess oath. The
poor burgesses are entitled to a horsegate and cowgate in several large pastures that
have been long ago given by benefactors and appropriated to that purpose, as also
to right of common in several meadows, as the Siddals, the Old Meadows, &c.
after the hay is got off, which ought to be by Midsummer-day. Free burgesses pay
no toll of lead or other goods passing or repassing through or laid in any part of
the town, which others are liable to. The burgesses of Derby are said to be free

of toll in London, though the Londoners are not in Derby. Mr. Woolley, in 1712, says, the tolls are the mayor's, for which he pays to the crown yearly £70. or thereabouts, and that the corporation had then about £500. a year to support their dignity, and charities arising out of lands at Little Chester, the Rooditches and several large closes between Derby and Mickleover, which were, 24th Edward III. held by Robert le Breton under Thomas, Lord Touchett, and by him left to Isabel, his daughter, married to John de Loudham. In the reign of queen Elizabeth, the said land belonged to Sir Godfrey Foljambe, which land was purchased about 1630, by Mr. Crowshaw, who left it to the corporation of Derby for several charitable uses mentioned in the several parishes.

The corporation are Trustees of Sir Thomas White's, and other charities.

By the Charter of Charles II. 1680, the representatives for the borough were to be chosen by the corporation, freemen, and sworn burgesses, the Mayor being the returning officer. The burgesses were then estimated at 655. In 1791 Mr. Hutton states their number at about 900. The act for reforming the representation of the people in the House of Commons, which received the royal assent on 7th. June, 1832, extends the elective franchise to householders, at £10. a year rent, throughout the borough. The number of electors registered in 1832 was 1384; viz. 372 freemen, and 1012 ten pound occupiers. In 1839-40 the number of borough electors was 1820, of whom 1375 were occupiers of houses rated at £10. and upwards, 445 freemen, 111 of these were possessed of qualifications as £10. renters.*

There is also a Court of Requests for the recovery of debts under 40s. which was established in 1766. The Commissioners, under the direction of a clerk, meet every third Tuesday, at the Town Hall, to decide cases. John Frear, esq., is clerk to the commissioners.

Commissioners.

Mr. Ralph Lomas,	Mr. Joseph Handford,	Mr. Michael Hallam,	Mr. Thomas Darby,
Mr. William Barton,	Mr. Robert Ward,	Mr. John Mason,	Mr. George Hood,
Mr. J. Henry Cock,	Mr. John Corden,	Mr. John Radford,	Mr. Samuel Watson.
Mr. George Cox,	Mr. John Wright,	Mr. Thomas Tunaley, sen.	

IMPROVEMENT ACTS.—In 1768 an act was passed " for selling part of a Green called *Nuns' Green*, in the borough of *Derby*, and for applying the money arising from the sale thereof in the improvement of the remaining part of the said *Green*," the preamble of which recites, " Whereas there is within the borough of *Derby*, a certain piece of Ground called *Nuns' Green*, containing by estimation forty-eight acres or thereabouts, on which the Freeholders, Owners, and Occupiers of Messuages, Lands, and tenements, and Burgesses within the said borough, have right of common : And whereas several small buildings have lately been erected thereupon and great damage has been done to the said Green by Persons digging gravel thereout, to the no small detriment and loss of the said Freeholders, Owners, Occupiers, and Burgesses having right of common thereon, as well as to the prejudice of the health of the Inhabitants of the said borough, by reason of the stagnated water and other nuisances : And whereas the said borough is by the increase of trade become very populous, and there is a real want of more dwelling houses for the Inhabitants : And whereas if the said nuisances and incroachments on the said Green were removed and prevented, and power given to sell part thereof for the purpose of erecting dwelling houses and buildings thereon, and the money arising from such sale were applied in removing the said nuisances and incroachments, and improving the said *Green*, it would greatly tend to the benefit and advantage of the said Freeholders, Owners, Occupiers, and Burgesses, as well as of the other Inhabitants of the said borough." The land sold under this act

* In the Appendix to the first volume of the History of the County, will be found a list of the chief magistrates for three hundred and twenty years, and of the representatives of the borough for five hundred and thirty-eight years. It is curious to observe the rude state of letters which those lists exhibit. There seems no fixed principles in the use of the alphabet; for a man seldom spelt his name twice alike, nor is it a wonder we see confusion in those early documents, as but few of the principal inhabitants were capable of using the pen. A gradual improvement may easily be traced. We also observe the fluctuation of parliaments. In some years three or four were held, and then again thirteen or fourteen years elapsed without any.

was "such part of the said *Nuns' Green* as extends in length from the late
dwelling house of *Gilbert Cheshire*, esq., to the dwelling house of Master *George
Manyfold*, known by the sign of the *White Lion*, and in depth not exceeding
forty-five yards (except such part thereof as is included within the site of Ground
belonging to the Gaol for the County of *Derby*.") The powers of this act were
vested in certain trustees, consisting of the principal inhabitants of the town and
immediate neighbourhood, but they were invested with no permanent authority.

In 1792 an act was passed " for paving, cleansing, lighting, and otherwise improving the streets, lanes, and other public passages and places, within the borough
of *Derby*; and for selling a certain piece of Waste Ground, situate within the
said borough, called *Nuns' Green*, towards defraying the expence of the said Improvements."

This continued in existence till 1825, but the powers given by it, and the rates
allowed to be raised under it, being found insufficient for the increasing wants—
and, we may add, the increasing desire for improvement in the town; a further
act was obtained " for better paving, and otherwise improving the borough of
Derby." Under this act, power was given to take down the then Town Hall,
which was an isolated building in the market place, and to build an enlarged one
on the present site; to build the new market—to make various alterations for the
widening and straightening of streets and lanes; and generally, to take measures
for the better paving, draining, cleansing, and lighting of the town—for establish-
ing a regular night watch—and for the preventing, and removing of nuisances.
The powers of the act were vested in commissioners, consisting of the mayor and
aldermen, and all owners and occupiers of houses, or other buildings of the value
of thirty pounds a year. The commissioners were empowered to borrow the sum
of £20,000. at 4 per cent. to be laid out in improving and lighting the town. The
passing of this act has had a very beneficial effect on the appearance of the town.

The town of Derby is becoming distinguished among the provincial capitals of
the kingdom for improvements, which blend the two characteristics of perfection,
elegance and utility. The streets, particularly the main thoroughfares, are
gradually being divested of obstructions, and with the approaches to the borough
in every direction, have undergone the process which gives smoothness and safety
to the carriage ways. We cannot look around us without discovering proofs that
the improvement Bill has been acted upon with energy, taste, and judgement;
and that the commissioners merit the thanks of the community for the spirit, intelligence, and prudence, with which they have employed the parliamentary powers intrusted to them.

The streets have been greatly improved, and additional streets have risen in every
quarter, particularly in the Castle-fields, Nun's-green, and the Normanton road.
The following have been built within the last forty years:—

Albion-street.	Erasmus-street.	North-street.
Albion place.	Exeter-street.	Nun's-street.
Ashbourn road.	Fingal-street.	Orchard-street.
Back Sitwell-street.	Forester place.	Osmaston-street.
Bath-street.	Fowler-street.	Osmaston road.
Bloom-street.	George-street.	Ossian-street.
Bradshaw-street.	Goodwin-street.	Parker-street.
Britannia-street.	Green-street.	Park-street.
Brook-street, Upper.	Grove terrace.	River-street.
———— Middle.	Grove-street.	Rivett-street.
———— Lower.	High-street.	Sacheverel-street.
Canal-street.	Hill-street.	Sheffield-street.
Cannon-street.	Hope-street.	Siddals-lane.
Castle-street.	John-street.	Sitwell-street.
Carrington-street.	Kensington-street.	South-street.
Cavendish-street.	Large's-street.	Talbot-street.
Chapel-street.	Leaper-street.	Traffic-street.
Charles-street.	Leonard-street.	Union buildings.
Cherry-street.	Litchurch-street.	Uttoxeter road.
Chester place	London-street, part of.	Vernon-street.
City road.	Midland terrace.	Waterloo-street.
Curzon-street.	Mundy-street.	Waterloo place.
Darwin terrace.	Normanton-street.	William-street.
Derwent-street.	Normanton terrace.	Wilmot-street.
Devonshire-street.	North parade.	Wright-street.
Duke-street.	North Midland terrace.	York-street.
Eagle-street.		

A new road leading from the Burton road into Curzon street, and a new road along the Cross lanes between Curzon street and Green lane, each thirty-six feet wide; also a new street from the Cross lanes to the Burton road is now being formed. The Brook course which has been a nuisance for centuries will be arched over, which will be another great improvement effected in the borough.

The fairs either granted or confirmed by king James's charter, were, Friday in Easter week, May 4th, Thursday before Midsummer, and September 26th, each fair being for two days. The charter of Charles II. grants or confirms seven fairs: viz. Friday after the Epiphany; Friday in Easter week; Friday after St. Philip and St. James; Friday in Whitsun week; Friday before the nativity of John the Baptist; St. James's day, and Friday before September 29th, most of them being for two days. In 1732, the corporation had a grant of two new fairs, one for three days, beginning September 16th, the other for two days, beginning on the festival of St. Paul. In 1734, the corporation appointed an annual meeting for the sale of latter made cheese to continue three days, beginning on the 12th of March, altered four years afterwards to the 21st of March, and two following days.

The fairs for cattle, horses, sheep, pigs, cheese and pedlery are generally well attended. They are held on Monday after January 25th, for cattle, horses, sheep, pigs and pedlery; on the 21st and 22nd days of March, for cheese; on Friday in Easter week, on Friday after May-day, on Friday in Whitsun week, and on the 25th of July, for cattle, horses, sheep, pigs and pedlery; on the last Tuesday in August, a market for cheese; the 27th, 28th and 29th days of September, for cheese, horses, cattle, sheep, pigs and pedlery; and on the 10th of October, for cattle, horses, sheep, &c.

The markets are well supplied with corn, butchers' meat, poultry, butter, eggs, fruit, vegetables, &c. They are held on Wednesday for butter and vegetables; on Friday, the principal, for butter, eggs, butchers' meat, vegetables, fruit, corn, earthenware, &c.; and on Saturday, for butchers' meat and vegetables. A market for cattle, sheep and pigs is held at the Smithfield in the Morledge, every Tuesday.

Few market towns are better situate than Derby for a plentiful supply of all sorts of provisions, and were it not for the immense quantity of fruits and vegetables bought up by the dealers from the Staffordshire Potteries, and from the High and Low Peak, Derby would be as cheap a market as Nottingham for those necessaries of life. The weekly Tuesday's cattle market is numerously attended, and of great importance to the agriculturists, and to the butchers of Derby and the surrounding towns and villages. The supply of fat cattle, sheep, pork, &c., are generally equal to the demand, and sell at as high a price per pound as at most country markets. The meeting of gentlemen, farmers and factors, at the Friday markets is large, and the extent of business transacted in corn is considerable, and notwithstanding the additional accommodation afforded to the inhabitants of the borough and the surrounding neighbourhood by the new market and shambles, the markets are still crowded and inconvenient for want of more space. The new shambles are chiefly occupied by butchers from the country villages. The Saturday's market is now numerously attended. Some few years ago, Wild, a gardener, who lived on the Osmaston road, first commenced with a stall at the top of the Piazza, or market head, and his example has been followed to a very considerable extent. Early vegetables are supplied from Melbourne, Foremark, Repton, and other villages south of the Trent.

The market-place is about 110 yards by 55. The increased population of the borough, and the number of country people who regularly attend on the principal market-day, caused the market-place to be exceedingly crowded and inconvenient. This induced the Corporation to purchase premises, and to build a new market on the south side of, and communicating with the old market. The new market, consisting of one hundred shops for butchers, &c. a butter market, and a covered space for fruit and vegetable stalls, &c. occupies a space of ground at the back of the town hall, between the Corn-market and the Morledge, and communicating with both.

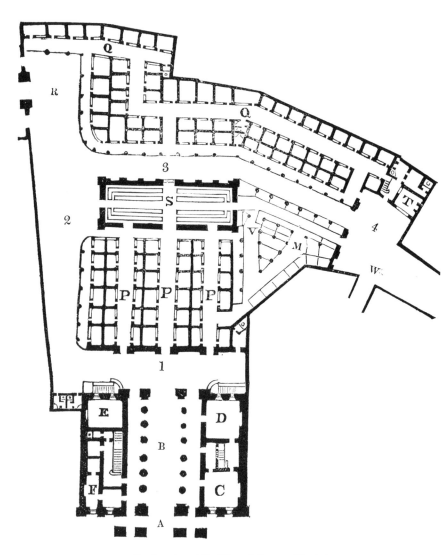

Explanation of the Plan of the new Market.

No. I. represents the ground plan of the late Town Hall.

The new Market-place occupies the ground at the back of the Town Hall, between the Corn-market and the Morledge; and is represented by the remaining part of the plan.

Immediately behind the Hall is an open space (marked 1) and beyond that, rows of shops (marked P) with walks between them, and a colonnade of slender iron pillars to the east and west. The shops along the middle avenue are larger than the rest, and contain from 70 to 80 square feet. Beyond these shops is the *Butter and Egg Market* (marked S) fitted with forms on iron supports, sufficiently large to accommodate a hundred persons, allowing the space of a yard to each. The *Vegetable Market* occupies nearly the whole space westward of the Butter and Egg Market, and the above named shops. It is marked in the plan (V M). This is fitted up with stalls, tables, &c. having lock-up places underneath them.

Standings for fruit are attached to the stalls, and these are marked out by grooves in the pavement. Beyond these last-mentioned markets is a road way, which divides them from the farther shops (marked Q). The shops toward the eastern entrance from the Morledge (marked R), and some of those at the back of the Market, contain from 70 to 80 square feet. There are altogether 30 of these sized shops, and 70 of smaller dimensions, containing from 40 to 50 square feet, and they are so contrived that any two of the shops may be thrown into one. The whole number of shops are 100.

The carriage ways, open spaces, &c. are marked 1, 2, 3, 4. The whole are well lighted, ventilated and drained.

T—is the Superintendant's House.

W—the entrance into the Market by the Tiger Inn.

PARISHES.

The town of Derby is divided into five parishes: All Saints', St. Alkmund's, St. Michael's, St. Peter's, and St. Werburgh's. Of these, St. Alkmund's lies to the north and east—St. Peter's to the south—St. Werburgh's to the west —and All Saints' and St. Michael's in the centre of the town, surrounded by the other three.

St. Alkmund's parish is bounded on the west by St. Werburgh's parish and Markeaton township; on the north by the chapelry of Allestree and the parish of Duffield; on the east by Chaddesden and Breadsall; and on the south by St. Michael's and All Saints' parishes. It contains 649 acres of excellent land, watered by the Derwent, which lets at from 40s. to £5. per acre, and small quantities occupied as gardens, let for £10. per acre, besides the land occupied by the buildings. The estimated annual value of all the land and buildings is £21,400. The population of this parish, in 1841, consisted of 4154 males, 4469 females, residing in 1678 houses; of these, 15 males and 12 females were in the workhouse. This parish is divided among about 360 proprietors, and contains the following streets:—

Bath-street.
Brook-street, part of.
Bridge-gate and courts.
Bridge-street and courts.
Chapel-street.
Charles-street.
Cherry-street.
Chester road.
Chester-place.
City-row and courts.
Darley-lane.
Darwin-terrace.
Duffield road.
Duke-street.
Erasmus-street.
Exeter-place.
Ford-street.
Goodwin-street and courts.
Green-street, part of.
Island-place.
Kedleston road.
King-street and courts.
Lodge-lane.
Mundy-street.
Navigation-row and courts.
North parade.
Nottingham road.
Nun's-street, part of.
Orchard-street and courts.
Parker-street and courts.
Plumtree-place.
Queen-street, part of.
River-street.
St. Alkmund's church yard.
St. Helen's-street and courts.
St. Mary's-place.
Upper Brook-street.
William-street.
Willow-row and courts, part of.

In St. Michael's parish there is no land but what the buildings stand upon, with the exception of a few gardens. It is chiefly bounded by St. Alkmund's parish north, and All Saints' parish south. There are but few streets in this parish. It includes the west side of the Iron-gate, from the Talbot Inn to the Globe wine vaults, and the greater part of the Old George Inn yard in the Sadler-gate; both sides of Queen-street to Messrs. Wilkins and Sons' shop; the left hand side of the Full-street to the Silk Mill lane, including the silk and corn mills; St. Michael's-lane, and Walker-lane on one side, as far as the Hen and Chickens public house, and on the other to the premises of William Evans, esq. The estimated annual value of all the land and buildings is £3200. The population in 1841 consisted of 533 males, 542 females, residing in 188 houses; of these, 4 males and 7 females were in the workhouse. This parish is divided among about 80 proprietors, and contains the following streets:—

Full-street, part of.
Iron-gate, part of.
Queen-street and courts.
Sadler-gate, part of.
St. Michael's lane and courts.
St. Michael's church yard.
Silk Mill lane.
Walker lane and courts, part of.

All Saints' parish contains the Holmes, of about 15 acres, besides the land occupied by the buildings. It is bounded by the Derwent east; St. Peter's parish south; St. Werburgh's parish west, and St. Michael's parish north. The estimated annual value of all the land and buildings is £17,880. The population in 1841 consisted of 2147 males, 2318 females, residing in 825 houses; of these, 12

males and 10 females were in the workhouse. This parish is divided among
about 260 proprietors, and contains the following streets :—

Amen alley.	Green-street and courts, part of.	St. James's lane and courts.
Bold lane and courts.	Iron-gate, great part of, & courts.	St. Mary's-gate and courts.
Brook-street, part of.	Jury-street.	Sadler-gate, great part of, &courts.
Cockpit hill and courts.	Market-place.	Tenant-street.
Corn-market, part of.	Morledge and courts.	Walker lane, part of.
Derwent-street.	Nun's-street, part of.	Wright-street and courts.
Full-street, great part of, & courts.	Rotten-row.	

St. Werburgh's parish is bounded by the parishes of St. Peter's, All Saints',
and St. Alkmund's east ; the chapelry of Normanton, in St. Peter's, south ; and
Markeaton and Littleover west and south-west. It contains 664a. 2r. 30p. of
good land, watered by two small rivulets, partly consisting of a strong clay (which
furnishes excellent bricks) and loam ; let at various sums, from £2. to £5. per
acre, besides the land occupied by the buildings. The estimated, annual value
of all the land and buildings is £25,360. The population in 1841 consisted of
3740 males, 4106 females, residing in 1557 houses. There were also 195 males
and 23 females in the County prison, and 19 males and 21 females in the workhouse. This parish is divided among about 400 proprietors, and contains the
following streets :—

Abbey Barns.	Forester-place.	St. Werburgh's church yard.
Agard-street and courts.	Friar-gate.	Searl-street and courts.
Ashbourn road.	Fowler-street.	Short-street and courts.
Baker's lane.	George-street.	South-street and courts.
Becket-well lane.	Green lane, part of.	Summer-hill.
Brick-street.	Green-street and courts.	Talbot-street.
Britannia-street, Burton road.	Haarlem-street.	Union-buildings.
Brook-street and courts.	High-street.	Upper Brook-street and courts.
Burton road.	Kensington-street and courts.	Uttoxeter road.
Cannon-street.	Large's-street.	Vernon-street.
Cavendish-street.	Manchester terrace.	Victoria-street.
Cheapside.	Markeaton-street.	Wardwick and courts.
Cross lane and courts.	Mill-street.	Waterloo-street.
Curzon-street.	Normanton road.	Waterloo-place.
Dam-side and courts.	Nun's-street, part of.	Welch's buildings.
Drewry lane.	Sadler-gate, part of.	York street.
Ford-street and courts.		

St. Peter's parish is bounded by the parishes of All Saints' and St. Werburgh's
north and west ; the chapelries of Alvaston and Normanton, and the townships
of Litchurch south. It contains 179 acres of excellent meadow and garden land,
besides the land occupied by the buildings, which lets at from £3. to £10. per
acre. The estimated annual value of all the land and buildings is £27,240. The
population in 1841 consisted of 5103 males, 5351 females, residing in 2086 houses.
There were also 16 males and 22 females in the workhouse, and 41 males and
44 females in the infirmary. This parish is divided among about 480 proprietors,
and contains the following streets :—

Albion-street and courts.	Grove terrace.	Rivett-street.
Albion place.	High Park corner.	Sacheverel-street.
Babington lane.	Hill-street and courts.	Station-street.
Bag lane and courts.	Hope-street.	St. James's lane, part of.
Baker's buildings.	John street.	St. Leonard's-street.
Bloom-street and courts.	Litchurch-street, in the township	St. Peter's church side.
Bradshaw-street.	of Litchurch.	St. Peter's bridge.
Bourne-street.	Liversage street.	St. Peter's-street and courts.
Canal-street.	London street and courts.	Siddals lane.
Carrington-street.	Morledge, part of.	Sitwell-street.
Castle-street.	North-street.	Station-street.
Cockpit-hill, part of.	Osmaston-street and courts.	Temple terrace.
Corn-market and courts.	Osmaston road.	Thorn-tree lane.
Devonshire-street.	Park-street.	Traffic-street.
Eagle-street and courts.	Railway terrace.	Wilmot-street.
Grove-street.		

In the parish of St. Alkmund there were 20 void houses, and 6 building ;
in St. Peter's 81 void houses, and 90 building ; in St. Werburgh's 31 void houses,
and 11 building ; in All Saints' 28 void houses ; and in St. Michael's 6 void houses,
and 2 building.

The whole of the rateable property in 1842, at 6d. in the pound, amounted to £2377.; the actual sum collected on the gross, is about 5d. in the pound.

The borough of Derby contained in 1377 lay persons, above fourteen years of age, exclusive of paupers, 1040. In 1712 the number of inhabitants was supposed to be about 4000; in 1788 there were 1637 houses and 1563 inhabitants; in 1801, 10,828; in 1811, 13,043; in 1821, 17,423; in 1831, 23,627; and on 7th June 1841, 6334 houses inhabited, 116 houses uninhabited, 112 building, and 32,875 inhabitants, viz.

Population of the Derby Union in 1831.

Parishes.	Males	Fe-males.	Total	Inhabited Houses	Void Houses	Houses building
St. Alkmund's.	2854	3150	6004	1234	58	31
St. Peter's.	3170	3534	6704	1368	117	10
St. Werburgh's.	3039	3330	6369	1315	89	2
All Saints'.	1797	1979	3776	749	56	1
St. Michael's.	409	365	774	176	12	—
Litchurch.	251	265	516	104	16	—
Little Chester.	96	95	191	46	—	1
Darley Abbey.	487	683	1170	172	—	—
	12103	13401	25504	5164	348	45
Census of 1841	16805	18120	35015	6695	122	120

Parish of St. Alkmund's in the Workhouse 27
St. Peter's 38
St. Werburgh's 40
All Saints' 22
St. Michael's 11
In the Infirmary 85
County Jail 195 males—23 females 218
Asylum 17 males—14 females 31

All in the Census taken June 1, 1841. ...... 472.
Including 605 Irish—138 Scotch—and 91 Foreigners.

Population of the Parishes and their Townships, &c.

BOROUGH OF DERBY.	POPULATION.						Acreage.	Estimated Annual Rental.
	1801. Persons.	1811. Persons.	1821. Persons.	1831. Persons.	1841. Houses.	1841. Persons.		
St. Alkmund's Parish	2002	2516	3462	6004	1707	8623	649 0 0	21,400 0 0
Darley Abbey Chap.	615	796	841	680	170	1059	324 2 28	3550 9 0
Little Eaton Chapelry	395	429	547	610	156	712	553 0 0	2523 10 0
Little Chester Towns.	181	173	177	191	77	364	436 0 0	1424 13 3
Quorndon Chapelry...	357	427	458	487	120	556	700 0 0	1765 0 0
St. Michael's Parish...	771	815	925	774	196	1075		3200 0 0
Alvaston Chapelry ...	503	341	399	439	99	491	1284 0 0	3012 6 0
All Saints' Parish	2862	3211	3745	3776	853	4465	15 0 0	17,880 0 0
St. Werburgh's Parish	2966	3805	5317	6369	1599	8135	664 0 0	25,360 0 0
Osmaston	108	116	168	175	29	177	742 3 24	1932 5 0
St. Peter's Parish	2231	2696	3974	6704	2207	10577	174 3 31	27,240 0 0
Boulton	114	112	159	172	37	171	811 0 0	1440 11 0
Litchurch Township	35	52	93	516	128	717	704 2 31	3290 15 0
Normanton Chapelry	214	230	294	290	63	309	1328 2 27	2657 17 0
	13154	15719	21439	27190	7441	37431	8388 2 6	96,617 6 3

Total of the Population of the 5 parishes in 1831, 23582
Ditto   Litchurch, Darley, and Little Chester 1922
in 1831   25504
1841   35015
increase   9511

In this historical sketch I have noticed several periods of the population and enlargement of the Borough, so as to afford a general retrospective view of its gradual growth. During the last thirty-five years, Derby has trebled its inhabitants. The streets and principal thoroughfares have been greatly improved, and additional streets have risen in every quarter, particularly in the Castle

Fields, Nuns Green, Kensington, between the Derwent and North Parade, North of Bridge Gate, City Road, Canary Islands, Burton Road, and between the Normanton and Osmaston Roads. The improvement act, obtained in 1825, has been productive of many alterations tending to the health and convenience of the inhabitants. Within this period three Protestant and one Roman Catholic Church, and ten Dissenters' Chapels have been built, besides numerous Schools and charitable institutions for the benefit of the present and future generations. Public institutions for the encouragement of science and education are almost daily increasing, and there are two newspapers published in the borough. The late Town Hall, erected in 1826, and burnt down on the 21st of October, 1841, was an elegant building, the exterior of which surpassed the interior, while the new interior of the County Hall, remarkable for the utility as well as the beauty of its arrangements, remains in possession of its grotesque facade, built in the style of the 17th century. The front of the New County Gaol may be classed among the finest specimens of Doric Architecture in the kingdom, but unfortunately it has been thought necessary, on account of the riots in 1831, to rear two martello towers, more suited to the old feudal times than the present era, one on each side of this truly classical portico. In addition to that noble establishment the Infirmary, the medical wants of the poor find relief in a Dispensary, established upon a very admirable plan. The Market Place has been enlarged and improved, and the facilities of trade have been every where objects of attention. Within fifteen years, Coaches, or what are called *Flies*, have been called for, and set up, and since the introduction of three important lines of Railway into the Borough, Omnibuses have been established on account of the increasing intercourse of the community, while the old sedan chair is retained only for the conveyance of invalids. The social amusements of the theatre or concert-room, are probably not so well attended as they were when the town was much smaller ; and the oratorios triennially performed for the benefit of the Infirmary, have latterly scarcely paid their expenses. In fact, as the comforts of the domestic circle increase, the recreations that were formerly sought for from public society every where diminish. There were no public walks, such as Darley Grove and the Holmes, formerly afforded the inhabitants of the borough, until 1840, when Joseph Strutt, esq., presented to the town the munificent gift of the Arboretum ; and bowling-greens, the constant evening amusement of respectable tradesmen during the greater portion of the last century, are now but little encouraged. Scientific lectures succeed best when delivered at the Mechanics' Institution, and without supposing that the higher classes of society do not make use of the extensive means in their power of privately acquiring knowledge more perfectly in their libraries, we see in the open manner in which the humble classes come to the fountains of instruction, a strong proof of the enlargement of mind among the manufacturing operatives, and the handicraftsmen of the rising generation. The literary and philosophical institutions will be described under their proper appellatives, but I cannot here omit to mention as an eminent proof of the improving taste displayed to the honour of the borough, the Picture Gallery of Joseph Strutt, esq., which comprises many of the best paintings of ancient and modern times, to which visitants obtain access with a facility worthy of the amiable and intelligent proprietor ; and the Museum at the Athenæum Rooms which is open to the public. The introduction of Railways will add materially to the importance of this town. Three of those vast modern undertakings having their termini one mile from the Market Place, on the south side of the borough. Two of these, the Midland Counties, and the Birmingham and Derby Junction Railways, are competing lines for the London traffic. The Midland Counties' Railway has a direct line between Derby and Nottingham, $15\frac{3}{4}$ miles in length ; and at a little more than midway between those towns, the London line from Derby is joined by one from Nottingham, near the bridge over the Trent, and the entrance to the Red Hill tunnel, and it thence proceeds to Loughborough and Leicester, joining the London and Birmingham Railway at Rugby. The distance from Derby to Rugby, is $49\frac{1}{4}$ miles, and from Rugby to London, 83, ($132\frac{1}{4}$). The Birmingham and Derby Junction Railway joins the London and Birmingham line at Hampden in Arden, and is $38\frac{1}{2}$ miles in length, from Hampden to London, 103, ($141\frac{1}{2}$) and $9\frac{1}{2}$ miles to Birmingham, (48). The North Midland Railway runs from Derby, by Belper, Alfreton, Chesterfield, (within 6 miles of Sheffield,) Masbro', for Rotherham, Barnsley, Wakefield, to Leeds, $72\frac{3}{4}$ miles. At Normanton, the Manchester and Leeds, and at Altofts the York and North Midland runs on to the North Midland. The Railway Station at Derby is superior to any in Europe for its extent and accommodation. The town of Derby has been much enlarged and improved within the last few years, and its public buildings have increased materially both in number and importance. There are now eight churches connected with the establishment, and one Catholic church, besides many large chapels belonging to various denominations of Christians. The chief branch of the manufacture is silk-sewings, doubles, velvets, sarcenets, &c., lace, hosiery, small wares, porcelain, spar ornaments, marble chimney pieces, watches, jewelry, colours, patent shot, white and red lead, patent lead piping, copper and tin plates, sheet iron, tobacco pipes, soap, wrought iron boilers, tanks, boats, &c., steam engines, iron lathes, printing presses, &c., besides several extensive iron foundries, breweries, and establishments for dying and bleaching.

The Police force of the Borough consists of twenty constables under the direction of a superintendent. The constables are allowed 18s. per week, and their clothing. Mr. John Abraham Thompson, Superintendent, Market Place.

POLICE CONSTABLES.

1 Hardy, Samuel, Silk Mill Lane.
2 Hanson, Richard, Bridge Gate.
3 Broughton, John, Hope Street.
4 Gee, William, Upper Brook Street.
5 Gallimore, Richard, Castle Street.
6 Wragg, William, St. Peter's Church Yard.
7 Hill, William, Normanton Road.
8 Hardy, George, St. Peter's Street.
9 Hunt, Joseph, Goodwin Street.
10 Moorcroft, William, Union Buildings.
11 Denstone, James, Drewry Lane.
12 Wibberley, Ralph, Lock-up, New Market.
13 Picken, Richard, Bridge Gate.
14 Taylor, Benjamin, John Street.
15
16
17
18 Rouse, Thomas, Darley Lane.
19 Messenger, Henry, Union Buildings.
20 Clarke, George, Leaper Street.
Allen, James, Agard Street, Magistrates' Constable.
Tomlinson, James, Exeter Place, Do. Do.

CHURCHES AND CHAPELS.

" Majestic Pile! whose towered summit stands
Far eminent above all else that rise
In Derby's peopled vale; through many an age,
With changing form, but renovated strength,
Thou hast maintained thy native site; and still,
(If unprophetic hopes fulfilment gain)
Shall other centuries depart and leave
Thee Sovereign of the scene!"

Edwards's All Saints' Church.

" The stranger, who wanders through Derby in quest of objects worthy of remark, will find some defects, and more beauties: but when he arrives at All Saints', he arrives at the chief excellence—the pride of the place. It stands as a prince among subjects; a giant among dwarfs. Viewed at any distance, or in any attitude, the associated ideas of taste, grandeur and beauty, fascinate the mind; the eye is captivated and continually turns to its object, but never tires. Some pride, more sense, and still more judgment must have combined in our forefathers in the construction of this noble tower: they wrought, and we enjoy the credit of their labour.

" A church in Derby, where the stone is not of a loose texture, will endure much more than a thousand years. As time has worn out one church and one steeple, we may fairly suppose this was erected early in the Saxon government, and is the oldest in Derby, being the only one known to have been rebuilt, St. Werburgh's excepted; nor is it to be much doubted, as this spot is the most inviting, that the Britons had a temple here." *(Hutton.)*

The tower of All Saints' is very justly the boast of Derby: it may be said, according to an observation of Mr. Hutton, not only to rank as " a Prince among subjects" compared with the buildings in its immediate vicinity, but to maintain a very conspicuous place among similar buildings, taking the more extensive range of the kingdom. The tower of Boston church alone is of a greater height: this however was built one hundred and fifty or two hundred years previous, and has an octagonal lanthorn or louvre at the top, to the summit of which from the ground, is said to be 300 feet. With the heights of those few other celebrated towers of parochial churches to which it alone can be compared, it bears the following proportion:

All Saints', Derby	174 feet.	Wrexham, Denbighshire ...	132 feet.
Taunton, Somersetshire ...	153	St. Stephen's, Bristol	124
Doncaster, Yorkshire	152	Magdalene Tower, Oxford	122

A similar parallel cannot, with equal propriety, be drawn with the heights of cathedral churches, as their construction is of a different nature; having as their highest part the central tower, which rises from the roof, and not, as in most of the instances above given, in one direct elevation from the ground. As it may, however, assist in giving a more correct idea of the relative altitude of All Saints', we shall just name, that with the exception of those that have spires, the following alone are higher: Lincoln, 288 feet; Canterbury, 235; York, 234; Gloucester, 225; Durham, 214; Ely, 210; and Worcester, 196: whilst Bath, which is 162 feet; Wells, 160; Peterborough, 150; Winchester, 133; Exeter, 130; Carlisle, 128; Chester, 127; and Bristol, 127, are lower.

But, prominent as it thus stands in its dimensions, it is to the beauty of the outline and proportion, to the purity of its style, and to the chasteness and elegance of its enrichments, that its chief claim for admiration rests, and which will ever cause it to be looked upon with pleasure, and continue to make it a most distinguished object. A general description will serve to illustrate each of these particulars, and confirm its superior claim to the attention of all lovers of Gothic architecture.

With regard to its *outline*, the angle buttresses rising with a bold projection from the ground, form in their gradual ascent to the top, by means of slopes, gables, niches, &c. what is termed the logarithmic curve, in other words, the line, or natural sweep made by the trunk of trees. These lose themselves in the four square turrets that rise above the roof, and which are crowned by pinnacles and crockets, and each by a gilt vane. The top of the tower is finished by open battlements, with a small centre turret between each.

Its general *proportion*, compared with the churches before named, has a rather more solid appearance, being only about four and a half diameters in height, whilst some of those are four and three quarters, and five diameters.

The body of the tower is divided into three stories, of nearly equal heights, by two beautiful lines of octangular and circular tracery, with shields and small battlements above. The lower story on two sides is quite plain, and in the front it has the entrance door with a niche, on each side, and a line of circular tracery and shields above, on which rests a window with four divisions. Each of the four sides of the second story consists of beautiful tracery, having the general feature of a window, but a very small part of which is pierced for light. The upper division forms the belfry, each side of which has a window with three mullions in two heights, filled in with sound boarding, and having surrounding tracery similar to the story below. The battlements above, as well as the buttresses, are also richly pannelled with tracery. The whole is in a tolerable good state of preservation, except the doorway, the niches and enrichments of which are a good deal defaced ; these are now undergoing repair, and will soon be restored. (Sep. 1842.)

The style is a remarkably chaste specimen of what is generally termed, the Florid, or highly decorated Gothic, or, according to a designation preferred by others, the Gothic of the fifteenth century. The more particular date of its erection, is the latter end of the reign of Henry the Seventh, or the former part of Henry the Eighth, and hence it may be considered as one of the last specimens of this then matured species of architecture in the kingdom ; for after this period a complete stop was put to the erection of ecclesiastical edifices, the art of building in this style was lost, and the Italian mode was gradually introduced.

From an inscription of "young men and maydens" which still remains on a fascia running round three sides of the tower, it is supposed by some that it was erected to that height by the contributions of young people of both sexes. By others this is supposed to be merely part of a quotation from the bible; and this latter opinion is most probably correct, as there are to be found partial scriptural inscriptions on other churches of about the same age.

The ancient body of the church was of Gothic architecture, and we regret that we have not been able to discover any description or print of a building that was probably in some measure adapted to this beautiful tower. In the old view of Derby, now in the possession of Mr. Harwood, of St. Peter's-street, the eastern gable of the church body partially appears. It is double, and each part seems to have contained a large Gothic window differing from the other in its style of ornament and form. This indicates that one part of the body of the church was more ancient than the other. From such a document it would be presumptuous in us to pretend to surmise any detail of the structure.

The modern body attached to this fine relic of Gothic proportions is in the style of the Roman Doric, and although it must be admitted to be an elegant and chaste design, it is lamentably incongruous with the tower. It was the design of the classical Gibbs, the architect of St. Martin's church, London, Gainsborough church, and the Radcliffe library, Oxford. It was built of beautiful freestone, the produce of the neighbourhood, in the years 1723, 1724, and 1725, and is 130 feet long by 83

c

feet wide. The present church was opened for public worship November, 25th, 1725, when a sermon was preached by Dr. Hutchinson, at that time minister, from *Psalm* cxxii. 1. " I was glad when they said unto me, Let us go into the house of the Lord." The expenses of the erection of this fabric were principally defrayed by voluntary contributions, which were raised by the Doctor, who not only subscribed £40. but being a man of genteel address, charged himself with raising the whole money, and executing a masterly work without a shilling expense to his parish. It is said he was a complete master of the art of begging. The people to whom he applied were not able to keep their money ; it passed from their pockets to his own as if by magic. Wherever he could recollect a person likely to contribute to this desirable work, he made no scruple to visit him at his own expense. He took a journey to London to solicit the benefaction of Thomas Chambers, esq. ancestor of the Earl of Exeter, who gave him £100. If a stranger passed through Derby, the doctor's bow and his rhetoric were employed in the service of the church. His anxiety was urgent, and his powers so prevailing, that he seldom failed of success. When the waits fiddled at his door for a Christmas-box, instead of sending them away with a solitary shilling, he invited them in, treated them with a tankard of ale, and persuaded them out of a guinea. He procured five hundred and eighty-nine subscribers, who gave the sum of £3249. 11s. 6d. But it appears he could procure a man's name by his eloquence easier than his money ; for fifty-two of the subscribers never paid their sums, amounting to £137. 16s. 6d. The remaining £3111. 15s. being defective, he procured a brief, which added £598. 5s. 6d. more. Still, though assiduity was not wanting, money was ; he therefore sold six burying places in the vault for six guineas ; and twelve of the principal seats in the church, by inch of candle, for £475. 13s. which were purchased as freeholds by the first inhabitants.

" Pride influences our actions ; nor will it bear contradiction. As the doctor raised the money, he justly expected to have the disposal ; but the parishioners considered themselves neglected, and repeatedly thwarted his measures, till, provoked by reiterated insults, he threw up the management, and left them in a labyrinth of their own creating. The result was, a considerable expense upon themselves. Some things he intended, were never finished, and some never begun."*

1735. " In this year the steeple of All Saints' was within a few minutes of being consumed by fire. This was occasioned by a plumber, who, going to close some leaks in the leaden roof, made a fire on the top of the steeple, upon a hearth of loose bricks, which he carelessly left unextinguished. Some days elapsed before a smoke was observed issuing from the battlements, and it was some time before any one would venture upon the dangerous, but necessary business of exploring it. At last, however, this was done ; the aspect was dreadful ; the roof was melted, the sleepers burnt, and the main beam consumed to the very edge of the wall which supported it."

The steeple contains a good set of ten bells and chimes. This church has, in all probability, been twice rebuilt since its original foundation. In ancient writings it is called All Hallows ; a name which it still retains in the dialect of the common people.

The church of All Saints was formerly collegiate, and had seven, and at one time, eight prebendaries. It is generally supposed the prebendaries of this church

* Hutton.

The Doctor having occasion to go to town, deputed the Rev. H. Cantrell, then vicar of St. Alkmund's, to the care of his parochial duties during his absence, but on the first and second Sundays of the Doctor's absence, Mr. Bagnold, then mayor, with a part of the body corporate, with their mace, &c. attended divine service, and ordered two other clergymen of the town, the Rev. William Chambers, and the Rev. Joshua Winter, to take possession of the pulpit and reading desk, and to perform the duties of the day. Mr. Cantrell, who was in attendance, remonstrated against their proceedings, and produced his authority for that purpose, not only by the Doctor's own letter, but also a letter from his diocesan. These disputes grew warm, and Mr. Bagnold was accused of using improper language and behaviour in so sacred a place, for which he was afterwards prosecuted in the Ecclesiastical Court. Such, however, was the ingratitude and ill treatment which the Doctor received from many of his parishioners, that he was at length compelled to relinquish that church, the erection of which had cost him such unwearied exertions, and to take up his residence for the remainder of his life in London.   *MS. Notes of Derby.*

resided in the house still designated " The College," and which is situate on the north side of the church. To this college formerly belonged two acres and a half of land, lying in Bridge-croft, in Derby ; all manner of tithes of corn, grain, hay, wool, lamb, and all other tithes whatever within the town and fields of Quorndon ; tithes of the same articles in Little Eaton ; one messuage, with lands, meadows and pastures appertaining to it ; a barn with lands, meadows, and pastures, lands and hereditaments called " The two small Prebends," a messuage and tenement, and one close of land with the appurtenances, all situate in Little Chester ; together with all manner of tithes within the liberty. The revenues of this college were estimated, in 1547, at £39. 12s. yearly income. The college house, which had been the habitation of the canons, passed into lay hands soon after the Reformation. It was some time in the possession of the Allestree family, who sold it to the Goodwins ; it is now by descent from the latter the property of John Coke, esq., of Debdale House, Mansfield-Woodhouse, who, since it came into his possession has modernized and improved the property.

There was in this church also the chantry of our Lady, and the guild of the Holy Trinity. Queen Mary, in the first year of her reign, granted one of the prebends of All Saints', called The Stone-house Prebend, and two small prebends, with several lands, tithes, &c. which had belonged to this college, and certain premises belonging to St. Mary's chantry and Trinity guild, to the Corporation. Directing at the same time, that the bailiff and burgesses should pay £13. 6s. 8d. to two priests, celebrating divine service, and having the cure of souls of the parish church of All Saints. There is now only one vicarage, formerly in the gift of the Corporation, who paid the vicar a stipend of £80. per annum. Archdeacon Walton, who died in 1603, gave £6. per annum towards augmenting the incumbent's stipend. The Rev. E. Lillingstone is the present vicar. Hutton says the living is a curacy worth £130.

The interior of the church is particularly light, elegant and spacious : the roof is supported by five columns on each side : the windows are large and handsome ; and the symmetry and harmonious proportions of the building have a very pleasing effect. At the west end is a spacious organ gallery furnished with an excellent organ. The gallery is wainscotted and of exceeding good workmanship. The east end is separated from that part of the structure appropriated to public worship by a rich open screen work of iron, fabricated by Bakewell, at an expense of £500. The portion thus cut off from the body of the church is divided into three parts. On the north side is the vestry and the east entrance into the church. Here the corporation meet for the the purpose of choosing the mayor ; here also the parish meetings are held. The centre part forms a very excellent chancel. The communion-table, altar-piece, and pavement within the communion rails, are of beautiful Derbyshire marble. Over the window is a painting by *Rawlinson*, representing the appearance of the tomb after our Saviour's resurrection, the attendant angel, the visit of the pious women, and the sleeping guards, which he presented to the corporation. Underneath the chancel is a spacious vault, called the Town Vault, in which many families have their places of interment, a small acknowledgment being paid to the corporation for this privilege. The southern side is the dormitory and contains the monuments of the Cavendish family. Underneath this is a spacious vault, in which many of that noble family are interred. In this dormitory is a monument nearly 12 feet high, which stands near the centre, and was erected to the memory of William, Earl of Devonshire, who died on the 20th of June, 1628 ; and Christian, his Countess, the only daughter of Lord Bruce, of Kinross, in Scotland. Each side of the monument is open ; and in the middle, under a dome, are whole length figures, in white marble, of the Earl and his Lady, standing upright. The angles on the south side are ornamented with busts of their four children ; William, the eldest, successor to the Earl ; Charles, lieutenant-general of horse in the civil wars, Henry, who died young ; and Anne, married to Robert, Lord Rich, son and heir to Robert, Earl of Warwick.

The Countess was much celebrated by the wits of her day, to whom she was a great patroness; she was buried with great funeral solemnity on the 18th of February, 1674–5; and at the same time were deposited in the vault, pursuant to her express desire, the bones of her beloved son, the brave Colonel Charles Cavendish, a most distinguished officer in the royal army, who was slain near Gainsborough, in the month of July, 1643, and had been interred at Newark. All the Earls and Dukes of Devonshire, of the Cavendish family, lie buried in the vault at Derby, except the first Earl (who was interred at Edensor) with their ladies, besides many of the younger branches of this noble family. Henry Cavendish, grandson of the third Duke of Devonshire (one of the most eminent chemists and natural philosophers of the age, of whom it has been said, that since the death of Sir Isaac Newton, England has sustained no scientific loss so great as that of Cavendish) was interred in the family vault at Derby, in the month of March, 1810. In this vault also lie the remains of the brave Earl of Northampton, who was killed at the battle of Hopton Heath, near Stafford, March 19, 1643.

On the south side of this repository is a splendid mural monument, to the memory of the celebrated Elizabeth, Countess of Shrewsbury, which was erected during her life time, and under her own inspection. In a recess in the lower part is the figure of the Countess, arrayed in the habit of the times, with her head reclined on a cushion, and her hands uplifted in the attitude of prayer.

The following is a translation of the inscription.

To the memory of Elizabeth, the daughter of John Hardwicke, of Hardwicke, in the county of Derby, esq.; and at length co-heiress to her brother John. She was married first to Robert Barley, of Barley, in the said county of Derby, esq.; afterwards to William Cavendish, of Chatsworth, knt., Treasurer of the Chamber to the Kings Henry VIII. and Edward VI. and queen Mary, to whom he was also privy counsellor. She then became the wife of Sir William St. Lo, captain of the royal guard. Her last husband was the most noble George (Talbot) Earl of Shrewsbury. By Sir William Cavendish alone she had issue. This was three sons, namely, Henry Cavendish, of Tutbury, in the county of Stafford, esq.; who took to wife Grace, the daughter of the said George, Earl of Shrewsbury, but died without legitimate issue; William, created Baron Cavendish of Hardwicke, and Earl of Devonshire, by his late majesty King James; and Charles Cavendish, of Welbeck, knt., father of the most honourable William Cavendish, Knight of the Bath, and Baron Ogle, by right of his mother, and on account of his merit created Viscount Mansfield; Earl, Marquess, and Duke of Newcastle-upon-Tyne; and Earl Ogle, of Ogle. She had also the same number of daughters, viz. Frances, married to Sir Henry Pierpoint; Elizabeth, to Charles Stuart, Earl of Lenox; and Mary, to Gilbert, Earl of Shrewsbury. This most illustrious Elizabeth, Countess of Shrewsbury, built the houses of Chatsworth, Hardwicke, and Oldcotes, highly distinguished by their magnificence, and finished her transitory life on the 13th day of February, in the year 1607, and about the 87th year of her age,* expecting a glorious resurrection, lies interred underneath.

Charities belonging to All Saints' parish.

		£. s. d.		
Ash Francis	....	3 0 0	Poor	Paid by the Corporation
Bateman, Sir Hugh....	Property at Derby, messuages, &c. to the Goldsmiths' Co.	....	6 gowns to poor wid.	Paid by R. T. Bateman, esq.
Beaumont Alice	Rent charge	0 10 0	Poor	Paid by Mr. Roger Cox.
Botham William	....	0 16 0	....	Paid by the Corporation.
Crowshaw Robert	Land	20 0 0	For a lecture	Ditto ditto.
Ditto	Land	15 0 0	Poor	Ditto ditto.
Devonshire Countess of	Rent charge	2 8 0	Poor	Ditto ditto.
Duffield William......	2 houses in Friar-gate	15 10 0	6 gowns to poor	Will, 22nd Dec. 1639.
Ditto	1 house in Bag lane ..	8 5 0		
Goodwin Francis......	Rent charge	1 8 0	Four gowns	Will, 11th Nov. 1626.
Glossop Anthony......	Rent charge	0 12 0	Poor	Paid by the Corporation.
Harpur Joyce	£10.	0 10 0	Poor	Ditto ditto.
Hough Peter	....	1 0 0		
Kilby Richard	....	1 0 0	Poor	Ditto ditto.
Moore Isabel..........	6 acres of land in Darley Slade	44 0 0	For binding out poor boys	Inden. March 31, 1673.
Osborne Edward	Land at Chester Green	1 0 0	Poor	Paid by the Corporation.
Shrewsbury Countess of	Rent charge	2 0 0	Minister for 2 Serm.	1st March, 1599.
Ditto	Rent charge	2 0 0	Poor	Ditto.
Stone Elizabeth	Rent charge	0 10 0	Ten poor widows	Will, 12th July, 1717.
	Rent charge	0 10 0	Poor	Paid by Mrs. Edge.
	Rent charge	0 6 8	Poor	Paid by Mrs. Thorpe.
Swetnam Rev. J.	Rent charge	0 16 0	Sixteen poor wid.	Inden. 21st Sept. 1652.
Walthall William	Rent charge	1 12 0	Poor	Paid by the Corporation.
Walton Jane..........	Rent charge	1 4 0	Poor	Ditto ditto.
Ward Samuel	5½ acres of land in Darley Slade	43 0 0	Poor	Deed, 15th and 16th August, 1707.

* If Collins be correct in his statement, that she was fourteen when married to Robert Barley, who died in 1533, her age must be here somewhat under-rated, and she must have been in her ninetieth year, even if her first marriage had not been of twelve months' continuance. *Lysons,* page 116.

St. Alkmund's Church.—This church is situate at the north end of the town, in Bridge-gate. It is supposed to have been founded as early as the ninth century, in honour of Alkmund (son of Alured, the deposed king of Northumberland) who was slain in battle whilst endeavouring to reinstate his father. Fuller's account is this: " St. Alkmund (son of Alured, king of Northumberland) slain in a battle on the behalf of Ethelmund, viceroy of Worcester, pretending to re-cover lands against Duke Wolstan, who detained them, was therefore reputed Saint and Martyr. It would pose a good scholar to clear his title to the latter, who lost his life in a quarrel of civil concernment: on which account all battles betwixt Christians, such as are slain on one side may lay claim to martyrship. However, it befriendeth his memory that his body, translated (from Lilleshull, in Shropshire) to Derby, was believed to do miracles, being there with great veneration interred in a church called St. Alkmund, on the right hand as passengers (from the South) go over the bridge, whither the Northern people made many pilgrimages, till discomposed by the Reformation."

This church is undoubtedly the oldest in Derby, and though built posterior to the Saxon times, it is a very ancient Gothic structure, with a square tower and embattled. The architecture appears to be the style of the fourteenth century. The spouts are formed of rude carved figures, and the string courses are ornamented with sculptured heads, and other sculptures, as ornaments, in different parts of the building. It consists of middle, north and south aisles: there are galleries on the north and south sides and west end, and the west gallery contains a good organ. In very early times this church was granted to the abbey of Derley, and continued till the dissolution, when Henry the Eighth seized it; and it rested in the crown till his daughter, Queen Mary, gave it to the corporation of Derby, who have sold the presentation to Jedediah Strutt, esq.; and his son-in-law, the Rev. E. H. Abney is the present vicar. It is a vicarage, valued in the king's books at £11. 6s. 8d. This, as Mr. Hutton observes, must have been a mistake, or some of the emoluments were lost; for in the reign of George the First, the income was only

£8. per annum, and divine service was performed once a quarter. Ever since the
year 1712, it has enjoyed an endowment bequeathed by a gentleman of the name
of Goodwin, which Mr. Hutton hands down to us in the following words: "An
old bachelor, of the name of Goodwin, descended from an ancient family in Derby,
possessed an estate of £60. a year. 'How will you dispose of your fortune?' says
Mr. Cantrell, minister of St. Alkmund's. 'I am at a loss,' replied Goodwin, 'for
I have no near relations.' 'My church,' says the parson, 'stands desolate;
instead of being a place of regular worship, it is only a nursery for owls and bats.
No act of charity can surpass that of promoting religion.' 'Then I will give £10.
per annum to St Alkmund's at my death,' says Goodwin, 'and the residue at the
death of my nephew:' which last happened about the year 1734." This estate is
situate at Plumley, in the parish of Eckington, and at that time produced £60. per
annum, but now about £210. The steeple contains six musical bells. The parish
includes Little Chester, Little Eaton, Darley, and Quarndon. The income is
about £350. per annum.

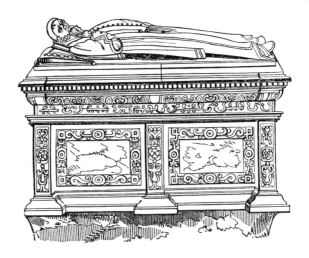

To the wall in the east end of the south aisle is erected a worthy tomb of alabaster, well adorned with
carved work, upon it is the effigy of a man in his gowne, and a booke in his left hand, his head resting
upon his right hand, and under his head a booke. In two tables on the side of the monument has been a
deal of writing in gold letters, but now not to be taken. On the north end of a tombe in a shield, the following coate of armes, vizt. *Ermine*, a chief, *Gules*, and a labell of five points, for Bullock, empaling a fesse
engrailed between six cross crosslets. Crest, seems to be a sheaf of arrows in a coronet.

Charities belonging to St. Alkmund's parish.

		£.	s.	d.		
Ash Francis	Rent charge ...	0	18	8	Poor	Paid by the corporation.
Botham William	Rent charge ...	0	5	8	Poor	Ditto ditto.
Crowshaw Richard	Land	1	10	0	3 poor, 3s. every 5th Sund.	Ditto ditto.
Devonshire Countess of	Rent charge ...	0	16	0	Poor	Ditto ditto.
Glossop Anthony	Rent charge ...	0	4	0	Poor	Will, 4th February, 1666.
Nayler Christopher	Rent charge ...	0	10	0	Poor	Paid by the corporation.
Osborne Edward	Land	0	6	8	Poor	Deed, 1667.
Parish land	4a. 2r. 36½p. ...	16	0	0	Poor	Paid by the corporation.
Shrewsbury Countess of	Land	0	13	4	Ten poor widows	1652.
Swetnam Rev. J.	Rent charge ...	0	10	0	Poor	Paid by the corporation.
Walthall William	Rent charge ...	0	10	8	Poor	Ditto ditto.
Walton Jane	Rent charge ...	0	8	0		

St. Michael's Church stands in Queen-street, about midway between the churches of All Saints' and St. Alkmund's, and, like the latter, was a member to Darley abbey, until it was seized by Henry the Eighth. This church is a Gothic structure, with a square tower and embattled. It is very ancient and built upon a small scale, but at what time it was erected cannot exactly be determined. About the latter end of the twelfth or the beginning of the thirteenth century it was given by one of the Freschevilles, to the convent of Darley. In the first year of Queen Mary's reign she gave this church to the bailiffs and burgesses of the town of Derby. It is a vicarage, valued in the king's books £4. 14s. 11d. according to Ecton, £11. 6s. 8d. and yearly tenths 9s. 6d. This church was united with St. Werburgh's; it contains about two hundred and eighteen sittings. Service was performed in 1791, once a month, now alternately morning and afternoon, every Sunday. There is also a lecture on Tuesday evening. The steeple contains three small bells. The patronage of this church is vested in the crown. The present vicar is the Rev. John Garton Howard. The living was augmented by a private benefaction of £400.; royal bounty £400.; and a parliamentary grant of £2000. It is now worth according to the commissioners report, £79. 6s. 10d. viz. Land at Sturston, £21. 12s. At Ockbrook, £40. Funds, £6. 14s. 10d. Alvaston, £3. Easter dues, and Fees, £8.

Charities belonging to St. Michael's parish.

		£.	s.	d.		
Botham William	Rent charge	0	2	8	Poor	Paid by the Corporation.
Crowshaw Richard......	Land		......		2s. 3d. every 5th Sund.	Ditto ditto.
Deane Daniel	....	0	5	0	Poor	Will, 1st April. 1637.
Devonshire Countess of	Rent charge	0	8	0	Poor	Paid by the Corporation.
Duffield William.........	Rent of ho. Walker la.	0	9	0	Poor	St. Michael's and St. Alk.
Glossop Anthony	Rent charge	0	2	0	Poor	Will, dated 1639.
Nayler Christopher ...	Rent charge	0	10	0	Poor	Paid by the Corporation.
Osborne Edward	Land at Chester Green	0	3	4	Poor	Ditto ditto.
Parish lands	2 houses in Queen-st.	4	19	0	Poor	Pd.by ten.of L.Scarsdale.
Stowman Edward	Rent charge	0	10	0	Poor	
Shrewsbury Countess of	Rent charge	0	6	8	Poor	Paid by Duke of Devons.
Walthall William	Rent charge	0	5	4	Poor	Paid by the Corporation.
Walton Jane..............	Rent charge	0	4	0	Poor	Ditto ditto.

St. Werburgh's Church is situate on the western side of the town, on the Markeaton brook. Like that of All Saints', it has a tower and body of different orders,
though probably both were built during the seventeenth century. The church
which originally stood on this spot, is supposed to have been built before the
Conquest, but from being so near the brook, its foundations were sapped by floods,
and, in the year 1601, the tower fell to the ground. To gain firmer ground, it was
erected on the east side, which is contrary to the situation of steeples. In 1698,
on the 5th of November, the church fell, owing to another flood. It has a Gothic
tower and a Tuscan body, with a lantern in the centre of the roof. In the chancel
is a much admired altar-piece, consisting of the arms of Queen Anne, and other
ornaments; under which are the Lord's Prayer, the Creed and the Ten Com-
mandments, all in gilt and painted plaster work, date 1708. There is a gallery on
the north and south sides, and west end, in the latter there is a good organ, built
by Gray of London. St. Werburgh's church is calculated to contain eight hundred
persons. It is 60 feet by 58 feet, with a chancel 38 feet by 16 feet. In this
church there was a chantry of the Virgin Mary, which was endowed with various
messuages, lands, cottages and gardens, which, in the reign of Queen Mary, were
granted by her to the Corporation of Derby. The living of St. Werburgh's is a
vicarage, in the gift of the crown. Its clear annual value according to the
Commissioners report is £318. The impropriation is vested in Lord Scarsdale.
The steeple contains five bells. The Rev. Edward Unwin is the vicar.

Charities belonging to St. Werburgh's parish.

		£.	s.	d.		
Ash Francis	{ Property at Derby, } messuages, &c. to { the Goldsmiths' Co. }	10 3 7	0 0 0	0 0 0	Vicar Poor Put out one appren.	Paid by the Corporation.
Bloodworth John	{ £100. to be laid out } { in land. }	5	2	8	Poor	Ditto ditto.
	Rent charge	0	17	4	Minister, &c.	Ditto ditto.
Botham William	Rent charge	0	8	0	Poor	1603.
Brough Theodosia	Rent charge	1	0	0	Ten poor widows	Will, dated 1723.
Cheshire Isaac	Rent charge	1	0	0	Poor	Pd. by R. H. Cheney, esq.
Crowshaw Richard......	Land	0	5	0	5s. 3d. every 5th Sun.	Paid by the Corporation.
Cundy Dorothy	{ Rent charge .... } { Land 8a. 1r. 11p. ... } { £7. per anum .... } { 9 acres of land .... }	2 5 2	10 0 0	0 0 0	Cloth, 4 poor people 2 fellmo. or their wid. Poor, in bread Vicar for 2 Sermons	Will, 1697. Pd. by Mr. Jas. Lovatt.
Devonshire Countess of	Rent charge	1	4	0	Poor	Paid by the Corporation.

		£.	s.	d.		
Day Mary	Rent charge	2	12	0	Poor, in bread	{ Will, 25th Sept. 1669. { Pd. by Chs. Clarke, esq.
Deane Daniel	Rent charge	1	0	0	Poor	{ Will, dated 1637. { Pd. by Trust of Ass. R.
Fletcher Samuel	{ 2 acres of land { called Park Field		....		Ten poor widows	Will, 15th June, 1695.
	A rent charge of	1	0	0	only is paid by	W. Leaper Newton, esq.
Fowler Rebecca	7 acres of land	12	0	0	Instruct. 14 poor chil.	
Gisborne John, gent. ...	Tithes of C. Broughton	5	0	0	Poor	Will, 3rd May, 1689.
Gisborne John, the Son	....	1	4	0	Poor	Will, 16th April, 1704.
Glossop Anthony.........	Rent charge	0	6	0	Poor	Paid by the Corporation.
Haughton Thomas......	{ House & land, 22a. { 2r. 24p. Int. of £85. { 7s. 5d. in Messrs. { Crompton & New- { ton's hands	51	10	0	{ Four boys and one { or more girls to be { put out apprent.	Deed, 24th Oct. 1729.
Jones's Dole	....	0	4	0	Poor	Paid by the Churchward.
Osborne Edward........	....	0	10	0	Poor	Paid by the Corporation.
Parish lands	2 acres in Old Meadows					
Potter William	{ £50. .... {	2 2	10 10	0 0	Poor Minister	} Vested in the Parish } Officers.
Spateman John	£10.		....		Poor	Will, 1729.
Shrewsbury Countess of	Rent charge	1	0	0	Poor	Pd. by Duke of Devonsh.
Walthall William	Rent charge	0	16	0	Poor	Paid by the Corporation.
Walton Jane...............	Rent charge	0	12	0	Poor	Ditto ditto.

St. John's Church is an elegant structure, erected in a bad situation, on a flat site, on the south bank of the Markeaton brook, in Bridge-street. It is built in a mixed style of Gothic architecture, prevalent in the fourteenth, fifteenth, and sixteenth centuries, in imitation of one of the public buildings at Cambridge. It was designed by Mr. Francis Goodwin, of London, architect, and built under the direction of Mr. Thomas Mason, of Derby. The contractors were Mr. Thomas Cooper, who has executed the masonry in a very superior style of workmanship ; Messrs. Bridgart, who did the joiner's work ; the late Mr. William Horsley, the plumbing and glazing ; Messrs. Weatherhead, Glover and Co. the iron-work ; Mr. William Searle, the plastering ; and Messrs. Welsh, the painting. The inhabitants subscribed nearly £5000. and the remainder was from the parliamentary fund for building churches. It cost nearly £7500. It is lighted by 22 elegant cast-iron Gothic windows, has a double embattlement, and the six projecting buttresses on each side of the nave is ornamented with caps and consols. At each corner is an octagonal tower or turret 71 feet 3 inches high. The body of the church is 69 feet 6 inches long, 53 feet wide, and 38 feet 9 inches high, with a chancel 20 feet 3 inches by 7 feet 4½ inches. It has a gallery on the north and south sides and west end, and is capable of holding 1200 persons. The entrances to the body of the church and galleries are on the north and south sides and west end. It is a chapel of ease to St Werburgh's, and the Rev. Philip Gell, M. A. is the minister.

St. Peter's Church is situate near the centre of St. Peter's-street, towards the southern extremity of the town. It was given in the reign of king Stephen to Darley abbey. In pope Nicholas's *Taxatio*, the revenues of the church of St. Peter, at Derby, were estimated at £13. 6s. 8d. and the tenths at £1. 6s. 8d. It is a very ancient Gothic structure, with a square tower, ornamented pinnacles, and embattled. It is 58 feet by 48 feet, with a chancel 36 feet by 24 feet. This church having galleries all round is calculated to accommodate a large congregation. It has also a good organ in the west gallery.

Some years ago the late Mr. Wilson planted ivy round the walls of the church, which now nearly covers the building, and gives it a pleasing appearance.

In 1819, a piece of land was purchased by the parishioners for the enlargement of the church-yard from Dr. Forester. This new burying ground is a great acquisition to the parish. Another opportunity now presents itself of further enlarging the church-yard, by purchasing of Mr. Gascoyne the adjoining piece of land.

"Robert Liversage, a dyer, of Derby founded a chapel in this church in 1530, and ordered divine service to be celebrated every Friday. Thirteen poor men and women were to be present, each to be rewarded with a silver penny; as much in those days as would support a frugal person. The porches, like those of Bethesda, were crowded with people, who waited for the moving of the doors, as the others for that of the water. While the spiritual sergeant beat up for volunteers at a penny advance, recruits would never be wanting. A sufficient congregation was not doubted; nor their quarrelling for the money. The priest frequently found his hearers in that disorder which his prayers could not rectify; they frequently fought, but not the good fight of faith; nor did ill neighbourhood end with Friday. The hearer used to pay the preacher, but here the case was reversed. We learn that no scheme is so likely to fill a church as the silver penny; that good silver will draw more than good sermons; that no devotion is valid that is bought with a price; and that a penny will make a hypocrite." The patronage of the living is in the gift of the Rev. Charles Wright, who is the present Vicar. The living is about £150. per annum.

Charities belonging to St Peter's Parish.

		£.	s.	d.		
Babington Augustine...	Rent charge	1	0	0	Poor	Paid out of manor of Normanton.
Botham William, gent.	Rent charge	0	6	0	Poor	Paid by the Corporation.
Brough Theodosia	Rent charge	1	0	0	10 poor widows	Will, 1723.
Cundy Dorothy	Rent charge	2	10	0	4 gowns or coats	Will, 1697.
Devonshire Countess of	Rent charge	1	4	0	Poor	Paid by the Corporation.
Glossop Anthony	Rent charge	0	6	0	Poor	Ditto ditto.
Jackson George, M. D.	Rent charge	2	10	0	Poor	Paid by the Duke of Devonshire.
Osborne Edward	Land	0	10	0	Poor	Paid by the Corporation.
Osborne Rev. William	£35.	1	8	6	Poor and clerk	Paid by Trust of Liversage estate.
Shrewsbury Countess of	Rent charge	1	0	0	Poor	Paid by the Corporation.
Staples James	£5.	0	5	0	Poor	Paid by Trust of Liversage estate.
Walthall William	Rent charge	0	16	0	Poor	Paid by the Corporation.
Walton Jane...............	Rent charge	0	12	0	Poor	Ditto ditto.
Wilcox Elizabeth	{ ¼th of rents of } { mes. in Derby }	11	15	0	Poor	Will, 20th April, 1646.

Trinity Church is situate on the London road, it is of Gothic architecture; the extreme length of the building is 92 feet, and the width 52 feet. At the west end is a square Gothic tower, terminated by four domed pinnacles, the base of which comprises the porch and entrance, at the east end is a light oriel window, with opaque glass in large plates, designed and prepared for painting; by this, and twelve square headed side windows, an excellent light is thrown into every part of the interior. It has a gallery on the south and north sides and west end, and is calculated to hold 800 persons. The church-yard completely surrounds it; at the east end a school room is built, the scholars of both sexes are instructed on the national system. The Rev. E. Wade is the officiating Minister.

Mr. Botham, a Builder from Sheffield, purchased 1530 square yards of land, belonging to the Castle fields estate, and built this church on speculation at the cost of about £3500. He afterwards became a bankrupt, and the church was sold for the benefit of his creditors, for about £2000. which sum was raised by subscription.

Christ Church, Normanton road, in memory of the late Bishop Ryder, is built on the highest point in the town. The first stone of this beautiful church, designed by Mr. Habershon, architect, of London, containing 860 sittings, of which 300 are free, was laid on Friday, the 6th day of July, 1838, and was opened for public worship, by license granted by the Bishop of the Diocess in March, 1840; from which time to the present, the number of Persons attending divine worship, has fully proved the great importance of the undertaking; while the Sunday Schools attached to the church, evidently show, that a stated ministry in that part of the town, was of the utmost importance, and loudly called for; and it is no small gratification to see the effects produced amongst the poor, by a visiting and clothing Institution, lately established in that district, allotted to Christ church, containing a population of nearly four thousand, the greater proportion are the poorer classes.

The tower is 50 feet high, by 20 feet wide at the base, with buttresses, pinnacles and embattled, terminated by a spire 60 feet high. The length of the body is 85 feet, the width 50 feet, and the height 30 feet. It is lighted by six lancet shaped windows on each side, and a large window over the entrance door in the tower. On the stone over the door, immediately under the window, is this inscription.— To the memory of Bishop Ryder. The other end of the church is finished by a convenient vestry, 15 feet by 10 feet. The church is well heated by a descending stove near to the altar, and an ascending one at the entrance, and ventilated by Fair and Co's. patent ventilators.

Messrs. Bridgart were the contractors, at the sum of £2985. in addition to this the side galleries and extras, made the total cost about £3250. Mr. Wood contracted for the stone work under the Bridgarts, it was built by subscription. The sum of £1000. is raised for the Endowment. The patronage is vested in five Trustees, viz. W. Evans, Esq. M. P. Rev. E. Unwin, Vicar of St. Werburgh's, Rev. Samuel Hey, Rector of Ockbrook, Rev. Philip Gell, minister of St. John's, and Henry Cox, esq. Morning and Evening service is performed in it every Sunday, by the Rev. Roseingrave Macklin, Minister.

The *New Catholic Church of St. Maries,* was designed and executed under the celebrated architect, Mr. Pugin, of London. This Church, when completed according to the original design, will be among the most imposing and Catholic which have been raised since the time of the Reformation. It is built entirely of an excellent bright stone, and the style is of the earliest decorated kind which prevailed about the commencement of the reign of Henry the Sixth. The extreme length from the entrance door under the tower window to the sanctuary windows is 127 feet, and the width 45 feet; the nave 80 feet long, the chancel 27 feet by 20, and the tower 20 by 14 feet. Before quitting the ground-plan, we may remark that there are two sacristies, each of them 14 feet 6 inches, by 13 feet.

It would hardly be possible to have chosen a plot of ground more suitable than that which forms the site of the Church. Though occupying a most central position, it is nearly surrounded by the gardens of Edward Strutt, esq., M. P., one of the representatives for the town, and is therefore, protected from the noise to which great thoroughfares are usually exposed. The ground is also hilly, and requires thirteen steps to conduct us to the doors, whilst a stone wall, tastefully divided without any iron fence, and so low as not to conceal the entrance that separates the building from the main street.

The tower is 100 feet high to the top of the embattled parapet, and 117 to the top of the pinnacles, and when it is found possible to raise the spire, it will add 100 feet to the height; thus making the elevation of the whole about 217 feet above the level of the street. Considerable expense has been incurred in the foundations, and in the tower itself, for receiving finally the spire, which has been very much admired for its beauty, being richly ornamented with crockets, figures, niches, &c., &c., but at present this noble addition cannot be made; in the meanwhile the tower itself must always be pronounced exquisitely beautiful; so much so, that many have believed the building more attractive and symmetrical without the spire.

Above the doors of the tower is a large window 28 feet high, by 13 feet, with mullions, admirably arranged; and above this window, in a large and highly ornamented niche, stands the ever blessed mother of our Lord. The figure is about 6 feet 4 inches high, and the infant Saviour is represented reclining in her arms, having in his hand a lily, the emblem of purity.

As we look higher we might reasonably request attention to other parts of the building, as the belfry windows, a great variety of singular and striking forms used as gargonillas, &c., and above all, to the four evangelists bearing scrolls, and surmounting the graduated parapet, which form a very happy finish to the tower.

The ground cost £1400. the church about £7000. and when the houses, school, &c., are completed, an outlay of about £10,000. will be incurred. The first stone of this beautiful structure, was laid on 28th June 1838, the day of her Majesty's coronation, by the Honourable and Rev. George Spencer, who preached a sermon on the occasion, the subject of his sermon was, the politics of Catholics proved Loyal. He took his text from 2nd Esdras, viii 10. " And he said to them : Go, eat fat meats, and drink sweet wine, and send portions to them that have not prepared for themselves, because it is the holiday of the Lord, and be not sad."

The interior is beautifully fitted up. The dedication took place on Wednesday, October 9, 1839. There is a gallery at the south end, in which there is an excellent organ.

The Church is flanked by a comfortable and handsome residence for one of the priests, of brick, with stone quoins, and a minor style of decoration. On the other side is to be a larger and more decorated residence. The Rev. Thomas Sing and the Rev. Joseph Daniel are the present priests.

The *Unitarian Chapel*, situate in the Friar-gate, was the first nonconformist chapel erected in Derby. It is a plain brick building, 45 feet by 40 feet, and 20 feet high, lighted by 24 windows, with a school and vestry-room and burying ground at the back. The interior is handsomely fitted up with pews, and a gallery on the east and west sides and north end, which is ornamented with an excellent organ. Over the pulpit is placed the arms of William the Third, out of gratitude, as Mr. Hutton informs us, to that monarch for the granting them that liberty they had a right to demand. The congregation, in 1697, obtained a lease for 300 years, of the piece of ground on which the chapel is built, subject to a ground rent of £2. a year. In 1766, Mr. Abraham Crompton left £200. towards increasing the minister's salary. The Rev. Noah Jones is the present minister.

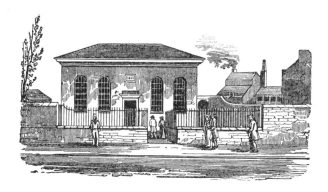

The *Friends' Meeting house*, erected by subscription in 1808, is situate in St. Helen's-street. It is a plain stone building, and has all that simplicity which distinguishes the sect to which it belongs. It appears from the Journal of George Fox, their founder, who was imprisoned for nearly twelve months at Derby, that the Quakers first obtained at Derby the appellation by which they are generally known. Justice Bennett, of Derby, says he, was the first that called us Quakers, in the year 1650, because I bid him "tremble at the word of the Lord."

The *Independent Chapel*, situate in Victoria-street, is a plain brick building, 54 feet long, and 48 feet wide, lighted by twenty-two windows, to which is attached a convenient vestry. This chapel was erected 1783–4, on or near the spot where St. Thomas-à-Becket's chapel stood, at the sole expense of Mr. Wilson. It is well pewed and neatly fitted up with a gallery on the east and west sides and north end, and calculated to accommodate from seven to eight hundred persons. The Rev. James Gawthorne, of Hoxton Academy, was ordained pastor over the congregation on the 10th of June, 1801, and is the present minister. This chapel was raised 10 feet, new fronted, and remodelled internally in 1836, and an excellent organ by Smythe, a celebrated German builder, introduced. Mr. William Mansfield Cooper was the contractor for the alterations at the sum of £1200.

Messrs. Thomas Jones, of Oathall, and Griffiths, in 1778, preached a few times in the market-place, at Derby, and on the 10th of September in that year, was announced in the Derby Mercury to preach on the morning of the following Sabbath, in a school room at the back of the Town hall. As the engagements of these ministers only permitted them to visit Derby occasionally, it was usual to send the public crier round the town to announce their intention to preach. In this manner the congregation was raised. In 1779, Thomas Wilson, esq., undertook to procure ministers to supply the congregation constantly.

The *Congregational Chapel*, London Road, is built on a plot of land containing 1600 square yards, formerly belonging to the Castle Fields' estate, purchased by Mr. Copeland, of Lincoln, from the late Thomas Borough, esq., and resold by him to the late Mr. William Collumbell, was purchased from the executors of the latter gentleman by the Trustees of the Chapel for the sum of £900. This beautiful Chapel, designed by Mr. H. J. Stevens, of Derby, is built of brick and stuccoed, and lighted by five circular-headed windows on each side, and a large square window at the eastern end. The portico and pediment supported by four columns is of the Corinthian order, and built with Hollington stone.

This Chapel is 70 feet long, by 45 feet wide, and 37 feet high. The vestibule and lobbies, including the staircases at the west end, are 61 feet 2 inches, by 8 feet. The vestry at the east end is 22 feet, by 14 feet. Over the vestry is the organ gallery ; and at the west end is a gallery for the school children. The ceiling is coved. The approach to the portico is by eight steps. The space between the four columns is 9 feet 4 inches. There is an area of 2 feet 8 inches round the chapel. The school room under is of the same length and width as the chapel. The contractors were Messrs. Gascoyne, who does the brick and stone work, plastering, plumbing, painting, glazing, &c., at the sum of £2280., and Mr. William Mansfield Cooper, the carpenter's work at the sum of £726. The pallisading and fence wall, gates, &c., will probably cost the additional sum of £250. The pulpit and interior fittings are in character with the exterior, elegant, and of the best workmanship. The total cost will be about £5000. The contributors to it are numerous and extremely liberal, the amount of £3000. having been raised. Amongst the largest contributors are Thomas Wilson, esq., of London. Joseph Handford, gent. Robert Forman, gent. John Hill, esq. John Moss, esq. William Goodale, esq. Thomas Boden, esq. Mr. Gascoyne. Mrs. Cooper. Mr. Richard Bryer. Mr. Bryer, of Vicar Wood. Mrs. Glover, of Birmingham, &c. &c.

The *General Baptist Chapel*, situate in Brook-street, is a brick building with stone front, erected in 1802, and opened July 20, in the same year, and enlarged in 1814, and again in 1819, and is now calculated to accommodate 700 persons. It is 58 feet by 34 feet, and 26 feet high, lighted by fourteen windows, and well fitted up with pews, and has a gallery on the south and north sides and west end. Attached to this chapel are two school rooms, each 55 feet by 18 feet, and a vestry room.

The celebrated Rev. Daniel Taylor was the first minister who preached at this chapel. In May, 1789, he delivered a sermon in the open air. In 1791, the first baptism took place, when nine persons were baptized; since that time continual additions have been made to the society then formed, which now consists of upwards of 340 members. The Rev. J. G. Pike, author of several popular works, has been minister thirty years.

The *Baptist Chapel*, St. Mary's Gate. The Trustees of the above connexion have purchased St. Mary's Gate House, and a plot of land containing one acre, extending from St. Mary's Gate to Walker Lane. This house was erected by a Mr. Osborne in 1750, whose family for some time continued to reside in it. From the Osbornes it passed to the Bateman family; it was purchased from that family about 60 years ago by the late eminent banker and merchant, Thomas Evans, esq., who for many years made it his principal residence, and at his decease left it to his grandson, William Evans, esq., M. P., of Allestree Hall. In 1841, the latter gentleman conveyed the premises to the Chapel Trustees for the sum of £4000. The house stands in a recess on the north-eastern side of St. Mary's Gate. It is a large and handsome brick and stone mansion of the Roman style of architecture, enriched with fluted Corinthian pilasters, a pediment and vases. The interior has been taken out, and the outer walls have been extended under the superintendance of Mr. Fenton, an eminent architect, from Chelmsford. Mr. Winterton, of Derby, contracted to make the alterations, including the old materials for £1500., making the total cost £5500. The chapel is 66 feet from front to back, and 65 feet from side to side. The North end is octagon. There are three entrances into the chapel. The front leads to the body of the chapel, and the two side entrances to the body and the galleries. The chapel is galleried all round, and is calculated to seat 1200 persons. The school-room, which will hold 400 scholars, and the vestry rooms, are underneath the chapel. The Rev. J. G. Pike is minister of this chapel, together with the one in Brook-Street. The minister's house adjoins the bank. The collections at the various services at the opening of this commodious and beautiful chapel, on 18th of May, 1842, amounted to the handsome sum of £425.

The *New General Baptist Chapel*, situate in Sacheverel-street, is a handsome brick building, 43 feet long, 36 feet wide, and 22 feet high, lighted by eighteen windows. This chapel, erected in 1830, cost about £1000. It is well pewed, and has a gallery on the east and west sides and south end, and contains about 750 sittings. On the north end is a convenient vestry and burial ground.

The *Particular* or *Calvinistic Baptist Chapel*, situate in Agard-street, is a brick building with a portico, erected about 50 years ago at the sole expense of the late Archer Ward, esq. of Mill-hill house, in this town. It has since been enlarged, and is now 43 feet long, 36 feet wide, and 20 feet high, lighted by eleven windows, and will accommodate twice the number of persons originally intended. The interior is neatly fitted up with a mahogany pulpit, good pews, and a gallery on the east and west sides and south end. In 1827, it was furnished with an organ by Mrs. Swinburne, at the cost of £170. At the north end is a convenient vestry and burying ground.

The largest *Wesleyan Methodist Chapel*, situate in King-street, was built in 1805: it was 53 feet long, 50 feet wide, and 30 feet high, lighted by eighteen windows. There was a deep gallery on the east and west sides and north end. This chapel was taken down, and the present one built on its site.

The *New Wesleyan Methodist Chapel*, King Street, rebuilt in 1841, was designed by James Simpson, esq., of Leeds, and the Messrs. Bridgart were the contractors. The portico is of the Doric order; and the pilasters above, Ionic. The chapel is 90 feet long, 64 feet wide, and 40 feet high, lighted by twelve semi-circular headed windows on each side, eight on the South-west end, and five on the North-east end. It is galleried all round, and will seat about 1600 persons. The pulpit is of the Doric order, veneered with beautiful Spanish mahogany. The family seats in the centre of the chapel are lined and cushioned with crimson cloth and carpeted. There is a small organ built by Mr. John Gray, of London. Underneath the chapel is the school-room, that will contain upwards of 500 children, vestry-rooms, &c. The whole is lighted with gas, and heated with hot water. The cost, including the old materials, was about £5000. Mr. Turner gave the handsome sum of £1000.; Mr. German, £100.; Mr. Holmes, £100.; Mr. Joseph Harpur and family, £100.; Mr. R. Chadwick, £50.; Mr. Shepherd, £20.; and several other smaller sums towards rebuilding this beautiful chapel. There is a cemetery approached from the chapel that will contain 130 coffins, and a burial ground in front. The amount collected at the various services at the opening of this elegant place of worship, on Wednesday, September 29 ; Sunday, October 3 ; Monday, October 4 ; Sunday, October 10 ; and Wednesday, October 13 ; was £712. 17s. 7½d.

The congregation is very numerous and respectable. On each side of the chapel, and attached to it, is a neat dwelling house for the accommodation of the stationary ministers.

The other *Wesleyan Methodist Chapel*, situate on Greenhill, is a plain brick building, 64 feet long, 38 feet wide, and 25 feet high, and lighted by twelve windows. It was erected in 1816, by Mr. Heathcote, Mr. Lane, and others, at a cost of nearly £1100. These parties not being able to procure a sufficient congregation to support the expenses of the chapel, and pay the interest of the debt incurred on the building, sold it to the Wesleyan Connexion some years ago for £700. The latter society have enlarged the chapel and erected a half circle gallery on the east and west sides and north end ; the lower part is well seated, and it is now calculated to accommodate upwards of 800 persons. At the back of the chapel there is a large school-house, consisting of two stories, which was built for the Sunday scholars in 1824. The chapel is attended by a numerous and respectable congregation.

The *Methodist New Connexion* erected a chapel in Devonshire Street, in 1824; it is a plain brick building, now used by St. Peter's Sunday scholars. This congregation took their name from the Rev. Alexander Kilham, who was a seceder from the Wesleyan Methodists. In 1834-5, they purchased the New Jerusalem Temple, situated in London Street. This handsome building has a stone front and portico in the Ionic style of architecture ; it was built by the late Mr. Madeley, Tape Manufacturer, about the year 1819, and was sold by his devisees for about the sum of £1500. This chapel is 44 feet long, 44 wide, and 34 feet high, lighted by twenty windows. It is neatly fitted up with pews and a gallery on the North and South sides, and West end, and contains about 800 sittings. Underneath is a large school-room for the use of the scholars who attend the school on sabbath days, and a small vestry-room ; it was opened February 1836. The Rev. James Henshaw, and the Rev. John Hilton, ministers.

The *Primitive Methodists* erected a small chapel in Albion-street in 1817. This chapel is 31 feet long, 23 feet wide, and the walls are about 10 feet high : it is lighted by four windows. This small congregation are seceders from the Wesleyan Methodists.

The *Arminian Chapel* in Babington lane, built in 1834, is now the property of R. F. Forester, esq. It is used by the Primitive Methodists.

The *Jerusalem Church*, or *Swedenborgian Chapel*, situate in King-street, was erected by Mr. James Robinson, draper, in 1820, at a cost of upwards of £1000. It is of an oblong octagon form, built of stone, with a portico. It has a gallery on the north end and east and west sides, and is lighted by seventeen windows.

Since the death of Mr. Madeley, the congregation, not being sufficient to maintain the current expenses of the chapel erected by that gentleman, in London Street, removed to the chapel built by Mr. Robinson, in King-street. Mr. Knight, minister.

Except the Quakers, all these chapels have Sunday schools attached to them, which are well attended : they are supported by the voluntary contributions of the respective congregations.

CHARITABLE INSTITUTIONS.

The *Derbyshire General Infirmary.*—This important and useful institution stands on the southern side of the town, near the London road. It is for the accommodation and relief of the sick and infirm poor It was at first established, and has been since conducted, upon the most liberal principles ; and the support it has experienced has enabled its conductors to distribute its benefits to an extent peculiarly gratifying to the humane and reflecting mind. Not only all proper objects, without distinction throughout the county are admitted, but it receives all those whom sickness or misfortune may lead to apply for assistance, from whatever quarter they may come, provided they are recommended by a subscriber, and their cases be such as come within the nature and purposes of the institution itself, but in cases of sudden accident the recommendation is dispensed with.

This excellent design was formed about the year 1806, when a subscription was opened by the principal inhabitants of the town and county, for erecting a building for the purpose, and a well selected field was purchased of the corporation, at the price of £200. per acre, on the west side of the London road, in an elevated, airy, and dry situation, abounding with excellent water and accessible by a good road. The design of the building was arranged by William Strutt, esq. F. R. S. according to which, working plans were drawn by Mr. Browne, who superintended the construction of a model, executed with architectural skill and ingenuity. The building is constructed of beautiful hard and durable whitish stone ; of cubical form, with an elevation handsome, yet simple and unornamented. The building consists of three stories ; the basement story being a little sunk, and surrounded with an area. The middle and principal story is a little elevated ; it is approached by steps, and a portico supported by four Doric pillars, of the same stone as that of which the walls of the building are formed, which is a hard and compact millstone grit. The upper story is approached by a staircase leading from a spacious hall in the middle of the building, which is lighted by several skylights placed in the dome over the hall in the centre ; this staircase terminates in a gallery, surrounding the interior of the hall on three sides, the central part being the hall into which the doors of the rooms open. The roof of the central part is drawn into a conical form, terminating in a dome containing six windows, which completely illuminate the hall from the floor of the principal story upwards. The roof of the surrounding rooms is separate from that of the central part, the sloping sides of which terminate in a gutter which surrounds the central roof. Within this central part is an outlet provided with a turncap, for the escape of the foul air, by flues communicating with each room appropriated for the patients. It may be proper here to mention, that the gutter which receives the water from the dome and the surrounding roof, has a contrivance to obviate the evils attendant on the gutters being filled with snow and ice, this is effected by covering the gutters with slates elevated by wood slips of about two inches square, with sufficient space between the ends of the slates, for the water of the melted snow to drain into the gutter and run off. The great inconvenience of removing the snow on these occasions, however deep it may be, is by these means entirely removed. The turncap above mentioned would of itself insure a certain degree of ventilation to the rooms; it is however strongly aided in this effect by another turncap, a short distance from the building, communicating with it by a subterraneous culvert: the opening from the former one, is by the power of a vane, presented in a direction opposite to the wind; while the latter is by a similar contrivance always turned to the wind. These being both connected with all the rooms occupied by the patients, a current of air is constantly passing through the same.

The committee, before the erection began, directed their attention to the means of obtaining the best plan; and in order to form a correct judgement on the subject, endeavoured to learn from the experience of similar establishments, what were the principal objects to be kept in view in the construction of an edifice of this nature. The result of their enquiries suggested several improvements, which have brought this Infirmary to a degree of perfection unknown to similar establishments. One considerable improvement, and which contributes much to the health and comfort of the patients, is, the construction of two light and spacious rooms (one for each sex) called day (or convalescent) rooms, in which those patients, to whom it may be agreeable, may eat their meals and pass the day, instead of being confined to the same room day and night, as is the usual practice. Another very great improvement is in the construction of a fever house, a place where relief is administered in case of infectious diseases. Such an establishment as this, has generally in large towns been separate from the infirmary; but here a portion of it is properly constructed for the reception, not only of those whose infectious diseases may commence in the hospital, but of those also which may occur elswhere. The entrance into this fever-house is on the side of the building directly opposite to the front, and has no internal connexion whatever with the Infirmary.

Besides the convalescent rooms and fever-house, before mentioned, another circumstance in which the plan of this Infirmary surpasses others, is, in providing superior accommodation for patients labouring under acute diseases. In general, the surgical and medical, the acute and chronic diseases, are assembled in one large ward, day and night; that this must be always painful, and in some cases highly prejudicial, cannot be denied. The better accommodation consists in providing for each sex, a set consisting of four small wards, containing one, two, three, and four beds respectively, with a water closet, nurse's bed-room and scullery. This enables the medical attendants to separate the diseases from each other, as may best suit their nature; and the whole of each set of rooms being shut off from the body of the house by one door, these together, procure for the patients silence and darkness (which is essential in some cases) as well as every other convenience, in a degree, perhaps, superior to many private houses. This plan, however, might not be eligible, unless it was constructed with another improvement, one which is of great importance, and which has hitherto been a desideratum in all hospitals; that is, a cheap and simple, and in every respect unobjectionable method of warming and ventilating effectually in cold weather. Both these have been effected perfectly in this Infirmary. And thus the ventilation will be copious, while, at the same time, the warmth may be regulated at pleasure; many lives will be preserved, which, owing to a certain state of the air generally pervading hospitals, might have been inevitably lost.

Particular attention has been paid to the construction of the water-closets, which, it is said, have not yet been managed so as to be unobjectionable in hospitals; for if they are ventilated externally, the draught, which should be from the house outwards, is the reverse, especially if the house is warm. A mode of construction has been invented for the occasion, in which every objection of this kind has been done away. A small steam engine has been erected to pump water, wash them, &c.

Warm, cold and vapour baths have been constructed; in short, it is furnished with every convenience, while, in the construction and arrangement of all the offices, every attention has been paid to adapt them to the various purposes with the greatest economy, which reflect the highest credit on the abilities of the late William Strutt, esq. F. R. S. who was the principal designer. It was opened on the 4th of June, 1810.

The magnitude of the building is equal to the accommodation of eighty patients, besides those with infectious diseases. This is doubtless a greater number than are likely at present to want relief at any one time; but considering the increasing population of the county and town, it cannot be considered too large. A statue of Æsculapius, emblematical of the object of the institution, modelled by Mr. Coffee, has been placed upon the centre of the dome.

The committee have secured about 14 acres of the surrounding ground, for the exclusive use of the institution, to prevent in future the too near approach of offensive objects.

By the report of the committee, dated the 1st of June, 1809, it appears that the expenditure for land purchased, building the Infirmary, &c. amounted to £17,870. 3s. 4d. From the same paper it also appears that the donations received by the treasurers for the institution, amounted, with their interest, to £31,238. 19s., so that the balance lodged in the different funds, &c. constituting the funds of the Infirmary, amounts to £13,368. 15s. 8d.

The medical board consists of three physicians, four surgeons, and a house apothecary. Mr. Dix, house surgeon. Mr. and Mrs. Rimington, are governor and matron.

The *Self-Supporting, Charitable and Parochial Dispensary*, was established in August, 1830. The house appropriated for this excellent Institution is in Bridge-gate. The objects of this Institution are,

Firstly, To encourage a provident and independent spirit amongst the working classes, by allowing such of them, as support themselves without parochial assistance, to become subscribers to this Institution, under the denomination of " Free Class," after the rate of one penny per week for persons above fourteen years of age, and one halfpenny per week, for persons under fourteen years of age; thereby entitling themselves to medical and surgical aid in case of sickness, and to certain privileges to be enjoyed exclusively by this class.

Secondly, To provide medicines and advice for those poor persons, who, though maintaining themselves without parish assistance, are unable to afford the means of subscribing to the Free Class, and who shall receive tickets of recommendation from honorary subscribers.

Thirdly, To procure surgical attendance and medicines for poor married women, being free members, during their confinement.

Fourthly, To provide medicines and attendance, under certain conditions, for paupers, the overseers of whose parishes are subscribers to this Institution.

Lastly, To consult the feelings and promote the comfort of the poor, by allowing, to all classes, the choice of being attended by any one of the medical officers of the establishment, who may be most agreeable to them; and by providing them with medical attendance at their own dwellings, in cases where severe illness renders them unable to attend at the Dispensary.

The spirited support that this important Institution has met with does great credit to the feelings and character of the inhabitants. In 1831, there were two hundred subscribers, whose annual subscriptions amounted to £211. 7s. The donations received from the 11th of August, 1830, to the 29th of September, 1831, was £214. 1s. The amount received from the Free Class of subscribers was £41. 6s. 6d. The utility of this establishment receives a striking illustration from the number of persons who have been cured of almost every kind of disorder to which the human frame is liable, through the assistance it has afforded. The number thus benefitted, from its commencement to October, 1832, has been 2212. In 1841, the total number of members on the books were 600. The annual subscriptions amounted to £175. 7s. 7d. Donations, £4. 13s. 6d. Two or more surgeons attend at the Dispensary every day: one of them regularly visits such sick poor as cannot personally attend.

This charity is conducted by a committee of subscribers, a consulting physician, and eight surgeons. The Duke of Devonshire is President; the Earl of Burlington, Lord Vernon, Lord Scarsdale, Sir George Crewe, and Sir Oswald Moseley, barts. W. Mundy, W. Evans, and W. Leaper Newton, esqrs. Vice-Presidents; and S. Evans, esq., Treasurer, and J. W. Gallimore, Secretary, and resident dispenser.

Ladies' Charity.—The object of this institution, which was begun in 1815, is the relief of poor married women in child-bed, at their own houses ; who not only receive medical assistance but the use of bed-linen, food, and every other necessary that their situation requires. This institution is patronised and chiefly supported by ladies of the first respectability, and its affairs are conducted by a committee. No public building is connected with this charity, as the present mode of relief is considered superior to that afforded by an hospital. The liberality with which its benefits are dispensed, places it among the first charities which distinguish the town of Derby.

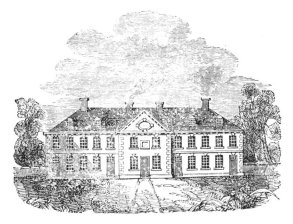

Large's Hospital.—Edward Large, of Derby. gent. by his will, bearing date 3rd June, 1709, devised all his lands and tenements situate on Nuns' Green, in Derby, being about the yearly value of £50. in trust to John Curzon, son and heir apparent of Sir Nathaniel Curzon, of Kedleston, bart. and two others, and their heirs, that they should, out of the profits thereof, erect and build five small almshouses for the habitation of five poor parsons' or vicars' widows for ever, the same to be elected, chosen and put in by the choice and election of his said trustees, or any two of them ; and that the rents and profits of the said estate should be equally divided amongst such five poor widows for their support and livelihood respectively for ever.

Mary Broom, by her will, bearing date the 6th April, 1721, devised as follows: " I leave to my brother, Nathaniel Doubting, all my land, free from debt, for his life, and after his death to that hospital upon Nuns' Green, where I now live, in Derby, which was left by Mr. Edward Large for parsons' widows, and after my brother's death, I leave my land to the care of the same trustees which Mr. Large left for that hospital, viz. Sir John Curzon, of Kedleston, bart. Robert Wilmot, of Osmaston, esq., and Counsellor Robert Holden, of Aston, esq."

The property belonging to this charity consisted of the edifice or building called Large's Hospital, and the gardens and appurtenances belonging to the same, situate upon Nun's Green, containing 1 a. 2 r. 23½ p. and six closes of land, situate in the parish of St. Werburgh's, containing together 20 a. 3 r. 36 p. also 7 a. 2 r. 9 p. of land in the parish of Alvaston.

Within the last few years two exchanges have been made by the trustees. The exchange made in 1823, with Mr. Thraves of Sandiacre, took place in consequence of a site being required for a new jail for the county of Derby, viz. six acres, at the rate of £400. per acre. But as the trustees had no power to sell this land, it was agreed that it should be exchanged under the Act of 1 and 2 George IV. for an estate at Sandiacre, belonging to Mr. Thraves, containing 43 a. 2 r. 26 p. which he agreed to sell for the sum of £2650. The sum which was to be paid by the county for the six acres being of less amount, two other parcels of the charity land were disposed of, one containing 2945 square yards, at 2s. 9d. per yard, and the other 482 square yards, at 4s. 6d. per yard, which were, together with the six acres intended for the use of the jail, conveyed by the deed of 1823 in exchange for the estate of Mr. Thraves. All the expenses of this exchange were paid by the county.

The following is a Statement of the Account.

	£.	s.	d.		£.	s.	d.
Purchase money of six acres for the site of the jail......................................	2400	0	0	Mr. Thraves' purchase money for estate at Sandiacre	2650	0	0
Interest on ditto from April 6th to August 8th	41	13	1	Interest on ditto to August 8th............	44	17	9
Paid by the county for building and a tree on the land............................	17	4	0	Balance...........	277	7	1
Miss Prime's purchase money of 2945 square yards	404	18	9	Out of this balance the trustees agreed to lay out on the premises at Sandiacre £100., leaving the balance £177. 7s. 1d.			
Mr. Ward's ditto of 482 yards	108	9	0				
	£2972	4	10		£2972	4	10

The other exchange, to which the deed of the 6th of August, 1825, relates, was made in consequence of its being advantageous to the charity. The trustees conveyed to Mr. Turner 4 a. 2 r. 26 p. of land, which was valued at £500. per acre, amounting in the whole to £2331. 8s. and the estate at Sandiacre, received by them, containing 31 a. 2 r. 25 p. was purchased by Mr. Turner for the purpose of making the exchange for £2050. The expenses of this transaction amounting to £238. 0s. 6d. was equally borne by Mr. Turner and the Trustees, which, after deducting some interest and a moiety of the expenses, left a balance in favour of the charity of £75. 11s. 1d. which, with the balance of £177. 7s. 1d. was placed in the bank of Messrs. Smith and Co.

The following rental will show the present state of all the property now belonging to this Charity, except the site of the hospital and the garden belonging to it.

Parish.	Tenants.	Description of Property.	Quantity. a. r. p.	Rent. £. s. d.
St. Werburgh's.........	Joseph Banister	A close	2 0 10	10 8 9
Ditto	The late T. Trafford	Ditto	3 3 50	19 11 3
Ditto	Mrs. Potter	Ditto	3 0 20	15 12 6
Ditto	Thomas Bent, M. D.	2 parcels of land	(626 sq. yards)	6 4 0
Alvaston	William Sherwin	Closes	7 2 9	18 0 0
Sandiacre	John Thraves	Nine ditto	45 2 26	80 0 0
Ditto	John Abbot	Seven ditto	31 2 25	56 0 0
				£205 16 6

The alms' houses, called Large's Hospital, which is situate in the Friar-gate, consists of five dwellings under one roof, with a wash-house at one end thereof, a small court in front, and a garden behind, divided amongst the inmates: each of whom, since 1821, has received £15. half yearly.

Byrom Thomas, house in Rotten-row, £20. to teach poor children to read (by his will, dated 14th July, 1714) an annual sum of £9. 12s. paid to a school-mistress for teaching 32 poor children by the late Mr. Leaper, one of the trustees, who had a balance in his hands belonging to this charity, in 1826, amounting to £143. 11s. 10d.

Society for the Relief of the Families of Distressed Clergymen.—This society for the relief of the widows and orphans of clergymen, and the families of dis-tressed clergymen, within the deaneries of Derby, Ashbourne, Repington, and Castillary, in the archdeaconry of Derby, was instituted at Derby, May 17, 1721.

Countess of Shrewsbury's Almshouse.—By indenture, bearing date 1st of March, 1599, Elizabeth, Countess Dowager of Shrewsbury, granted to the Warden, Brethren, and Sisters of an almshouse at Derby, founded by the said Countess under letters patent, bearing date the 3rd of March, in the thirty-ninth year of the reign of Queen Elizabeth, an annual rent of £100. to be issuing out of the manor of Little Longsdon, in the county of Derby, and after appropriating parts of the said rents to the said poor persons of the almshouse, she directed that 40s. thereof should be paid to the minister or curate of the church of All Saints', being a preacher, and in default thereof to the minister or curate of any of the other churches in Derby, being a preacher, for his pains to visit and see the said poor of the said almshouse there, to be kept in good order, according to the rules and orders of the said almshouse.

By the same deed, the said Countess also gave out of the said rent to five score of the other poor of the said town of Derby, 12d. each, to be yearly distributed on Good Friday. This is distributed under the direction of the mayor of Derby for the time being.

The alms' people were to receive £1. 13s. 4d. each, quarterly, and 20s. per annum for a gown. The warden was to have 20s. over and above as his salary for keeping clean the monument of the foundress. This almshouse was founded for the maintenance and support of eight poor men and four poor women. The original building, which was of stone, was taken down, and the present one erected by the late Duke of Devonshire, about the year 1777 ; before his death he gave an additional endowment of £50. per annum. The additional payment took place at Lady-day, 1811. Each of the alms people receives £2. 13s. 4d. quarterly, and the gown and coals annually.

It has been justly remarked that " whatever convenience the interior of the present structure may now possess, the design of the front but ill accords with the nature of the establishment. The simplicity and modest plainness that should exist in a structure devoted to the purposes of charity, are sacrificed to a style of architecture, that would be more in character when employed in the entrance to a nobleman's park or pleasure grounds."

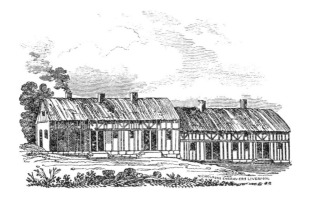

Wilmot's Almshouses, formerly called the Black Almshouses—are situate in Bridge-gate, Derby. Robert Wilmot, the elder of Chaddesden, by his will, bearing date — day of July, 1638, and proved in the prerogative court of Canterbury, in the same year, gave to his son, Edward Wilmot, and his heirs, all the tithe of corn, grain and hay arising within the limits of the manor of Denby, in the county of Derby, and appointed that his said son and his heirs should, out of the rents and profits thereof, pay the several sums of 12*d.* a piece weekly, from his decease, to ten poor people, viz. six poor men and four poor women, of good and honest life, by him already placed in ten little houses, situate in Bridge-gate, Derby, which houses he had built for the said number of poor people to dwell in, and to be maintained by such weekly allowance ; and he appointed that when any of the said poor people should die, his said son and his heirs should, within a month, appoint others in their room. And he appointed that out of the rents and profits of the said tithes, his said son and his heirs should every year, at Christmas, give to every of the said poor men and women a black gown, faced with red, of the like cloth as the poor people then in the said houses used to wear, or otherwise 10*s.* ; to the men every two years a red cap, of about 2*s.* a piece, similar to the caps then worn by them, and should also provide yearly, at Christmas, thirty yards of linen cloth at 12*d.* the yard, to be distributed amongst the said ten poor people ; and should also provide a dinner yearly for the said poor at Christmas, or otherwise allow every of them 8*d.* for the same. And he further appointed that his son and his heirs should, for ever, out of the rents and profits of the said tithes, repair the said houses so often as need should be.

Sir Henry Sacheverel Wilmot, of Chaddesden, bart. is the present owner of the tithes of Denby, mentioned in the founder's will ; and in respect thereof, pays to each of the eight alms people 1*s.* a week, and yearly, at Christmas, 13*s.* 8*d.* each, instead of the gown, cloth and dinner ; and the men are entitled to a cap each every two years.

Each of the eight alms' people also receive of Sir Robert Wilmot, of Osmaston, bart. 6*d.* a week, making in the whole the annual sum of £13. mentioned in the award of 1729. The almshouses are kept in repair by Sir Henry Sacheverel Wilmot, of Chaddesden, bart. The late Sir Robert Wilmot, bart. took down the old houses and erected a new range of buildings in their stead, for the accommodation of eight poor persons, four men and four women, A. D. 1814, at an expense of more than £250.

Linacre's Charity.—George Linacre, by will, bearing date the 27th of September, 1703, left a messuage and 19 *a.* 3*r.* 21 *p.* of land in Findern, now let for £31. 10*s.* 6*d.* and a messuage, &c. which lets for £5. to put forth two poor boys, being the sons of honest inhabitants in the town of Derby. All the parishes partake of the benefit of this charity.

Liversage's Charity.—By deed of feoffment, bearing date 2nd of August, 21 Henry VIII. (1529) Robert Liversage granted and confirmed to William Collyer, clerk, vicar of the parish of St. Peter's, Derby, Roger Smith, and six others, and their heirs, a tenement in the borough of Derby, situate at the north end of a bridge, called St. Peter's Bridge, with a garden ; a tenement, situate in the street called Corn Market Street ; a tenement, situate in the same street ; a tenement, near St. Peter's well ; a tenement with chambers, near the burial ground of St. Peter's, called a School House ; a messuage, in the Morledge, with three cottages, and twenty acres of arable land in the fields of Derby ; a close, lying in a lane, called Wandell Lane ; a barn, lying between the land of John Brookhouse and the land of St. Leonard's ; a tenement, situate in the parish of St. Peter, near the bridge ; a tenement, situate in the street near the church of St. Peter ; and a tenement, situate in Bag lane ; to the use of the said Robert Liversage and Alice his wife, and the survivor, and after the death of the survivor, to the use and intent of performing the will of the said Robert Liversage.

By a writing, bearing date 3rd of November, 21 Henry VIII. and annexed to the above-mentioned deed, the said Robert Liversage directed that his feoffees should stand seised of all his lands and tenements, specified in the said deed, after the death of the survivor of himself and his wife, to the fulfilling of his will, as follows: viz. that Ralph Ley, his priest, and his successors, his priests, should receive all the rents and profits of the said premises, and have the letting to farm of the same, by the advice of the vicar and churchwardens of St. Peter's, to the intent that the said Ralph and his successors should say mass daily in a chapel which the said Robert Liversage had built within the parish of St. Peter, for the souls of the said Robert and Alice his wife; and he directed that on Fridays, weekly, the said Ralph and his successors should say mass in the said chapel, and that thirteen poor men and women should be present, and should each receive one silver penny; and that his yearly obiit should be kept on the anniversary of his death, within the parish church of St. Peter, and certain payments therein specified made to the vicar, the priests, and others attending at such obiit, all the costs and charges of which he directed should be borne out of the rents and profits of the said premises.

The *Liversage Alms Houses*, London road, were erected in 1836, out of the Liversage estate, at a cost of £3000. They were designed by Mr. Mason, and built by Mr. Joseph Gascoyne. They consist of thirteen brick houses, in the Gothic style of architecture, each house having a front room, small kitchen, pantry, one bed room, and closet, with gardens at the back, and a grass lawn in front. If a man and his wife occupy a house, they receive 4s. per week, and one ton of coals annually. If two widows occupy one house, each receives 4s. per week, and the one ton of coals, and a gratuity of a cloak or coat, or another ton of coal. The Liversage charity estate is let on lease for fourteen, twenty-one, and sixty years, and a small portion of it yearly. The yearly rental in 1830, was £590. 8s. 4d. It is now (1842) £730. 12s. 4d. and will increase as the leases expire.

The trust deeds of 1824 contain a particular description of the state of the property at that time. Of the trustees therein mentioned, Daniel Parker Coke, esq., Bache Heathcote, esq., Richard Sutton Barrow, esq., William Strutt, esq., Francis Mundy, esq., Edward Miller Mundy, esq., and Sir Robert Wilmot, bart. have died since the date of those deeds.

When the trustees are reduced to four, others are to be appointed from the parishioners. The present trustees are Richard Forester Forester, esq., Joseph Strutt, esq., Edward Sacheverel Chandos Pole, esq., Godfrey Meynell, esq., William Evans, esq., M. P. and the Rev. Charles Evelyn Cotton.

On the 12th of June, 1722, it was ordered that twelve houses should be built at the edge of St. Peter's church-yard, for twelve poor people; for building which the trustees allowed the old materials of the houses then standing and £120.; and in the following December, twelve poor persons were placed in these houses, which houses at the time the Commissioners appointed to look into charitable institutions in 1826, formed the Workhouse for St. Peter's parish, and it appeared to them necessary for the welfare of this charity, that the appropriation of its funds should be regulated, and a scheme adopted for the future disposal thereof, under the sanction of a court of Equity.

After a seven years' suit in chancery, which cost £2781. 7s. a scheme was approved by the court which is now acted upon by the commissioners. Under this scheme the rents are collected by Mr. John Corden, who is agent to the vicar and secretary to the estate, and paid over by him to the account of the vicar and churchwardens of St. Peter's, into the bank of Messrs. Smith, who now have a balance in their hands belonging to the charity of £384. The vicar and churchwardens draw the money out of the bank by checques, to pay the alms'-people and other expenses, and appoint the alms'-people when any vacancy occurs. The candidates must be parishioners who have not received parochial relief, and of the best moral character. There are now in the almshouses 9 men and 8 women. The Rev. William Fisher is Lecturer of St. Peter's, for which service he receives £35. and Mr. Harwood, Surgeon, with a salary of £13. a year out of the charity estate.

SCHOOLS.

The *Free Grammar School*, in St. Peter's Church yard, is supposed to be one of the most ancient endowments in the kingdom. Queen Mary, by charter bearing date 21st May, 1554, gave and granted to the bailiffs and burgesses of the town of Derby, and their successors, for ever, divers messuages, lands, &c., in that town and elsewhere in the county of Derby, subject to certain yearly payments, therein mentioned; and her majesty ordained and granted that thenceforward there should be one free grammar school for the instruction and education of boys and youths in the said town of Derby, to be for ever supported by the bailiffs and burgesses of that town, and that the said bailiffs and burgesses and their successors, out of the revenues of the premises thereby granted, should yearly, for ever pay to the master and under master for the time being of such free grammar school, £13. 6s. 8d. The Rev. W. Fletcher is appointed head master by the corporation, at a salary of £60. per annum; second master, Mr. Rowell.

St. Peter's *National School*, in Traffic-street, was established in 1829, by the Rev. Robert Simpson, author of the History of Derby, at a cost of £350. The boys' room is 40 feet by 20 feet, and 10 feet high. The girls' room is of similar dimensions. The boys are instructed in reading, writing, and arithmetic, towards which each scholar pays 3d. per week. They are furnished without further charge, with copy and account books, ink, pens, slates and reading books. The girls pay 2d. a week, for which they are taught to sew, read and write. There are about 100 boys, and 70 girls on the books. Mr. Pescud, the master, and Mrs. Bartlett, the mistress, receive the amount paid by each scholar. The remainder of the expenses are paid by voluntary contributions and annual subscriptions. The Rev. William Fisher superintends all the schools belonging to this parish. The Infant schools in Siddals-lane and Bag-lane, are supported from the same fund.

The *Infant School*, in Siddals lane, was established in 1827, under the auspices of the Rev. Robert Simpson, on the system of Mr. Wilderspin, for children of from two years to six years of age. The school-room is 50 feet by 24 feet, and about 20 feet high, and is lighted by seven large windows. The average number of children taught is about 80. The school is supported by annual subscribers and voluntary contributions, and by the 2d. a week paid by each scholar. This school was purchased in 1833 for the sum of £773.

St. Peter's *Church Sunday School*, for boys and girls, in Traffic street, is numerously attended, the number of scholars on the books are, 120 boys, and 85 girls.

St. Peter's *Church Sunday School*, for boys, in Devonshire-street, in a building 36 feet long, and 30 feet wide, lighted by nine windows, formerly used as a chapel, by the Kilhamite Methodists. It was purchased for the use of the scholars for the sum of £260. There are 80 boys on the books; Mr. Herbert Holmes is the superintendant.

St. Peter's *Church Sunday School*, for girls, in Bag-lane, was built in 1839, at the cost of £550.; it is a handsome room, 42 feet long, 22 feet wide, lighted by 4 windows. There are about 100 scholars on the books. The Infant school is held in it during the week; there are about 70 scholars on the books, who pay 2d. per week for their instruction; Miss Jane Greaves, mistress.

For all these schools there has been received from the National Society £390., and from the Treasury, £370. The Sunday schools are supported by voluntary subscriptions, and annual Sermons.

St. Alkmund's Church Sunday Schools are attended by about 500 scholars, viz., 200 boys under the superintendance of the Vicar, the Rev. E. H. Abney, are instructed in the Lancastrian School room, and 290 girls, under the superintendance of Mrs. Abney, are instructed in the British girls' school room.

St. Werburgh's Church Sunday School is held in the National school, in Curzon street; there are about 140 boys, under the superintendance of Mr. Ayres, and 160 girls, under Miss Taylor.

All Saints' Church Sunday Schools are attended by about 100 boys, under the superintendance of Mr. Barnett, and 200 girls, under Miss Sanders and Miss Gibson.

St. Michael's Church Sunday School is held in the church, and is attended by about 50 boys, under the superintendance of Mr. James, and 50 girls' under Miss Howard.

St. John's Church Sunday School is attended by about 380 scholars, viz., 220 girls, under the superintendance of Miss Cox, and 160 boys, under Mr. Ratcliffe. The school room is in Mill-street.

Trinity Church Sunday School is attended by about 240 boys, and 210 girls. There are upwards of 500 scholars on the books. They are under the superintendance of the Rev. E. M. Wade.

Trinity School, Liversage-street, opened 14th October, 1830, was designed by M. Habershon, jun., of London. It is a neat plain brick building, adjoining Trinity Church-yard. Messrs. Thompson and Wood were the joint contractors. The total cost of the building, land, and furnishing, was about £1000. The school room is 71 feet long, by 35 feet wide, lighted by eleven windows, and the entrance by a large oriel window. The boys' part is 42 feet long, and the girls' part is 29 feet long, by 35 feet wide. There are two class rooms. There are 120 boys, and 65 girls on the books, who pay 3*d.* per week for instruction and the use of books, &c. The master receives 1*d.* per week from each boy, and a salary of £35. per annum. The Rev. E. M. Wade superintends the school, and provides every additional expense beyond the weekly pay of the scholars. Mr. R. G. Aldridge, is the master, and Miss Martha Adams, the mistress.

Christ Church Sunday School is attended by about 210 children, viz., 90 boys, and 120 girls, under the superintendance of the Rev. Roseingrave Macklin. The school is held in a room on Burton road.

St. Mary's Catholic Church Sunday School is attended by upwards of 300 scholars, viz., about 150 boys, and 150 girls, under the superintendance of the Rev. Thomas Sing, and the Rev. Joseph Daniel.

The *National School* was established in 1812, for the education of poor children of both sexes on the plan of Dr. Bell. The principle of this Institution is, that all children attending for the benefit of education, shall be required to attend the established Church, the catechisms and creeds of which form a leading part of the instruction. In 1817, the building in Bridge-street, in which the School was held, was consumed by fire, and the books belonging to the Institution were also burnt. The supporters of this school bought a mill in Bold Lane, for which they gave £700. The children are now removed to the new National School, Curzon-street, which is built of brick and stone, in the Tudor style of architecture. It was designed by Mr. H. J. Stevens, our respected and talented townsman, and ranks among his best performances. Messrs. Thompson and Wood, were the joint contractors. The total cost was about £1500. It was commenced in 1839, and opened in January, 1842. This school contains one room on the ground floor, 63 feet by 30 feet, for boys, and a spacious class room adjoining which may be used for the meetings of the Committee, a similar arrangement is preserved in the upper floor for the girls; the two schools are capable of accommodating 500 scholars. Henry Cox, esq., is treasurer, Mr. Henry Cumming, master, who has a salary of £60. per annum, and the pence paid by the scholars, Miss Warner, mistress. There are now 230 boys, and 195 girls on the books, who pay 1*d.* per week each. The remaining expenses are provided by annual Subscriptions and Donations.

The *Diocesan School,* Friar-gate, is of the Elizabethan style of architecture, designed by Mr. Henry J. Stevens, and built by Mr. George Thompson, at the cost of about £1500. of which sum the late Thomas Cox, esq., contributed £1000. towards the building, and £100. towards the interior fitting. The school-room is 52 feet long, 30 feet wide, and 20 feet high, lighted by nine windows. The entrance hall and staircase is lighted by a large oriel window. There is a committee room lighted by 2 windows, and a smaller room. The Rev. Philip Gell, is the treasurer, and Mr. P. E. Hammond, is appointed the master. The terms for instruction are five pounds per annum. It was opened in 1842.

The *Lancastrian School* was founded in 1812, for boys only, who are educated on the plan of Mr. Joseph Lancaster. The supporters of this school took part of a mill in Full-street on a short lease, and, on its expiration, the committee built a commodious room 72 feet long, 35 feet wide, and 20 feet high, lighted by ten windows, situate in Orchard-street, at a cost of £2160. Besides the school-room, there is a master's or committee-room, 16 feet long, and 12 feet high, and a play ground. There are now 250 boys on the books, who each pay a penny a week for their education, the remainder of the expenses are paid by annual subscribers and donations. The annual receipts are about £190. The Rev. James Gawthorne and Mr. S. G. Smith are the secretaries, and Mr. Alexander Britton, the master, who receives a salary of £80. a year, and the surplus children's pence, above 150 per week. Since its establishment, up to June 1842, it is stated in the report that 4740 children had been admitted.

The *British Girls' School*, situate in Chapel-street, is a plain gothic building, of stone, 60 feet by 30 feet, formerly used as the Catholic Chapel. It was purchased by the trustees of the chapel for the sum of £560. There are 112 scholars on the books, (about 70 of whom daily attend,) who are taught reading, writing, arithmetic, plain sewing, and knitting; each scholar pays 1d. per week. Miss Pitman is the mistress.

The *Infant School*, in Mill-street, is a brick building, two stories high, and lighted by fourteen windows. The rooms are 46 feet by 24 feet. The school was built by subscription, and is supported by annual subscribers and voluntary contributions, and by 2d. a week paid by each scholar. There are 130 children of both sexes on the books. The Sunday school children belonging to St. John's church are also instructed in these rooms.

The *Wesleyan Methodist Sunday Schools*, in King-street and Green-hill chapels, are attended by about 700 scholars. The superintendant of the King-street chapel girls' school, is Mr. Peacock; boys' school, Mr. John Cockayne; and of the Green-hill chapel girls' school, Mr. Dallison; boys' school, Mr. Gregory.

The *Wesleyan Methodist Day School*, in Chapel-street, for the education of children of all denominations, conducted by Mr. Rogers, on the Glasgow Normal training system. There are 88 boys on the books, who pay the following terms quarterly, in advance.

TERMS PER QUARTER.

Including a Bible Training Lesson, and a Secular Lesson on the
Elements of Science &c., to be given every Scholar each day.

	s.	d.
Reading, Spelling, and Writing on Slates	3	0
———— with Writing in Copy Books, and Arithmetic	4	0
———— with English Grammar, Sacred and Modern Geography, Natural History, Mental Arithmetic, Mensuration, Book-keeping, and the principles of Vocal Music ...	6	0
———— with Etymology of English words as derived from the Latin, Greek, and other Languages, Classical and Modern History, Drawing of Maps, &c..............	7	6
———— with English Composition, Natural Philosophy, and the Elements of Elocution	10	0

N. B. In the above terms, the following will be provided at the expense of the Committee, viz., Slates, Pencils, Pens and Ink, and a copy of the Wesleyan Catechisms.

The school room is a long narrow room, lighted by 23 windows, and is the property of Mr. Turner.

The *New Connexion of General Baptists' Sunday Schools,* in St. Mary's-gate, are attended by 485 scholars, and 40 teachers. There are 426 members belonging to this chapel.

The Sacheverel-street *General Baptists' Sunday Schools,* are attended by 220 scholars, 33 teachers, and 204 members. From the minutes of the 73rd annual association held in London, it appears there are 16,237 members, 194 chapels, 20,870 scholars, and 3,240 teachers.

The *Independent Chapel Sunday Schools,* are attended by 250 girls, under the superintendance of Miss Storer, and 120 boys under Mr. Tomlinson. The number of children belonging to the Chester-place school, connected with this chapel is about 160.

The *Methodist New Connexion Chapel Sunday School* is attended by about 170 boys and girls, under the superintendance of Mr. Kirk.

The *Agard-street Chapel Sunday School* is attended by about 100 children of both sexes, under the superintendance of Mr. Robotham and Miss Burnett.

The *Unitarian Chapel Sunday School* is attended by 100 children, 40 boys, and 60 girls, under the superintendance of Mr. Hirst.

The *Primitive Methodist Chapel Sunday School,* in Babington-lane, is attended by 240 children, viz., about 100 boys, and 140 girls; Mr. Robert Webster and Mr. Mather, superintendants.

The *Swedenborgian Chapel Sunday School* is attended by 300 children, viz., about 170 boys, and 130 girls; Mr. Corden, superintendant.

No reflecting person can entertain a doubt that the Infant School System is calculated to confer great blessings on the rising generation. The children are instructed through the medium of pictures, maps and other ocular representations. The whole range of animal biography, incidents from history, stories from the Bible, &c. Many of their lessons are in rhyme, and sung or chaunted to a number of plain and easy tunes. Even the most formidable of all lessons to an infant, the learning of the alphabet, is thus invested with a peculiar charm by its being taught in the simple and touching strains of a pretty Scotch air.

The importance of Sunday schools to the rising generation, first established in this kingdom by the philanthropic Mr. Raikes, Bookseller, of Gloucester, in 1780, is now almost universally acknowledged. The beneficial results effected by them on the morals of the labouring classes of society is too evident to need a remark. Sunday schools are attached to each of the churches and chapels in the town, and from five to six thousand children receive instruction and are kept under good moral government. Within a quarter of a century many excellent school-rooms have been erected by the voluntary contributions of benevolent individuals, and by the various congregations to which they respectively belong. For these charitable and intellectual uses many thousand pounds have been employed. Thousands and tens of thousands of young men and women, now filling useful situations in society, have received their education at these schools, and have reason to be thankful. Too much cannot be said in their recommendation; nor should we forget the praise due to those benevolent individuals who devote their time and talents in instructing the children of their poorer neighbours. Those parents who cannot pay for the education of their children, would be blameable indeed if they did not embrace with thankfulness the opportunities thus afforded by a benevolent public. It would be a disgraceful neglect on the part of parents to allow their children to remain ignorant of their duty towards God and their neighbour, when so many fountains of knowledge are opened for their benefit.

The sunday scholars attending the eight protestant churches, are 1160 boys and 1430 girls. Those attending the catholic church, 150 boys and 150 girls. Those attending the different chapels, 2845 children, making a total of 5735. The children attending the National and Infant schools amount to 1600.

THE TOWN HALL.

" Derby must have had a succession of Guildhalls for many ages ; but two only come under the pen. The last stood upon the same spot as the present. I knew it well ; it seemed to have stood more than 200 years, it was wood and plaister ; the roof was tiled in the form of a large old fashioned span ; it had two stories, the lower was called the town prison, and was divided into cells, as all prisons ought to be, that two rogues might not communicate their vices ; the upper was a large room for Corporation use, to which the company ascended by a steep flight of wooden stairs projecting into the market place, covered also with a roof of tiles. The hall, the stairs, the conduit and the cross, then in being, nearly choked up the little market place. In 1730 this venerable building was taken down, and the present hall erected, which is an honour, a beauty, and a use."*

This building Hutton also calls, from the situation in which it was built in the market place—a disgusting beauty. It was not built where the present one now stands, owing to the extravagant price required from the corporation by the owner of the property, who knew the corporation could not go to any other market. They offered an extravagant price, and the seller asked one more extravagant. Astonished at the enormous sum, the corporation refused to purchase and began to build, when he sunk his price to theirs, but it was too late. This town hall, which was a handsome, but rather heavy brick and stone, building, was allowed to stand for nearly a century ; but in 1825 the town improvement act was obtained, by which the Corporation were empowered to take it down, and rebuild it on the present site, on a line with the south side of the market place, thus adding very materially both to its convenience and beauty.

The new Town Hall, which was built in 1828, was in the Grecian style of architecture. Its principal feature was an extremely handsome and massive Ionic portico, which projected the clear width of the footpath, having four fluted Ionic columns about 27 feet in height, and finished by a pediment. This with the two wings flanked by pilasters, elevated upon a basement, the height of the ground story. In this basement, under the centre of the three openings formed by the columns of the portico, was a lofty archway for carriages communicating between the market place and the new market. The great room, or Court of Sessions, which occupied nearly all the front of the second story, was 58 feet long and 35 wide. The building cost upwards of £7000 ; the architect was Matthew Habershon, esq.,† But this building was not destined to last so long as its predecessor, for on the 21st of October, 1841.—the interior was completely destroyed by fire, leaving only the outside and centre walls standing ; but these were apparently but little injured, and, with the exception of the portico, will form part of the restored building. The external appearance of the new hall will differ materially from the one lately destroyed : having provided the accommodations required to render the building available for Judicial and Municipal purposes, the architect was requested by the Committee to make provision on the outside of the building for an Illuminated Clock, to be seen from a distance, and an Alarm Bell. To effect this object he appears to have had in recollection the ancient Hotels de Ville, and to have carried out the principle of design illustrated by them, by proposing to build a clock and bell tower as an integral portion of the *façade*, thus uniting architectural effect with strict utility, and in accordance with the dictates of common sense. Although this arrangement necessitates the pulling down of the old portico and the whole of the front, except the wings, its cost, according to the architect's calculation, will not exceed that of restoring the old work.

The Hall being entirely lighted by four 10 feet skylights from the roof, the windows in the front are not required, and we are glad to find the architect, instead

---

* Hutton, p. 41.

† Considerable improvements at the cost of from £600. to £700. had been made, and were just completed when the fire took place.

H. DUESBURY ARCHT.

J. GARFORTH. DERBY.

of occupying the plain spaces on each side between the tower and the two wings with blank windows or such commonplace and unmeaning decorations, proposes to enrich them with *bas reliefs*, from the hands of a talented sculptor Mr. Bell,—the one to have reference to judicial, the other to municipal proceedings—so that the building shall, as it were, speak to the spectator, and be explanatory of the purposes for which it is used : and, at the same time, produce an effect of repose and simplicity in harmony with the character and expression a building of this description ought to possess. We scarcely need add, that the present design is infinitely superior to the original one, and that it reflects great credit upon the taste and judgment of Mr. Duesbury. The foregoing engraving will however give a more accurate idea of it than any description.

HEIGHT OF TOWER.

	ft.	in.
Foundation to first floor	9	0
Opening or first story	18	9
Tower staircase from vestibule to the top of the hall	27	9
Ventilation chamber	15	4
Belfry	13	0
Clock-room	11	6
Dome	11	0
Finial	5	0
Floors	1	6
Total	**112**	**10**

THE EXTERIOR DIMENSIONS OF THE TOWER.

	ft.	in.
At the base 18 feet 6 inches by 15 feet 6 inches, and 16 feet 10 inches by 14 feet 8 inches, first pair of stairs.		
The opening or passage stairs under the tower is	8	0
Communicating with the cart way in length	61	0
In width	16	6
Two footways 9 feet 4½ inches each	18	9
Divided from the cart way by twelve cast-iron columns, 16 feet 6 inches high. Six on each side of cart way.		
Height from base line	103	10

There are 16 rooms or vaults in basement story 7 feet high.

The right wing contains
Magistrates' room, 21 feet by 17 feet
Waiting room, 16 feet by 12 feet
Magistrates'stairs at the back of waiting room, 16 feet by 8 feet 2 inches
Police office, 23 feet by 21 feet 4 inches

The left wing contains
Police station, or Constables' room, out of which is taken the weighing machine room } 20 ft. 9 in. by 19 ft. 4 in.
Hall and staircase, 21 ft. by 20 ft. 9 in.
Landing and ditto 20 ft. 9 in. by 16 ft. 10 in.
Town Clerk's office.

All these rooms are 16 feet 6 inches high.

The principal story contains—

The Hall or Court, 55 feet 4 inches long, 35 feet wide, and 28 feet 4 inches high, and a gallery over the lobby. This room will be fitted up in wainscoting, after the most approved plans. The gallery at the east end of the court is 7 seats deep.

The vestibule, 11 feet 8 inches, is entered from the landing of the principal stairs, at the north end of which is the stairs to the gallery ; at the west end of the court is the Recorder's room, 17 feet 9 inches, by 11 feet, and the back stairs 16 feet by 11 feet. The landing from the principal stairs communicates with the public corridor, 6 feet wide, leading to the centre of the court, and the waiting-room, 18 feet 3 inches, by 12 feet 6 inches. The private corridor leads to the Grand Jury Room, 22 feet 4 inches, by 18 feet 3 inches, and the water-closets and urinals, 18 feet 3 inches, by 6 feet 9 inches, and back stairs. The principal stairs 23 feet, by 20 feet 9 inches.

The total external dimensions of the building (exclusive of the tower) are 88 feet wide, by 64 feet deep ; the exterior dimensions of the tower are 18 feet 6 inches by 15 feet 6 inches, and the height from the ground is 103 feet.

The architects are Messrs. Lee and Duesbury of London, whose plan was selected from upwards of forty that were sent in, many of them of great merit, and its interior arrangement is considered much superior to the late one. The builder is Mr. William Mansfield Cooper, whose original contract was for the sum of £3771.

Let us hope that this building will be more fortunate than its predecessor, and that the present generation of the inhabitants of Derby will not have to witness the destruction of their Town Hall. The inscriptions on the building are as follows. On left wing, Deflagratum, A. D. 1841. On right wing, Restitutum, A. D. 1842. On Tower, Forum Municipale.

The *County Hall*, or *Court of Justice*, situate at the bottom of St. Mary's-gate, was erected of freestone in 1660.* It stands in a recess, as public buildings should do, and has a walk of flag stones in front. The court yard was once graced with an avenue of trees leading to the entrance. Mr. Hutton describes it as being handsome and convenient, long the pride of the midland circuit, longer the dread of the criminal and the client, but the delight of the lawyer. Were two evils cured (he adds) we should yet behold an accomplished piece of architecture: remove one house towards the east, and it would open the whole front; and eight vases placed upon the summit would relieve the heavy effect of the cornice. The former suggestion has been complied with, and, on the east side of the court yard, the Judges' lodgings have been erected and furnished at an expense of nearly £16,000. paid by the county.

The new county hall, though an edifice raised for the legal business of the county magistrates and the judges at assizes, may justly be regarded as one of the public buildings of the town in which it stands. It was opened for the business of the summer assizes on the 11th of August, 1829. The courts and accommodations of this structure are eminently commodious, and afford a fresh testimony of what may be termed the beauty of utility.

The courts themselves are ample and commodious, with an elegant neatness suitable to their purpose. They are about 50 feet by 30 each, and have galleries round three sides, which are supported by columns of an oriental form; and columns of a similar form, but lighter and more enriched, sustain the roof; these pillars are handsome and much admired. The ventilation of the courts, and the warming them by means of heated air, was effected very successfully, principally under the direction of the late George Benson Strutt, esq. They are well lighted by lanterns composed of double panes of glass, the one clear, the other ground; they are also remarkably free from that echo which in some courts has been found so great a hinderance to public business. The front of the Hall is the same as belonged to the old building erected in 1659, but the interior has been

---

* Mr. Hutton informs us that the masonry was executed by one ——— Reeve, who saved nothing by the undertaking, as he drank the profits as they sprang up; and the carpentry by Roger Morledge, father of him who attempted to curb the Derwent, who was said to have acquired as much as erected a house at the bottom of St. Helen's walk, since the residence of his family.

fitted up in character with the rest of the building. A balcony or gallery, four feet wide, along the whole width of the Hall on the side next the courts, communicates by means of doors with the galleries within them, and forms a convenient elevated place for ladies and others to witness the proceedings at public meetings, that may be held on various occasions in the Hall.

County Jail. Before the 23rd of Henry 8th (1532) the felons of the County of Derby, were taken to the jail at Nottingham, but in that year the Justices of peace for the county, were empowered by act of Parliament, to erect a jail within the limits of the county. This was probably the one mentioned in such strong terms of reprobation by Mr. Hutton, when he says, " Our ancestors erected one in a river, exposed to damp and filth, as if they meant to drown the culprit before they hanged him. A worse situation could not have been chosen: it extended across the corn-market, one of the principal streets, as if to hide the brook or bind the flood. The wretched inhabitant was open to the public and they to him. A vile arch admitted the horse passenger, and a viler the foot; inconvenient to both, hurtful to the stranger, dangerous to the inmate, a reflection upon the place, without one benefit as a counterbalance. But their wiser successors destroyed this ancient reproach of some centuries standing, erecting an elegant prison on Nuns' Green."*

In Mr. Hutton's time there were four prisons in the town, two of these were jails, and two houses of correction ; one of each for the use of the town, under the jurisdiction of the mayor ; the others for the county, under the sheriff. The town jail before 1730, was under the town hall, but when that was taken down to be rebuilt, a small erection was added to the county jail at the bottom of St. Peter's-street, to serve as the town jail. In 1756 both jails were removed from this locality, " the elegant prison in Nuns' Green," being then erected for the use of the county, and the town jail removed to a building in the Willow Row. The prison in Friar-gate continued to be used as the county jail till 1825, when the new one having been erected it was bought by the corporation for £3000. as a borough jail, the one in Willow Row having been long found miserably defective. It continued the Borough jail till 1840, when an arrangement having been made for the reception of the Borough prisoners in the county jail, it was sold for £2000. to Mr. Thomas Cooper, who is now erecting several handsome houses on its site.

The four prisons mentioned by Mr. Hutton having been taken down, or ceased to be used as such, it remains only to give some account of the one, the only one now existing. The county jail in Friar-gate, having been inadequate to the wants of the county, and also deficient in arrangement ; it was determined at the county sessions in October, 1821, to erect a new jail and house of correction, for the use of the county. For a site for this purpose, 6 acres of land at the back of Friar-gate, and adjoining the old road to Uttoxeter, were obtained from the trustees of Large's hospital, by exchange for 36 acres of land in the parish of Sandiacre.

The six acres were valued at £2400. The plans and designs of Mr. Francis Goodwin were approved by the committee at the Epiphany Sessions, on the 16th of January, 1823, and on the 12th of February, the committee contracted with Mr. Goodwin to be their architect, who estimated the expense of the proposed erections at £37,403. exclusive of the purchase money for the land, the tread-mill, and the furniture of the cells and lodges.

The committee submitted the plan to the Society for the improvement of Prison Discipline, and at their suggestion and recommendation the architect introduced various alterations, which increased the number of cells to 185, several of which are calculated to contain three prisoners each. This amended and enlarged plan the court approved and adopted, and the architect delivered a new estimate, which amounted to £46,208. 5s. 4d. exclusive of the purchase of land. The present jail, erected upon this plan, is capable of containing 333 prisoners. The amount paid to the contractors, architect, furniture, &c., was £65,227. 4s. 6d.

* Hutton, p. 49.

Derby County Gaol.—This Prison is in an open and airy situation in the outskirts of the town of Derby. It is enclosed with a brick wall, 25 feet in height, with 15 courses of loose bricks on the top, and defended by flanking towers, loophole1 for musquetry. The exterior front and gate presents a happy appropriation of the Grecian Doric, with columns and entablature. The lodges contain a hall, lodgings for two turnkeys, county store-room, three receiving cells, keeper's office, two drop rooms, and reservoirs for water in the roof. The interior of the prison consists of a central building (the keeper's house and chapel) with seven radiating wings, of two stories each, connected therewith by iron bridges. The portion assigned to the females consists of two small buildings, apart from the others. The infirmary is detached, and comprises a day-room, surgery, bathhouse, on the basement, airing yard, and four rooms on the upper floor. A detached building of a circular shape, is exclusively appropriated for refractory prisoners, and those sentenced to solitary confinement. It contains two floors with three cells in each. Those in the basement are dark ; they are of a fanlike shape, occupying two-thirds of the circle, which is completed by the staircase. The lower cells have the appearance of being damp. Communication can be carried on between prisoners in the adjoining cells, with great facility.

Dimensions of the sleeping cells, 6 feet by 8 feet, 12 feet high.

The solitary cells, basement 11 feet by 7 feet, 12 feet high.

The solitary cells, upper floor, 11 feet by 7 feet, 9 feet high.

The airing yards are not paved. The keeper's house contains in the basement three kitchens, store-room, cellarage ; first floor, four rooms ; second floor, eight rooms. The chapel, above, is quadrangular. The divisions for the prisoners are 17 in number, with open iron-work in front. There is some garden-ground and stabling without the prison, the property of the county, in the possession of the keeper ; likewise three small houses, at the angular points, and at short distances from the boundary-wall are tenanted by the officers of the prison, and conducing materially to its security. The water-closets, the drainage, and indeed all the fittings in this prison are perfect, and the general arrangement of the buildings most convenient, with the single exception of the one set apart for solitary confinement.

Since the riots in October, 1831, eight martello towers have been designed by Mr. Mason, and built by Mr. Thomas Cooper, at the cost of £1540. These are furnished with fire arms.

Extract from the Inspector of Prisons' Report.

The magistrates, impressed with the necessity of warming the cells in winter, have adopted a most ingenious process, invented by Mr. Sylvester, civil engineer, which not only supplies the requisite heat, but contains at the same time a stream of fresh air into each cell, which is continually renewing itself. The apparatus was applied in the first instance only to one wing of the prison, but its complete success has induced the extension of it throughout the prison. The governor, in a communication to me, says, " I am quite delighted with this plan of ventilation and warming. We have an atmosphere which appears to change in the course of a minute or two, by a current of air which would almost take up a pocket-handkerchief into the shaft upon the roof of the wing. We are able to raise the temperature of the cells to 62, 63, 64, and 65 degrees, and to about 33 and 34 degrees above that of external air.

Upon each section of the building there is a ventilating shaft erected. The prison is warmed by hot water. There are now 212 prisoners under confinement.

The boundary walls round the new prison enclose three acres of ground. The plan is upon the radiating principle, and consists of one hundred and eighty-five cells, having twenty-one wards for the classification of prisoners. The gateway is a bold and commanding edifice, exhibiting the strength of character of which the Doric order is capable. The governor's house stands in the centre, and overlooks the whole. It is one of the most complete prisons in England.

The following extract from the Third Report of the Inspectors of Prisons will explain more fully the system Mr. Sims has adopted.

" The management of Prisons should be as near as possible upon the same principles as a military organization. The prisoners should be formed into divisions, and officers appointed to their charge ; all orders and reports should be made in writing ; the responsibility, duties, and precedence of the officers should be defined ; the daily routine of services precisely laid down and never departed from ; the interior of a well-regulated prison should present the same aspect as a garrisoned fortress. In very few establishments have I found any approach to this desirable state of things ; but the County Gaol at Derby is an exception, where the advantages of it are strikingly exhibited.

Mr. Sims succeeded Mr. Eaton, as keeper of the prison, in 1832, with a salary of £360. a year, now advanced to £500. a year. Mrs. Sims, matron, with a salary of £40. a year ; and Mr. James Sims, their son, clerk in 1836, with a salary of £41. 12s. now deputy-keeper, with a salary of £200. a year. The Inspector of Prisons, in his Report of the County Prison of Derby, speaks in the highest praise of the discipline and management of this Prison under Mr. Sims, and the advancement of himself and family is a sufficient testimony that he has filled the situation with the highest credit to himself, and has at all times given the utmost satisfaction to the magistracy of the county in the responsible office he has so long and so ably held.

The Surgeon attends the prison and sees every prisoner daily ; and is present at the infliction of corporeal punishment. Mild inflammatory diseases are those most prevalent. Douglas Fox, Esq., was appointed Surgeon in 1822, and receives a salary of £100. a year, and £20. for medicine.

Moral and religious instruction.—The Chaplain performs two full services with sermons on Sundays, and in the intervals, or after the services, attends the schoolroom, where the prisoners in classes are catechized. A portion of the scriptures is selected by him and read to the prisoners, who are questioned as to their conception of its meaning, and the necessary explanations afforded them if required. On other days prayers are read at 9 o'clock in the morning, and the chaplain is engaged with convicted prisoners until eleven. Rev. George Pickering was appointed chaplain to the jail, in 1813, and receives £150. a year.

There are fourteen male turnkeys who receive 20s. each per week ; two females, 14s. each, and two watchmen, 14s. each.

TURNKEYS.

Benson John, Fowler street.
Birch Charles, South street.
Brown, John, Dogkennel lane.
Carrington Henry, Fowler street.
Hudson Samuel, Searl street.
Kerry John, Nuns' street.
Martin Anthony, Fowler street.
Mather Thomas,   ditto.
Payne John, Uttoxeter road.
Francis Eaton.

Payne Joseph, Uttoxeter road.
Potter Thomas, York street.
Thompson John, South street.
Tucker William, Fowler street.
William Millet, Fowler street.
White Joseph, Uttoxeter road.
Bryan, John, Watchman.
Mary Neiland.
Sarah Peat.

Dietary.—Breakfast, a quart of gruel, made from two ounces of oatmeal, and a portion of bread ; dinner, one pound of boiled potatoes, and a portion of bread ; supper, one quart of gruel, made from two ounces of oatmeal, and a portion of bread. One and a half pound of good wheaten bread, and one quarter of an ounce of salt per day. Prisoners, confined for a longer period than three calendar months, receive in addition to their daily allowance, two ounces of onions per day. When onions cannot be procured, a red herring is substituted every second day. The surgeon states, that he considers the diet sufficient in general cases.

The agricultural labourer in Derbyshire has cheese and a little bacon, but butcher's meat seldom forms a portion of his food. The diet is not sufficient in scrofulous cases, and when he observes prisoners to be of that habit he increases it.

The following is a copy of a letter sent to the visiting Justices by the Surgeon, in consequence of the prisoners having petitioned the Justices to increase their allowance of food, and his opinion being on that point required.

Gentlemen,

The prisoners have not of late experienced any unusual inconvenience from the present gaol allowance. From numerous experiments which I made several years since, I ascertained from the present diet most of the men lose weight, some considerably, others but slightly; growing youth increase in weight. Whenever prisoners are confined a considerable length of time, if they appear feeble, I allow them occasionally half a pound of meat three times a week, or daily. In other cases I allow the addition of a pint of milk daily to their ordinary food. In all cases whether the prisoners have been confined for a long or a short time if their health appears to suffer materially, I immediately increase their diet.

Therefore Gentlemen, if it is your wish that the prisoners should have a diet, rather less stimulating and nutritious than that they procure when at large, and such as is calculated to cause them to wish to keep out of prison, and you desire that it shall make them feel that a gaol diet is not a desirable one, then I think the present one need not be altered.

Taking all the circumstances of the case into consideration, I am of opinion it is not necessary to add to, or to alter the present allowance.

I am, Gentlemen, your most obedient servant,

Douglas Fox, Surgeon.

The convicts sent from the above prison from 1815 to 1832, are as under: transported for life, 144; for fourteen years, 65; and for seven years, 202. 413 from 1832, to 1842, inclusive of 342 males, and 16 females, making a total in twenty-seven years of 771 persons.

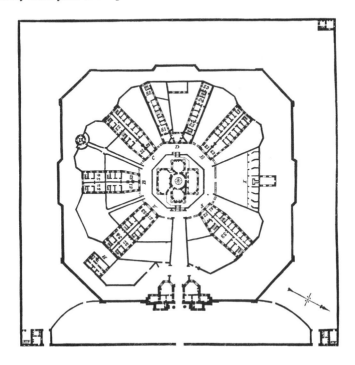

Plan of the new County Prison.

That the several wards or divisions of the said prison, shall be marked, and distinguished by the letters A, B, C, D, E, F, G, H, and I, and the sections or compartments of each ward, and the airing grounds attached thereto, shall be numbered progressively, beginning with each ward with the number or figure 1.

Common Jail for Male Prisoners.—That the whole of the wards A and B, and the sections or compartments 1 and 2 of the ward C, and the section or compartment 3 of the ward F, shall be the common County Jail, and, with the airing grounds attached to the same wards and sections or compartments, shall be appropriated for eleven classes of male prisoners.

That section 2 of ward A, and section 3 of ward F, with the airing grounds, shall be the debtors' prison.

FRONT ENTRANCE OF THE NEW COUNTY PRISON.

The new Assembly-room, situate on the east side of the Market-place, is elegant. It is built of stone in the style of architecture generally termed Roman, on a rusticated basement. It was built, by subscription, the whole sum subscribed amounted to £2,500—between the years 1763 and 1774. The dancing room is 30 feet high, 68 feet long, 32 feet wide, and contains an elegant loft for the musicians. It is fitted up with splendid chandeliers and sconces, which together with rich drapery adapt it for the reception of the nobility and gentry of the neighbourhood. On one side is a card room with a coved roof, supported by pillars, and below are the tea rooms. The property is in the hands of trustees.

The new Assembly-room is also appropriated to the use of the Derby Choral Society, for the performance of their annual series of concerts, consisting of four in each year, with occasionally a supernumerary one. These performances are respectably conducted, and have conduced much to the cultivation and improvement of the musical taste of the neighbourhood.

This Society was established in 1817, and was for several years conducted under the direction of Mr Alcock. It has now increased to the number of sixty members. The present leader and conductor is Mr. Gover, under whose judicious direction the combined talents of the society have progressed rapidly, and have been rendered available in a great degree to the furtherance of the charitable institutions of the neighbourhood.

The patrons are His Grace the Duke of Devonshire, and many of the nobility and gentry of the County. The Duke of Devonshire purchased the premises for £400. which he presented to the Committee appointed to build the Assembly Room.

Theatre.—The history of theatricals in Derby resembles that of every provincial town. There was formerly no regular theatre, and itinerant performers occasionally exhibited dramatic pieces in private rooms, or in the barns of inns. The back of the Old George Inn, between the Iron and the Sadler gates, was the principal site of these exhibitions, until the theatre was built in Bold lane, in 1773, by Mr. Whiteley. Mr. Manly, with a very good company of performers, who were frequently aided by the most popular actors and actresses of the London stage, attended here at regulated seasons, of which the principal consisted of six weeks from the Friday after Easterday ; and a short period at the races. He was manager for thirty years, and had a long lease of the theatre under the descendants of Mr. Whiteley. The theatre, we are informed, was erected in six weeks. It will hold about £90.

The first newspaper published in Derby, we have reason to believe was the *British Spy,* or *Derby Postman.* This publication made its appearance in 1726: it was published on a halfpenny stamped paper by S. Hodgkinson, and the price was 2d. or 2s. per quarter. This paper soon ceased after the appearance of the *Mercury,* which was first published on Thursday, the 23rd of March, 1732, by Mr. Samuel Drewry, in the Market-place, at 2d. each paper, or 2s. per quarter. This continued to be published by his descendants and was the only paper published in the county, with some slight exceptions, until 1823. Prior to which there had been several unavailing attempts to establish a second newspaper in Derby. The last was by Mr. Harrison, brother to the celebrated singer. The *Reporter* commenced on the 1st of January, 1823. It was at its publication edited by Mr. Noble, and has been spiritedly conducted by the proprietor, Mr. Walter Pike. This paper is published on the Thursday, and the proprietor has an increasing demand for it. The *Mercury* which has been established one hundred and sixteen years, takes the lead in the extent of circulation and in the number of advertisements. It is published by Mr. Burroughs, on the Wednesday.

The Philosophical Society, in St. Helen's-street, was established in February, 1783, by the following gentlemen, who met for that purpose at the house of the celebrated Dr. Darwin, in Full-street: Dr. Darwin, Mr. French, Mr. Sneyd, Dr. Berridge, Dr. Pigot, Mr. Leaper, Mr. Gisborne, Mr. Fox, and Mr. Strutt. The present Society consists of twenty-nine resident and seventeen non-resident members. Dr. Forester is the president. In 1815, the total number of volumes was 1486, and the members of the society thirty-nine. The building in St. Helen's-street contains a capital library, with mathematical and philosophical apparatus, specimens of fossils, &c.

The Athenæum, Royal Hotel, Post Office, and the Derby and Derbyshire Bank.—This group of buildings, from the designs of Mr. R. Wallace, forms a very striking improvement to the town, being situate immediately at the entrance of the Corn-market from the London-road, so as to present two lines of façade— one of 134 feet, towards the Corn-market, the other, 185 feet of frontage in Victoria street.

The erection of these buildings arose from the Derby and Derbyshire Banking Company having purchased some property, formerly occupied as shops, in the Corn-market, for the purpose of constructing a new Bank, afterwards they purchased the site and buildings of the Red Lion Inn, by auction, and the site and buildings of the White Lion, by private contract, from Mr. Thomas Cox. So large a property of old and dilapidated buildings in the centre of the town, naturally offered the opportunity of making important improvements. The Town Council, by an order made on the 9th day of April, 1836, resolved, that the Brook course from St. Peter's bridge to St. James's bridge should be covered over; this work, from peculiar circumstances, was not commenced until the 23d of May, 1837, and was completed on the 19th of August, in the same year; Messrs. M'Connel and Son were the contractors for this work, which was completed for the sum of £950. 16s. 6½d.—thus preparing the way for the following buildings: the plan of erecting a pile for public purposes was first suggested by Mr. Alderman Johnson, who named the project to Mr. Joseph Strutt, (the donor of the Arboretum) on the 15th of August, 1836, who at that time filled the office of Mayor; Mr. Johnson proposed to form a public company of shareholders, in shares of £25. each, to complete the undertaking, but the work not to be proceeded with until the sum of £10,000. had been subscribed. Mr. Strutt at once approved of the plan, and put his name down for £1000. Mr. Edward Strutt, one of the members for the borough, followed his worthy relative's example; a public meeting of the inhabitants was then held, and the project approved. In a short time shares exceeding £10,000. were subscribed, and a meeting of the subscribers was held at the Town-hall on the 9th of February, 1837, when a committee of twelve gentlemen was appointed to carry the objects of the Athenæum Society then formed, into effect. The society purchased the site of the present buildings from the Derby and Derbyshire Banking Company. Advertisements for designs were immediately published, and fifty-two designs were furnished by the several competing architects. The design by Mr. R. Wallace was approved by the committee, and that gentleman was employed as architect. The buildings were contracted for by Mr. Thomas Cooper, Brook-street, and were completed in 1839, at a cost (including the purchase of the site) exceeding twenty thousand pounds.

Though apparently only three, there are in fact, four distinct buildings, the Post Office forming externally a part of that end of the Hotel which adjoins the Derby and Derbyshire Bank, which faces the Corn-market, surmounted by ornamented sculpture, is built of Morley Moor stone, and has a frontage of 36 feet, set 5 feet back from the Hotel, that space being given up as the area. The ground-floor forms a rusticated basement, with four openings, viz., three windows and door, all arched, and the former ornamented with carved console keystones; the other with brackets. The first-floor windows have console-jambs, in addition to their architraves and other dressings; while those above have antæ-jambs, whose caps come immediately under the general entablature, which is of Ionic character, with a dentil cornice, carved architrave mouldings, and an inscription on the frieze in bold relief. The elevation is terminated by a conspicuous mass of decoration, composed of Grecian tracery or scroll-work, combined with the shields of the town and county arms, and a Caduceus on its apex; which symbolical ornament serves as an aëroterium, and gives a happy play and lightness of outline to the whole. Internally, the entrance-hall is separated from the dwelling-house part of the establishment by folding-doors, and has glazed doors of the same kind opening into the banking-office. This is 24 feet square, by 13 feet 6 inches high, and is fitted up with wainscot-framed enclosures, having frieze panels with open-work of brass ; which, with the mahogany desks and counters, give sufficient finish to the lower part. The ceiling consists of a circle, inscribed within the square cornice formed by a ring-band of Greek ornament, and having in its centre a large flower-shaped Greek boss, 4 feet in diameter : the spandrils are also filled in with enriched panels. From this office extends a corridor leading to the directors and managers' rooms behind, which has a berceau, or semi-cylindrical ceiling, formed in a groin, midway its length, in order to obtain a fan-light window. The whole of the ground-floor is of fire-proof construction—a system of iron-framing being introduced over it, of strength sufficient to carry brick arches and vaultings. Between the front office and the business-rooms behind it, is a strong room ; and there are likewise several lesser repositories of the same kind over it. Indeed, both convenience and security, as well as elegance, have been studied throughout.

The Hotel, which is at the external angle of the general pile of buildings, occupies the site of what were formerly the Red Lion and the White Lion inns ; the latter of which adjoined the brook that has now been covered over, and from which the road or street derived its appellation. Including the Post Office, the frontage of the Hotel towards the Corn market is 62 feet, and, towards Victoria-street, 98 feet. The style of architecture is Grecian Ionic, comprising two floors within the order above the basement. The order itself, however, is nearly confined to the curved compartment at the angle, which unites the two general elevations, and serves as a centre to the whole, when viewed directly in front and the other parts obliquely. On this account, therefore, it has very judiciously been treated as the principal architectural point in that portion of the mass ; a distinction the more suitable as the principal entrance is there placed. This part of the composition is further marked by the grouped pedestals at the angles above the antæ of the attic, which gives a boldness of outline to the summit, attended with considerable effect of light and shade. But we observe here one fault, in common with nearly every one of our modern Grecian designs, especially those of this species of the Ionic, namely, that the entablature generally, and the cornice in particular, so far from according with the florid character of the columns, is quite plain and meagre in appearance. Had its mouldings been carved, and a deep and enriched cymatium been placed above the corona of the cornice, the false concord of a masculine, or rather *neuter,* entablature, and *feminine* columns, would have been avoided. The entrance at this angle of the Hotel leads, through a small hexagonal vestibule, to the principal staircase (which is of stone,) and to a corridor communicating with the principal rooms on the ground-floor, and extending as far as the entrance beneath the gateway in the nearest pavilion of the Athenæum front.

This last-mentioned façade is decidedly the most important part of the whole design ; although, except in being somewhat loftier, it does not exceed that of the Hotel on the same side. It certainly possesses both greater originality and consistency ; and, although it has no columns, bears far more of the impress of the style than that elevation where they are introduced. In the view, however, it becomes little more than a secondary object, being seen too remotely to exhibit more than its general forms. The centre compartment has only five openings above, placed over three in the basement (viz., the entrance and window on each side of it,) owing to which a certain piquant contrast is produced, at the same time that the piers below acquire greater solidity. Above the five windows of the upper floor a deep panel is carried the entire length of this centre compartment of the elevation (45 feet,) which is filled with sculpture, by Henning, representing a portion of the Panathenaic Procession, of the same size as the original. Above the entablature here is an attic, or rather small upper order in pilasters, somewhat lower than the corresponding parts terminating the pavilions ; of which latter the height is further increased by grouped pedestals at their angles, supporting massive stone tripods, which serve as chimneys to the flues brought up in the piers beneath them.   In addition to the variety of outline thus obtained, considerable diversity of expression is produced by the upper part of the pavilions being made to assume somewhat of a loggia character, their windows being set back between square pillars, whereby much force of shadow is obtained.   The two larger windows, with the balconies, serve materially to keep up the distinct expression of these compartments, as compared with that of the centre one.

On the ground-floor are two entrance-halls (one in the centre, and the other in the farthest pavilion,) a news-rooms, 30 ft. 6 in. by 19 ft. ; a library, 35 ft. 6 in. by 15 ft. 9 in., with a recess, 15 ft. 10 in. by 5 ft. 9 in. ; a lobby, 15 ft. by 8 ft. 6 in. ; and a reading-room, 19 ft. by 14 ft. The large upper room, or hall, is 68 ft. by 30 ft. 6 in., and 23 ft. high. It is entered by folding doors at the west end ; and at the other, where the room is extended over the gateway in that pavilion, a division is made in the plan by two Ionic columns, owing to the greater width of the pier between the extreme window and the next one of the other five.   Above the west door is a small music-gallery, supported by boldly projecting consoles, and entered from an ˜upper landing on the staircase.   This latter also leads to a room over the hall, of the same dimensions, but of much lower proportions, its height being only 10 ft. 6 in.   As this room, however, is fitted up as a museum, its lowness is not disagreeable, especially as greater height is obtained in the centre portion, between the trusses of the roof, the tie-beams of which form chords to arches turned between the queen-posts, so as to disguise the construction, and carry the height to the level of the collar-beams, where light is admitted through glass panels or coffers, beneath external sky-lights.

The Town and County Museum in the Athenæum, Victoria street, contains some interesting specimens of minerals, fossils, preserved birds, native and foreign animals, insects, skeletons in comparative anatomy, &c.   The principal contributors to this collection of miscellaneous, attractive and instructive subjects, are Col. Gawler, sometime governor of South Australia, who presented to the Trustees a beautiful collection of birds and rare minerals which he had obtained during his residence in that country ; among the birds are two fine Albatros, one of which is displayed in the centre of the room. Lord Vernon, who presented the Wild Boar, a beautiful case of horned owls, the great buzzard, &c.   Joseph Strutt, esq., numerous rare specimens.   Godfrey Meynell, esq., a collection of fossils in chalk. Richard Wright Haden, esq., several rare specimens. Samuel W. Fearn, esq., a collection of skeletons, intended to display specimens in comparative anatomy.   We may mention amongst a few of the attractive objects, the dress of an Indian Chief, a richly carved Canoe, from the South Sea islands, the Bengal Tiger, the Mexican Deer, the Lion's Cub, a great variety of foreign snakes, several cases of insects, &c.   Admission 6d.

The News Room is supported by 102 subscribers, who pay one guinea each. The papers received are, the Times, Chronicle, Post, Standard, Sun, Globe, Examiner, Spectator, John Bull, Sunday Times, Derby Mercury, Derby Reporter, Liverpool Mercury, Nottingham Mercury, Leicester Chronicle, Manchester Guardian, Mark-lane Express, and Birmingham Herald.

The *Town and County Library*, in Amen Alley, has a very extensive Collection of Books of general Literature, and is especially rich in Travels and History.   The foundation of this Library may be considered to have been the Permanent Library, established in 1811, and which continued at Messrs. Wilkins' till 1832, when in consequence of there being a desire for an institution of a more enlarged nature, the proprietors agreed to transfer their stock and themselves to the Town and County Library, then in progress of formation.   This was first established in Full Street, but in 1839 it was removed to the present house, which was purchased for the purpose from John Chatterton, esq.   There are about 200 Proprietors, whose annual subscription is £1. 5s.

The *Mechanics' Institution*, established in August, 1825, commenced its operations with the most favourable prospects of success. The two first experimental courses of lectures, were delivered to the members, on the sciences of Chemistry and Anatomy, by Mr. Douglas Fox, surgeon, in a manner well adapted to the understandings of his audience, who, by the strong interest they manifested, afforded a striking proof of the immediate benefit of the institution, and excited a gratifying anticipation of its future advantages ; 274 individuals gave their names as members.

The *Mechanics' Hall* in the Wardwick.—The institution is now in a flourishing state, the number of members being about 800. In December, 1839, the number of honorary members was 73 ; senior members, 477, junior members, 195 ; 14 females had availed themselves of the advantages of the institution. There are classes for reading, writing, and arithmetic, drawing, music, French, and chemistry, and a class meets weekly for the purposes of discussing literary and scientific subjects. The library contains nearly 6000 volumes, which are classed with a view of forming a distinct division for juvenile members, and there is a museum and philosophical apparatus. The reading room, a comfortable and spacious apartment, is open from an early hour in the morning, to 10 at night ; it is well lighted, good fires are kept, and the table is amply supplied with periodicals and newspapers. In 1832, spacious premises were purchased for the use of the institution, for the sum of £1500. ; and its continued prosperity led to the erection of a lecture hall, the first stone of which was laid in 1836, by Joseph Strutt, esq., the President and fostering parent of this noble institution. It is an elegant and spacious room in the Grecian style of architecture, with fluted pilasters, 75 feet long, 40 feet wide, and 35 feet high, lighted by 16 windows, 12 branch gas lights, and a handsome chandelier. The walls are painted to represent grey marble. The room is ornamented with many valuable paintings, presented by Joseph Strutt, esq. The hall, including the necessary fitting up, cost £2000. ; to raise this sum a mortgage of £1600. was effected. It was opened October 18, 1837, by a public dinner, at which Lord Dunfermline, then Speaker of the House of Commons, presided, supported by the President and the Vice President of the Institution. About 500 Gentlemen dined on this occasion, many of whom were distinguished as the friends of education in this and neighbouring counties, and who by their presence, and by the speeches they delivered, testified their approbation of the Institution, and their regard for the interests of Literature and Science. To pay off the incumbrance of £1600. with which the institution was burthened, it was resolved to open an exhibition, and the gentry and others of the town and neighbourhood were solicited for the loan of articles ; for this purpose 400 individuals contributed 5000 different articles, including a Columbian printing press, a model of Fourdrinier's patent paper-making machine, electro magnetic apparatus, Jacquard loom, paintings, by eminent masters, sculpture, porcelain of Derby and foreign manufacture, models of various kinds, specimens in ornithology, entomology, mineralogy, and geology, and an extensive collection of curiosities. The managers wisely effected an insurance for £15,000. on the property thus liberally committed to their charge. The single admission was 6d., and season tickets for the 18 weeks, during which the exhibition was open, were 2s. 6d. 6000 catalogues were sold at 6d. each ; including the holders of season tickets, the number of persons who visited the exhibition was 96,000, and the total receipts amounted to £2119 9s. 8d., the expenses being £764. 9s. 8d., leaving the sum of £1355. to be applied to the liquidation of the debt. The inmates of the alms-houses, of the union poor-house, and the police and military, were admitted gratuitously ; the children belonging to the Sunday and charity schools of the town and neighbourhood, at 2d. each.

The hall is let for Exhibitions, Public Meetings, Balls, Public dinners, &c.

Front Entrance to the Arboretum, Grove Street.

VIEW OF NORTH LODGE, GROVE STREET,
FROM THE INTERIOR.

THE ARBORETUM.

THROUGH the noble munificence of Joseph Strutt, esq., (first Mayor of the Borough of Derby, after the passing of the Reform Bill in 1835, one of the Founders and President of the Mechanics' Institution,) the working classes of Derby have opportunities of enjoyment and gratification which few towns in the kingdom afford. This excellent, enlightened, and venerable man, observing the rapid increase of the population of Derby, and that while measures had been from time to time adopted for promoting their convenience, good order, and instruction, there existed no means by which the inhabitants with their families could take exercise and recreation in the fresh air, in public walks and grounds devoted for that purpose, appropriated nearly 11 acres of land to be laid out in the most advantageous manner, and to comprise an extensive collection of trees and shrubs, arranged in such a manner as to afford the means of instruction to visitors. This piece of land, to which Mr. Strutt gave the name of the Arboretum, was laid out at the donor's expense, by J. C. Loudon, esq., with great taste and judgment. Upwards of 1000 trees have been planted, besides several thousand evergreens, which form the belt of the gardens. The gravel walks are 6070 feet in extent. The principal walks are 15 feet wide, and the secondary ones 8 feet wide. Adjacent to them are placed seats in many convenient situations, and some portions of them are ornamented with vases, statues, and other sculptures. The grounds on either side of the walks are thrown up into mounds, varying from 6 to 10 feet in height; the easy and elegant forms of which are admirably adapted for exhibiting the trees and shrubs planted thereon. The ground was more particularly fitted for converting to its present purpose, from some portions of it having been already occupied with trees of considerable growth and graceful appearance; which would greatly contribute to facilitate the new formation, and its more speedy maturing into a beautiful landscape. In the recent work of plantation, a kind of zone has been formed consisting of thousands

VIEW OF THE SOUTH LODGE ENTRANCE, OSMASTON ROAD.

of evergreens ; and the numerous forest trees and deciduous shrubs which are in-
terspersed throughout the wide extent of the remaining space. have been disposed
upon the principle of classification—forming groups of such kinds as most nearly
resemble each other in their nature and properties.   This arrangement, though
not always the best adapted to please the eye by presenting variety in one single
or limited view, has the advantage of affording a greater facility to those who
may be desirous of acquiring a knowledge of the subject by repeated observations.

Two lodges have been erected from designs furnished by Mr. Lamb, of London ;
that at the principal entrance is situate at the north extremity of the gardens, and
is of the Elizabethan order ; and the one at the southern end of the gardens is of
the Tudor style of architecture.   Rooms for the use of the public are appropriated in each lodge, and have been furnished in a very neat and substantial manner at Mr. Strutt's expense.

VIEW OF THE SOUTH LODGE FROM THE INTERIOR.

Mr. Strutt's instructions to Mr. Loudon were as follows:

" That two lodges with gates, at the two extremities, should be built; and that each lodge should have a room, to be considered as a *public room*, into which strangers might go and sit down, taking their own refreshments with them, *without any charge* being made for the occupant of the lodge, unless some assistance, such as *hot water, plates, knives and forks*, &c., were required, in which case a small *voluntary* gratuity might be given.   That there should be proper yards and conveniences at each lodge for the use of the public, apart from those to be exclusively used by the occupant of the lodge.   That there should be open spaces in two or more parts of the garden on which large tents might be pitched, a band of music placed, dancing carried on, &c.   That certain vases and pedestals now in the flower garden, and also certain others in Mr. Strutt's garden in Derby, should be retained or introduced; and, finally, that some directions should be left for the management of the garden."

Conclusion of Mr. Strutt's Speech.—" I will only add, that as the sun has shone brightly on me through life, it would be ungrateful in me not to employ a portion of the fortune which I possess, in promoting the welfare of those amongst whom I live, *and by whose industry I have been aided in its acquisition.*"

There are two pavilions, one at each extremity of the principal walk.

Mr. Loudon has prepared a catalogue of the trees, shrubs, and plants for the use of the visitors, which is scientific, poetical, and anecdotical.   By the side of each plant a neat brick tally is fixed, the upper part of which exhibits under a glass covering the species, with other particulars, and a number referring to a fuller description in the catalogue.   A copy of Loudon's " Arboretum Britannicum," is kept in the lodge, to which those who desire more ample information may refer.   Mr. Loudon states that the soil of the Arboretum might have been prepared, and the trees planted at one tenth of the expense incurred; and this fact shows the liberal spirit with which Mr. Strutt has carried into effect every plan connected with his munificent gift.   Its value, including the ground and the buildings, is estimated at £10,000.   The duty of keeping the grounds in order devolves upon the public.   Mr. Strutt wisely conceiving that those who will enjoy and profit by the Arboretum will take an interest in its performance.

The Arboretum was opened on the 16th of September, 1840, and the event was celebrated by demonstrations in which every class of the inhabitants of Derby took a part. The day was a universal holiday, and the procession extending nearly a mile in length, was formed by the different trade societies and public bodies accompanied by banners, streamers, and music. On this day 6000 persons were assembled in the Arboretum, many of whom were young and full of animal spirits, but not a single shrub or plant was injured. Dancing, in which large numbers participated, was enjoyed in a field near the Arboretum to the music of a well appointed band. A ball took place at night in the Mechanics' Hall, and there were seldom less than two hundred couple dancing at the same time. Two days afterwards, the opening was celebrated by the children, and several thousands were admitted to the gardens, and the field was set apart for dancing and games of various kinds ; tea was provided in a large pavilion.

The gardens are " open to all classes of the public without payment, (subject only to such restrictions and regulations as may be found necessary for the observance of order and decorum,) on every Sunday, and also on the Wednesday in every week, from sunrise to sunset ; except that it shall never be open earlier than 6 o'clock in the morning, nor later than 9 o'clock in the evening ; and that it shall be closed between 10 and 1 o'clock on Sundays." It is under the management of the Mayor for the time being, and six other gentlemen, four of whom must be members of the Town Council.

The author and publisher is greatly indebted to the kindness and liberality of Mr Strutt, for allowing him the use of the engraved plans and views belonging to the Arboretum.

The residence of Joseph Strutt, esq., is situate at the bottom of St. Peter's-street ; it is a large and elegant modern brick mansion. Besides furnishing it in the most costly manner, the spirited proprietor has added a splendid gallery of paintings, which he has been many years in collecting. The works of the most celebrated artists are here brought together, and are gratuitously exhibited to the inhabitants and the stranger with a liberality and condescension rarely equalled.

The following is a list of some of the valuable Pictures, &c.

Interior with Figures, by P. De Hooge.
View in Holland—Jacob Ruysdael.
Education of the Virgin—Murillo.
Flemish Harvest Home—Teniers.
Head of a Jewish Rabbi—Rembrandt.
Children Playing at Soldiers—Morland.
Landscape and Figures—Sir Joshua Reynolds.
Portrait of Himself, seated at his easel—Ditto
Duke and Duchess of Hamilton—Ditto.
Landscape, River and Bridge—Claude.
Figure—Jan Meil.
Landscape, Ruins and Figures—Claude.
Virgin, Child and Angels—Lud. Caracci.
Landscape and Cattle—Bergham.
Return from Egypt—Langen Jan.
Christ Crowned with Thorns—Guido.
Virtue holding Revelry at bay, an Allegory—Titian.
Woods, Landscape and Figures—Waterloo.
Festoon of Fruit, Monkeys, &c.—F. Snyders
The Assumption of the Virgin—Crayer.
Horses going to Exercise, &c.—Cuyp.
With many other fine Pictures, by Holbein, Howard, Wright, Wilson, Salvator, Vandevelde, Dominichino, Moucheron, Fyt, Wemix, P. Neef, Collins, Danby, Wheatley, West, Corregio, Canaletti, Wilkie, Rubens, Vandelen, Vandernere, Guerchino, A. Caracci, Jordaens, Pollemberg, De Heem, Artois, Minderhout, Poussin, Martin, Van Dyck, Ostade, De Voies, Van Goyen, Gainsborough, De Witt, Hogarth, Terbourg, Fuseli, Etty, Opie, &c. &c.

Besides the Pictures, in Mr Joseph Strutt's collection, there are—

IN MARBLE—

A perfect copy of the Venus de Medicis, by Bartolini.
Venus Accroupie—Comolli.
Philoctetes—Comolli.
A magnificent Bust of Buonaparte.
A fine Apollo Belvidere.
A Bust of Roscoe—Gibson, of Rome.
A fine copy of the Borghese Vase, and many others.

IN BRONZE.

The Rape of Iole, by Hercules.
Buonaparte at the Head of his Army, and others.

A very perfect Egyptian Mummy.

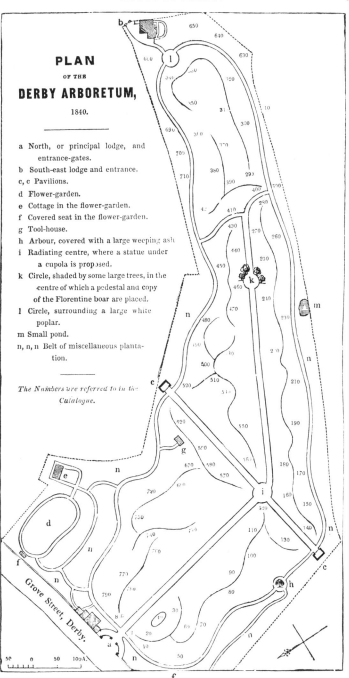

PLAN
OF THE
DERBY ARBORETUM,
1840.

a North, or principal lodge, and
    entrance-gates.
b South-east lodge and entrance.
c, c Pavilions.
d Flower-garden.
e Cottage in the flower-garden.
f Covered seat in the flower-garden.
g Tool-house.
h Arbour, covered with a large weeping ash
i Radiating centre, where a statue under
    a cupola is proposed.
k Circle, shaded by some large trees, in the
    centre of which a pedestal and copy
    of the Florentine boar are placed.
l Circle, surrounding a large white
    poplar.
m Small pond.
n, n, n Belt of miscellaneous planta-
    tion.

*The Numbers are referred to in the
Catalogue.*

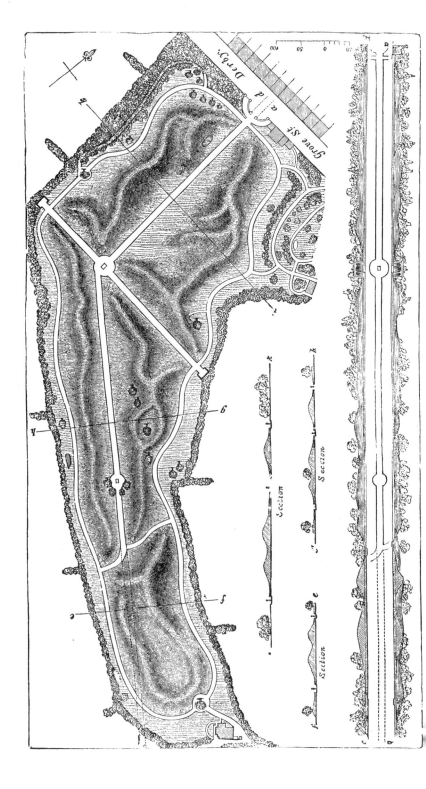

Grove Str. Derby.

Section — Section — Section — Section

The Derby Football.—Football continues to be played in many parts of England on Shrove-Tuesday and Ash-Wednesday; but the mode of playing this game at Ashbourn and Derby, differs very much from the usual practice of this sport.   In the town of Derby the contest lies between the parishes of St. Peter and All Saints, and the goals to which the ball is to be taken are, Nun's Mill for the latter, and the Gallow's balk on the Normanton road for the former.   None of the other parishes of the borough take any direct part in the contest, but the inhabitants all join in the sport, together with persons from all parts of the adjacent country.   The players are young men from eighteen to thirty and upwards, married as well as single, and many veterans who retain a relish for the sport are occasionally seen in the very heat of the conflict.   The game commences in the Market-place, where the partisans of each parish are drawn up on each side ; and, about noon, a large ball is tossed up in the midst of them.   This is seized upon by some of the strongest and most active men of each party.   The rest of the players immediately close in upon them, and a solid mass is formed.   It then becomes the object of each party to impel the course of the crowd towards their particular goal.   The struggle to obtain the ball, which is carried in the arms of those who have possessed themselves of it, is then violent, and the motion of this human tide heaving to and fro, without the least regard to consequences, is tremendous.   Broken shins, broken heads, torn coats, and lost hats, are among the minor accidents of this fearful contest, and it frequently happens that persons fall in consequence of the intensity of the pressure, fainting and bleeding beneath the feet of the surrounding mob.   But it would be difficult to give an adequate idea of this ruthless sport ; a Frenchman passing through Derby remarked, that if Englishmen called this playing, it would be impossible to say what they would call fighting.   Still the crowd is encouraged by respectable persons attached to each party, who take a surprising interest in the result of the day's sport; urging on the players with shouts, and even handing, to those who are exhausted, oranges and other refreshments.   The object of the St. Peter's party is to get the ball into the water down the Morledge-brook into the Derwent as soon as they can, while the All Saints' party endeavour to prevent this, and to urge the ball westward.   The St. Peter's players are considered to be equal to the best waterspaniels, and it is certainly curious to see one or two hundred men up to their chins in the Derwent or brook, continually ducking each other.   The numbers engaged on both sides exceed a thousand, and the streets are crowded with spectators.   The shops are closed, and the town presents the aspect of a place suddenly taken by storm.   The origin of this violent game is lost in its antiquity, but there exists a tradition, that a cohort of Roman soldiers, marching through the town to Derventio, or Little Chester, were thrust out by the unarmed populace, and this mode of celebrating the occurrence has been continued to the present day.   It is even added that this conflict occurred in the year 217, and that the Roman troops at Little Chester were slain by the Britons.   This game is played in a similar manner at Ashbourn, but the institution of it there is of a modern date.

There are two *Subscription Bowling Greens,* one on the Nottingham road and one in St. Peter's-street.   These are attended by the respectable tradesmen of the borough.   A billiard-table is kept in the Old George Yard.   There is also a cricket club, held at the Coach and Horses, Little Chester, consisting of about twenty-five members.   Many of the Innkeepers have skittle grounds attached to their houses for the amusement of their customers.

Among the private and ancient buildings of the town, the following are worthy of notice.

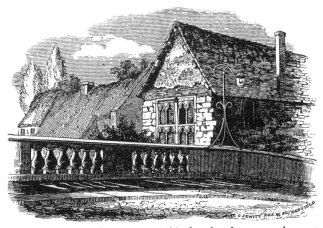

St. Mary's Chapel.—The remains of this chapel rank amongst the most ancient buildings now extant. It stands upon the verge of the river, formed a part of the old bridge, and was interwoven in such a manner with it, as to leave little doubt of its having been erected at the same time. There appears to have been a church in Derby dedicated to the Virgin Mary in very early times, and we think it is not hazarding a very erroneous opinion to pronounce this the same church as was given to the abbey of Burton, by William the Conqueror.

In the reign of Charles II. the Presbyterians made use of this chapel, and about a century ago it was converted into small dwellings. The only remains now in existence are a door case and two window frames, which formed part of the habitation of the late Mr. Thomas Eaton, surgeon.

The Castle.—There is great uncertainty respecting both the position and origin of Derby Castle, of which not a vestige can be traced with accuracy. The names of Castle-fields and Castle-street are the only indications of its site, and from them, Mr. Gibson, in his edition of Camden's Britannia, published about the close of the seventeenth century, concluded, that "on the south east corner of the town stood formerly a castle; though there have been no remains of it, within the memory of man." At a much later period, Mr. Hutton in his curious researches, believed that he had discovered the foundation walls of the castle in an orchard on the summit of Cockpit-hill. He says, "one of the mounds, eighty yards long, runs parallel with the houses on Cockpit-hill, perhaps one hundred yards behind them; also parallel with those in St. Peter's parish, but twice the distance." He adds, "this place of security then stood out of the town in an open field, no houses were near it. It was guarded by the Derwent on one side, and on the other ran the London road. This, I apprehend, was the chief approach, because the passage afterwards bore the name of Castle-street. From thence also the fields towards the east, Mr. Borough's park, acquired the name of Castle-fields." Since the days of Mr. Hutton, and indeed since the year 1815, almost the whole of Castle-fields and the space between Cockpit-hill and St. Peter's-street have been covered with new buildings, but we have not heard of any further vestiges of the castle being discovered; while in cutting down the hill on the west of St. Peter's-street, at the back of the Osmaston road, fragments of armour, heads of spears, and several skeletons were met with. Such an elevated and commanding situation, so near the ancient road to Repton, formerly the capital of Mercia, would more probably be chosen for a military fortress than Cockpit-hill, while the street and fields are as much in the neighbourhood of the one position as the other.

Mr. Woolley in 1712, notices a good house, erected by Mr. Beardsley, on the west side of the mill stream, on the Cockpit-hill. It is a good specimen of the early brick houses, erected in the latter end of the seventeenth century. There is one built in a similar style situate in St. Peter's church-yard. The house named by Mr. Woolley, taken down in 1819, is represented in the following engraving.

The same author mentions a good house on the south-east corner of Babington lane, built by the Mellors, who were a considerable family in this town. It afterwards belonged to the family of Degge, from whom it descended to E. S. Wilmot Sitwell, esq. It is a large old fashioned brick mansion with pointed gables, now the property of W. E. Mousley, esq.

The Babingtons had a large mansion on the north-west corner of Babington lane. A branch of which ancient and respectable family resided here. In 1712, the ancient stone gateway was standing. This gateway was ornamented with the arms of Babington, sculptured in stone, supported by Baboons upon Tuns. The hall was wainscoted with oak, on the panels were various devices and Baboons upon Tuns carved thereon, the same being a play upon the name of Babington. The following wood engraving represents one of the panels.

Exeter House.—The author has thought it right to give a sketch of Exeter House, the mansion house which communicates with the Full-street, from its connexion with the history of this county, in the year 1745.   At that time it belonged to the Earl of Exeter, and Prince Charles Edward, commonly designated " the Young Pretender," took up his abode there, and held his council of war in a fine old oak-wainscoted room (now used as a drawing-room) before he determined to abandon his project.   This house was subsequently occupied by an ancestor of the late celebrated William Strutt, esq., and by other families, and is now the residence of William Eaton Mousley, esq., to whom it belongs.

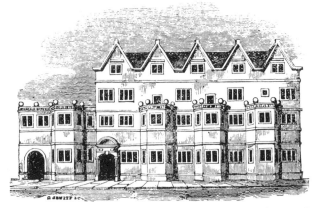

This house, which belongs to Francis Jessopp, esq., is a large and ancient pile of building, with projecting windows, and pointed gables, and an ornament to the street in which it stands.   Over the entrance door is the date of 1611, though it appears to have been erected at a later period.   It was originally built by an opulent ancestor of the Gisborne family, formerly residents in this town, and has attached to it two acres of ornamental pleasure grounds, very tastefully laid out.   From the Gisbornes it passed to the late Rev. Dr. Heathcote, from whom Mr. Jessopp purchased it about the year 1820.

St. Helen's House, situate at the top of Bridge-gate, opposite the site of St. Helen's priory, was built by John Gisborne, esq.* from whose descendant it was purchased by the late William Strutt, esq. F. R. S. who made great improvements in the interior, and additions to the gardens and pleasure grounds. This noble looking mansion has a stone front, with a handsome pediment ornamented with vases. It is elegantly furnished, and contains some excellent family and other portraits and pictures. The staircase railing is a fine specimen of wrought iron work. It is now the principal residence of his only son, Edward Strutt, esq. M.P. for the borough.

Abbot's Hill, the residence of Richard Forester Forester, esq. M.D., a magistrate of the county, stands on an elevated site, in the centre of the town ; it is a large brick mansion, distinguished by some noble elms tenanted by rooks ; the gardens and pleasure grounds are enclosed by a high wall.

The Friary, the residence of Henry Mozley, esq., is situate in the Friar gate, built by Samuel Crompton, esq., on the site of a religious house, which gave name to the house and the street in which it stands.

In the Friar-gate are many good houses, occupied by respectable families. That built by the late Thomas Cox, esq., is a large handsome modern brick house, the residence of his sister, Miss Cox ; and that recently built by Mr. Shaw, designed by Mr. Henry J. Stevens, has a handsome stone front, in the Italian style of architecture.

In the Wardwick, adjoining the Mechanics' Hall, stands the handsome brick mansion, the property and residence of William Lockett, esq., a magistrate of the county.

In the Iron-gate the most distinguished building is the bank of Messrs. Crompton and Newton, and the residence of John Bell Crompton, esq., Mayor of the borough of Derby. In St. Mary's-gate is the bank of Messrs. William and Samuel Evans, and in the Rotten-row, the bank of Messrs. Smith and Co.

In many of the streets, and within the vicinity of the town, are many respectable and beautiful residences, occupied by the clergy, gentry, and the principal inhabitants.

---

* Hutton says, "the most superb house in Derby, is that of John Gisborne, esq. in Bridge-gate, a house that would honour the first orders of nobility, but in a situation which does not merit a dwelling of £500. Wherever we find so expensive a work, we may fairly conclude the proprietor was either very rich, or did not dread poverty."

Derby being situate in the centre of the kingdom, with water and railway conveyance to every part; an abundance of good coal in the immediate neighbourhood, and two copious streams flowing through it, renders it extremely favourable for the institution and carrying on of manufactures which require the aid of water or steam power. These advantages have caused many capitalists to establish various works in the town and its vicinity. Their success has also been greatly promoted by the judicious application of machinery; and mills of the most improved construction have been erected for numerous purposes. Owing to the variety of the manufactures carried on here, the inhabitants seldom experience those serious changes caused by the temporary depression of any one in particular, which is so frequently felt in those towns where the manufacture is confined to one.

Mr. Hutton, after having described the leading manufactures in Derby, concludes with this remark: " Derby appears to have crept silently through ages without much connexion with commerce, except what arose from her own tailors, hatters, weavers, and shoemakers, till the beginning of the eighteenth century, when the frame, the river, the silk-mill, the porcelain, &c., awakened her drowsy talents to riches, increase and notice. The man who has known her threescore years can easily discover an improvement in her external buildings, and the extension of her borders. He may as easily prophesy, that like an infant whose powers are equal to its magnitude, it can stand upon its own basis, and will rise more rapidly towards maturity." Mr. Hutton's prophecy was correct. Derby has trebled her inhabitants since he made the observation, and her manufactures have immensely increased.

In 1199, in the reign of king John, an exclusive privilege was granted to the burgesses of Derby to dye cloth. This business continued to be the staple manufacture of the borough for some centuries; for we find three fulling mills are mentioned in queen Mary's grant to the burgesses of Derby.

The manufacture and dyeing of wool flourished until the introduction of the silk mill, by that ingenious mechanic, John Lombe, about 1717. Indeed, it appears that long after the silk mill was introduced, the woolcombers were numerous; for, in 1749, we find the woolcombers, who walked in procession to All Saints' church, on the celebration of the peace of Aix-la-Chapelle, formed a considerable body. In 1780, Messrs. Barber erected a machine to spin wool for the manufacture of carpets. The only woolstaplers now in the borough are Messrs. Cooper and Son.

There are no fairs, we believe, expressly held for the sale of the wools of this county, though some persons have at times advocated such an establishment, and formerly the July fair at Chapel-en-le-Frith was noted for the sale of this article. At Ashhopton, an attempt has been made to establish an annual fair for the disposal of wool. It is customary for the wool-staplers to go from farm to farm.

By the charter of Grants of Queen Mary in 1555, there appears to have been three fulling-mills on the river Derwent, which stood on the flats, where the old silk mill was afterwards erected; and the name of the " Full-street," still points out the particular part of the banks of the river, where the fullers carried on their branch of the wool-manufacture. Fulling-mills are now in use at Glossop, Simondley and other places.

About two centuries ago, according to Camden, the chief trade consisted in malting and brewing ale; which he speaks of as being in great request, and much celebrated in London, to which city large quantities were sent.

Fuller, in his usual quaint style, remarks, " to make malt for drink was indeed a master-piece. How much of philosophy concurred to the first kiln of malt! And before it was turned on the floor, how often was it tossed in the brain of the inventor thereof! First to give it a new growth more than the earth had bestowed thereon. Swelling it with water to make it last the longer by breaking it, and taste the sweeter by corrupting it. Secondly, by making it pass the fire, the grain (by art fermented) acquiring a lusciousness (which by nature it had not) whereby it doth both strengthen and sweeten the water wherein it is boiled." And he adds, " never was the wine of Falernum better known to the Romans, than the Canary of Derby to the English."

Ale was much used as a beverage by the Anglo Saxons. In the Saxon Dialogues, preserved in the Cotton library, in the British Museum, a boy is asked what he drank: he replies, " *Ale* if I have it, *water* if I have it not." Ale was sold in houses of entertainment, but a priest was forbidden to eat or drink at *Cape-ale-thetum*, a place for selling ale.

In 1712, Mr. Woolley says that the chief trade consisted in malting, and that large quantities of malt were sent into Cheshire, Staffordshire, and Lancashire, by which many persons raised good estates; and mentions also the trade of a baker; this town supplying most of the Peak country with bread of hard corn.

The same author tells us that Derby was famous for very good ale, which the brewers sent to London and other parts, to great advantage. There are at the present time several malting establishments, none of which are very extensive, and four wholesale breweries. The baking business is chiefly confined to the borough. A considerable quantity of grain, sent from hence to the northern division of the county, passes through the hands of the factors.

The hosiery trade forms so important a part of the trade of Derby, and employs so many of its inhabitants, that a detailed account of the trade will be both interesting and instructive.

Stockings were in former times, generally, if not entirely, made of worsted, and were knitted by hand; but for many years past, stockings intended for sale are frame-woven. In Derbyshire very few, if any, worsted stockings are made on the frame; and the framework-knitters of this county may be divided into two branches; namely, those who work in silk and those who use cotton only. In the silk branch there are eight hundred and fifty persons employed; in the cotton, not fewer than *six thousand five hundred*.—The stocking-frame was invented towards the close of the sixteenth century, by Mr. William Lea, M. A. of St. John's, Cambridge. He was born at Woodborough, a village about seven miles from Nottingham. It is related that he became enamoured with a lovely stocking knitter, who instructed and employed young girls in the same business. She rejected his addresses, and her admirer, in revenge of his slighted affections, conceived the design of inventing a machine that should render the hand-knitting of stockings a profitless employment. He produced the stocking-frame in 1589, and taught his brother and some of his nearest relatives the use of it. Having for some years practised this new art, at Calverton, a village about five miles from Nottingham, he proceeded to London, and solicited the protection and encouragement of the court. This was either at the latter end of the reign of Elizabeth or early in that of James I.; but though he and his brother are said to have made a pair of stockings in the presence of the sovereign, his invention was discountenanced, upon the grounds that it would tend to deprive hundreds of the industrious poor of their usual means of maintenance. The value of such improvements, by which the productions of industry might be increased, was not then understood in this country, and France was the place where the aid of machinery in various species of manufacture was beginning to be sought after. There Mr. Lea, at the invitation of the illustrious Henry IV., went with nine workmen, and settled at Rouen, in Normandy. The murder of that monarch, and the intestine troubles of the kingdom destroyed the expectations of Mr. Lea, who ended his days at Paris; a victim, it is said, to disappointment and grief. Seven of the workmen returned to England, and under the direction of a person named Aston, who had considerably improved upon the original invention, the foundation of the manufacture was laid in England.—The two workmen who remained in France attempted in vain to obtain encouragement; and endeavours were made with very little success to introduce the framework-knitting into Italy and Holland. The art, in the mean time, began to flourish in this country, and during the Protectorate, the framework-knitters petitioned Oliver Cromwell, to be incorporated by charter. In this petition, which is composed with much intelligence and spirit, they style themselves "the promoters and inventors of the art, and mystery or trade of framework-knitting, or making of silk stockings, or other work in a frame or engine." They wrought (as appears by the petition) generally, if not entirely, in silk, that material being "the best and richest of all others in use and wearing, and most crediting the artisans, and of the greatest advantage unto this State and Commonwealth, yielding several payments to the use of the State before it passes out of the hands of the traders therein, and increasing merchandise by both the ways of importation and exportation of the same material, imported raw at cheap rates ; exported ready wrought at the utmost extent of value : so that the distance of those valuations is totally clear gain to this Commonwealth, and esteemed upwards of six parts in seven of the whole quantity of this material in the highest value thereof, wrought up by this manufacture ; which has vindicated that old proverbial aspersion :—*the stranger buys of the Englishman the case of the fox for a groat, and sells him the tail again for a shilling.*—And may now invert and retort upon them ;—*The Englishman buys silk of the stranger for twenty marks, and sells him the same again for one hundred pounds.*"—Cromwell did not grant the prayer of their petition, but they obtained a charter from Charles II. soon after the Restoration, by which the exercise of their manufacture was restricted to a company, with a jurisdiction extending ten miles round London. In process of time, this company established commissioners in some county towns, where they compelled the country frameworkknitters to purchase their freedom ; but a spirited Nottingham artisan determined to try the question in a court of law. In this process, the company was cast, and the stocking manufacture has, since that occurrence, continued to be entirely open. Since the dissolution of the company, the manufacture of stockings gradually declined in London, and spread itself into various parts of the country. At Leicester, in particular, it flourished greatly during the early part of the last century, but the finest work was made at Nottingham and Derby. Some frameworkknitters established themselves at Towcester in Northamptonshire, and at Godalming in Surrey.

This manufacture which had been introduced into the town and county some time in the eighteenth century, acquired additional celebrity by the ingenious discovery of Messrs. Jedediah Strutt and William Woollatt, who, in the year 1758, produced a machine for making ribbed stockings. This was termed the Derby rib. From an imperfect idea furnished by a common workman named Roper, these ingenious gentlemen brought this important improvement to perfection, and obtained a patent, which gave them the exclusive use of it during a term of fourteen years. A kind of ribbed-work had been introduced in the knitting of stockings, even before the invention of the stocking-frame, and it has been asserted that a pair of ribbed stockings had been made by a man named Wright, at Ilkeston, in the year 1730, and by an old stocking-maker of Dale Abbey. The following account of the invention is from the late William Strutt, esq., F. R. S. " It was Jedediah Strutt, my father, who invented the Derby rib machine in the year 1758, or thereabouts. About that time he settled in Derby for the purpose of carrying on the manufacture of ribbed stockings, in conjunction with his brother-in-law, Mr. Woollatt, who was then a hosier in that place, and which partnership continued until the death of my father, in the year 1797. A great part of the time during which the patent was in force, Mr. Samuel Need of Nottingham was a partner, under the firm of Need, Strutt, and Woollatt. The patentright was tried twice in Westminster-hall : first, with the hosiers of Derby, and afterwards with those of Nottingham ; from which time it was enjoyed quietly to the end of the term."—This improvement has suggested others, and from it has arisen the art of making open-work mittens, gloves, pantaloons, shirts, and various fanciful articles.

The stocking frame invented by the Rev. William Lea, or Lee, of Calverton, in 1589, was very simple, with jacks only, and was a *twelve-guage :* the improvement introduced by Aston of Thornton, who was originally a miller, consisted in applying the lead-sinkers, which are still in use. Needham, a London frame-work-knitter, placed the trucks on the solebar, and in 1714, another London workman, named Hardy, added the caster-back and hanging-bits; and thus may be said to have brought the stocking frame to all the perfection of which it is capable, for nothing that has subsequently been devised has added any power or facility to its operations. The Derby-rib-machine, applied to the stocking frame, is known among the framework-knitters as the one-and-one, and the two-and-one rib machine; the invention of which, by Mr. Jedediah Strutt, has been already mentioned.

The principal of the stocking frame was applied to the knitting of various articles in the course of the last century. In 1766, a person named Crane, manu-factured a rich brocade for waistcoats on a similar frame, and about two years afterwards he attempted vandyke-work, by appending a warp-machine to a plain stocking frame. In 1769, Mr. Robert Frost, who lived at Arnold, near Not-tingham, invented the figured eyelet-hole machine, and in concert with Mr. Thomas Frost, now of Worcester, obtained patents for various inventions, which gradually led to the net and lace frames.

The first machine for making lace from a stocking frame was contrived in 1777; and the invention of it was disputed by Mr. Robert Frost, and a poor operative of Nottingham, of the name of Holmes. This was superseded by the point-net machine, the offspring of the ingenuity of Mr. John Lindley, senior; at whose death, Mr. Thomas Taylor, of Chapel-bar, having improved upon the principle, took out a patent. This subsequently was further improved by Mr. Hiram Flint, but it has been almost wholly superseded by the warp and bobbin net. This last was the invention, chiefly, of Mr. James Tarratt, about the year 1783; that ingenious man was very lately resident in the Charter-house, in Lon-don. The bobbin and carriage, for making bobbin-nets, is an important inven-tion, and has been claimed by various persons, among whom is Mr. John Lind-ley, resident at Loughborough. The other claimants were George Whitmore of Nottingham, who died greatly distressed in a London hospital, and Robert Brown, also of Nottingham, who some time before his death fell into a state of melancholy, occasioned by his pecuniary embarrassments and the failure of his fishing-net and upright warp machines. The bobbin and carriage machine was first worked, about the year 1799. In 1807, Edward Whittaker of Nottingham made the bobbin and carriage to traverse, after the manner now in use, in the Loughborough and Levers' machines. He died at New Radford, in impoverish-ed circumstances. The rack was applied to the lace machine by Handley of Nottingham, who was unfortunately poisoned with cantharides, administered to him in a frolic. In the succeeding years, the lace manufacture received nume-rous improvements, which it would be impossible to particularize with accuracy or distinctness in this compendious view of so interesting a subject: it will be sufficient to say, that Mr. William Morley, now of the firm of Boden and Morley, of Derby, introduced the straight-bolt bobbin-net and the circular-bolt bobbin-net machines, both of which are now in use; and we do not hesitate to say, that the machinery in Messrs. Boden and Morley's extensive mill is the best in the trade. To the family of the Levers this manufacture is indebted for various improvements, and indeed the more recent inventions have chiefly consisted of ingenious methods of adapting the Levers' bobbin-net machine to a variety of purposes; and in 1826, Mr. William Crofts and Mr. John Bertie applied the Levers' machine to make breadths by what is termed a treble-turn-again, which superseded all other methods. Of the Messrs. Levers, the elder died some years ago at New Radford; his son, Mr. John Levers, resides at Rouen in Normandy; and his nephew, of the same name, lives at Nottingham. The plat-net machine, still in use, was the invention of the unfortunate and misguided Jeremiah Bran-dreth, who was executed for treason at Derby, November 7, 1817.

The manufacture of the beautiful fabric called bobbin net-lace has been introduced into Derby within the last twenty years. Nottingham and Loughborough were some years the chief marts for it. Very extraordinary profits were obtained on its first introduction. This induced numbers who could raise a little capital to embark in it. The great demand for machines causing them to rise five or six times above their real value. Many tradesmen, who had been travelling steadily on in the old beaten tract, fancied they saw golden days at hand. The bobbin net machine was to be the means of realizing to the possessor a rapid and splendid fortune. In the brilliant prospect the speculative mind became dazzled, and the head giddy, with the thought of purchasing estates, building mansions, and driving four in hand. The picture was too glowing to be real. The scene, alas! soon changed; many soon found they had speculated their all, and that all had gradually sunk into oblivion. Others withdrew from the trade at an immense sacrifice. Lace manufactories and machinery became a drug in the market. A machine, which had originally cost from £600. to £800. might be purchased for £100., and even so low as £40. or £50. The article manufactured fell in proportion, and the trade vested among capitalists and the most eminent mechanics.

The largest lace manufactory of this description is the one in Castle-street, belonging to Messrs. Boden and Morley. It is a handsome structure, containing two hundred and ninety-eight windows, and occupying an area of 2124 square yards. The principal building is 56 yards long. It is fitted up with 150 machines worked by steam power, and contains an engine of twenty horse power, planing engine, casting, fitting-up and winding rooms, smiths' shops, and every convenience for such an establishment. It would be a difficult task to give a correct idea of the numerous and complicated movements of the beautiful machinery here employed. There are also several smaller manufacturers.

Silk, it has been noticed, was used as the principal material in hosiery soon after the invention of the stocking frame, but it was not until the beginning of the eighteenth century that the manufacture of that elegant article by machinery upon an extensive scale was introduced into this country. The Italians had previously possessed the art of throwing silk by means of machinery, and the French excelled in the fabric of piece-goods. Attempts were made in England to rival these productions without success. A person named Crocket endeavoured to throw silk at Derby in the year 1702; but his machinery was imperfect, and it was not until 1715, that a young ingenious and enterprising mechanic, whose name was Lombe, resolved to proceed to Italy and investigate personally the whole process. He encountered many dangers, but returned to England in 1717, with plans and drawings, and accompanied by two Italian workmen. He came immediately to Derby, and rented of the corporation a long swampy island in the Derwent for eight pounds per annum, and there erected THE SILK MILL, which was long esteemed a masterpiece of mechanical skill. While the mill was building, Mr. Lombe erected temporary machines (turned by hand) in the town hall and other places, by which he was enabled to pay for the erection of the grand machine as the work went on. In 1718 he obtained a patent for a term of fourteen years; but the Italians were enraged at his success, and he fell a victim to their vengeance, in the year 1722; it being supposed that a slow poison, administered to him by an artful woman from that country, occasioned his death at the early age of twenty-nine. One of the Italians who had accompanied Mr. Lombe from Italy, and whose name was Gartrevalli, remained at Derby for some time, and afterwards worked at a silk mill which had been established at Stockport, where he died in poverty.

Mr. John Lombe was succeeded by his brother William, a young man of a melancholy disposition, who committed suicide. The property then became the inheritance of Mr. Thomas Lombe, the cousin of the enterprising founder of it, and was conducted with much spirit and success; for about the year 1730, the works are said to have employed more than three hundred persons. In 1732, the patent expired, and the proprietor petitioned parliament for its renewal, alleging

" that the works had been so long a time in perfecting, and the people in teaching, that there had been none to acquire emolument from the patent." The application was not successful, but a remunerating grant of £14,000. was voted to him, and a model of the works was ordered to be deposited in the Tower of London. The proprietor was also introduced at court, and had the honour of knighthood conferred upon him. He did not long enjoy this reward of wealth and honour. On the 3rd of January, 1739, he expired, leaving to his widow an accumulated property, valued at little less than £120,000. On the 20th of February, 1739, the lease of the silk mill was assigned from Lady Lombe to Richard Wilson, esq. and the whole of the works were in the following July transferred to that gentleman for the sum of £4000. These premises were occupied for many years by Mr. Swift, who made many important additions to the machinery. The lease expired in 1803; the mill is now in the occupation of Mr. William Taylor, who has entirely renewed the works, erected a steam engine, and introduced numerous important improvements. On March 14, 1826, a fire broke out in the upper part of the old mill and did very considerable damage. This Mill is the property of the Corporation.

The Silk Mill, being the first and largest of its kind ever erected in England, brought Derby into particular notice. This original mill is designated THE SILK MILL, to denote its pre-eminence. Its history is remarkable, as it displays the power of genius and the astonishing influence which the enterprises of a single individual has on the commerce of a country. The Italians long enjoyed the exclusive privilege of the art of silk throwing, and the merchants of other nations were dependent on that people for their participation in that lucrative article of trade, until Lombe brought it into this country.

The raw silk is chiefly brought in skeins or hanks, from China or Piedmont.* That produced in the former country is perfectly white, but the produce of the latter is of a light yellow colour. The skein is first placed on an hexagonal wheel, or swift, and the filaments which compose it are regularly wound off upon a small cylindrical block of wood, or bobbin. To wind a single skein is the work of a day and a half, though the machine is kept in motion ten hours a day, so astonishingly fine are the filaments of which it is formed. In this part of the process many children are employed, whose nimble fingers are kept in continual exercise by tying the threads that break, and removing the burs and uneven parts, some of which are the cases that the silkworm fabricates for its own grave, or rather for its dormitory while nature prepares it for a new mode of existence. The silk thus wound upon the bobbins, is afterwards twisted by other parts of the machinery, and is then sent to the doublers, who are chiefly women, stationed in the same building. Here four, seven, or ten, of the threads are united into one, according to the uses for which they are designed ; the fine kind going to the stocking weaver, the other to the manufacturer of piece goods, &c.

The machinery is dispersed through six rooms, occupying the six stories. This is all put in motion by the water-wheel, on the west side of the building, and the steam engine. The elaborate machinery consists of many thousand reel bobbins, star-wheels, reels, and spindles ; but an adequate idea of the complicated assemblage of wheels and movements cannot be conveyed by words ; to be distinctly conceived it must be seen ; and even then considerably more time is requisite to obtain a knowledge of its parts, and of their dependence on each other, than is generally allotted to the casual visitant. All is

---

* It was not till the year 535, that two Greek monks, returning from the Indies to Constantinople, brought with them a number of silkworms, with instructions for hatching their eggs, rearing and feeding the worms, drawing out the silk, &c. upon which manufactories were set up at Athens, Thebes, and Corinth. In the twelfth century, Roger, king of Sicily, established a manufactory at Palermo, and another in Calabria, having brought workmen from the cities of Greece, which he had conquered in his expedition to the Holy Land ; and by degrees the rest of Italy as well as Spain, learned the art from the Sicilians and Calabrians. In the reign of Henry the Second, the French began to imitate their neighbours with good success; and James the First was very desirous of having mulberry trees planted, and silkworms propagated in his British dominions, where, from various experiments, it appears they will thrive and work as well as in any other part of Europe.

whirling and in motion, and appears as if directed and animated by some invisible power ; yet mutually dependent as every part is, any one of them may be stopped and separated at pleasure.   This arises from every movement being performed by two wheels, one of which is turned by the other ; but when separated, the latter preserves its rotary motion, while the other stops, as the impelling power no longer operates.*

In this preparatory sketch, we cannot pretend to describe this extraordinary combination of mechanism, except in a very cursory manner.   This mill stands on an island in the Derwent, upon large piles of oak, doubly planked, and covered with stone work ; on which are turned thirteen stone arches, that sustain the walls.   The length of the building is one hundred and ten feet ; its breadth thirty-nine feet ; and its height fifty-five feet and a half.   It contains six stories, beside the under-works, and is lighted by four hundred and sixty-eight windows. Mr. Lombe expended upwards of £30,000. in erecting and fitting up this mill. The whole of the rooms are filled with machinery constructed on the most modern principle.   This elaborate machine (for *only one* it is) though occupying six apartments, is put in motion by the water-wheel and the steam engine.   All operations are performed here, from winding the raw silk to organzining or preparing it for the weavers.   There are besides this mill 12 others in Derby.

Silks which are manufactured in Derby are equal to any in the kingdom.

The weaving of piece-goods in silk was first introduced into Derby by Mr. William Taylor, at his factory in Bag-lane, about twenty years ago.   His example was followed by Messrs. Bridgett and Son, Messrs. Wilson, Moore and Co., and Messrs. Robinson, and now sarcenets, gros-de-naples, velvet, and other rich silks are manufactured, in a style equal to those made by the weavers of Spitalfields.   There are now about two hundred and twenty looms in work.   The number of hands employed in this branch is about three hundred.

The weaving of silk ferrets, galloons, doubles, &c., was introduced by Messrs. Peet.   Messrs. Frost and Stevenson, Messrs. Madeley and Co., and others have established similar manufactories.

Silk hosiery is not the least important branch of the silk trade ; there are many excellent mechanics connected with this branch, and the manufacturers are Samuel Fox, jun., esq., Mr. Longden, Mr. Lewis, Mr. Morley, and others, some of whom also manufacture cotton hosiery.

Of the other branches of industry in which the inhabitants of Derby are chiefly employed, we must not omit to mention tape, ferrets and small-wares. Manufactories of this nature were introduced into the town of Derby in 1806, by Messrs. Riley, Madeley, Hackett and Co. and the manufacture of tape is now carried on by Messrs. Hackett and Son.

---

* Mr. Lombe procured, in 1718, a patent from the crown, to secure the profits during fourteen years. But he had not pursued this lucrative commerce more than three or four years, when the Italians, who felt the effects of the theft from their want of trade, determined his destruction, and hoped that his works would follow.

An artful woman came over in the character of a friend, associated with the parties, and assisted in the business.   She attempted to gain both the Italians, and succeeded with one.   By these two, slow poison was supposed, and perhaps justly, to have been adminstered to John Lombe, who lingered two or three years in agonies, and departed.   The Italian escaped to his own country ; and the woman was questioned, but nothing transpired except what strengthened suspicion.

Grand funerals were the fashion at this time, and Mr. Lombe's was, perhaps, the most superb ever known in Derby.   A man of a peaceable deportment, who had brought a beneficial manufactory into the place, employed the poor at advanced wages, could not fail meeting with respect, and his melancholy end with pity.   Exclusive of the gentlemen who attended, all the people concerned in the works were invited. The procession marched in pairs, and extended the length of Full-street, the Market-place and Iron-gate ; so that when the corpse entered All Saints', at St.Mary's-gate, the last couple left the house of the deceased, at the corner of Silkmill lane.   Besides a row of flambeaux on each side the procession, one person in every fourth couple, carried a branch, with four candles, weighing a pound.

Though the unhappy victim died at the early age of twenty-nine, and by a cruel death, yet the priest who preached his funeral sermon took for his text, " He is brought to his grave as a shock of corn in its season."—There is, however, a remark in favour of this ill-chosen text ; the good never quit the world *out* of season.

Mr. Lombe dying a bachelor, his property fell into the hands of his brother William, who enjoyed, or rather possessed the works but a short time ; for, being of a melancholy turn, he shot himself.   This superb erection then became the property of his cousin, Sir Thomas Lombe.

The largest cotton mill in Derby, and the first fire proof mill erected in England, was built by the Messrs. Strutt, in 1793. This mill is six stories high, 115 feet long, and 30 feet wide. The floors are constructed on brick arches and paved with brick, by which means it is rendered absolutely indestructible by fire. These gentlemen were extensive manufacturers of cotton thread, hosiery, figured waistcoat pieces, and numerous other articles, for many years, which contributed to the extension of this branch of business in a very eminent degree. This mill is now occupied by Messrs. Davenport and Humpstone, silk-manufacturers.

At these various factories upwards of five thousand persons are employed.

The porcelain or china manufactory of Derby has placed the reputation of this country on a level with that of Saxony or France for the production of this elegant article ; and equal to any other, for the finish and taste of the execution. This manufacture was introduced here about the year 1750, by Mr. W. Duesbury, who fabricated numerous elegant and costly articles, among which was an elegant dessert service, consisting of one hundred and twenty pieces, for the Prince of Wales, (late George IV.) The fineness of the material has subsequently been greatly increased, and much superiority in the colouring has been attained. The blue and gold had been brought to the greatest state of perfection, and now the green, in which alone this porcelain was surpassed by foreigners, is possessed of the highest degree of delicacy and lustre. The body of this elegant ware is fine clay, combined with fluxes, and is chiefly brought from Cornwall. The best kind is completely fusible. The biscuit figures are peculiar to this manufacture, and are in high estimation in almost every part of the globe. The urns, vases and ewers produced in this manufactory are from classical designs, and are adorned with landscapes, portraits, and figures by very superior artists. Among the splendid services executed at the Derby china works, the following may be enumerated ; one for the Earl of Shrewsbury, embellished with fruit subjects, upon a rich ground of the chrome-green ; another for the Duke of Devonshire, which was enriched with original views of Chatsworth, Hardwick, &c. Elegant services for Lord Muncaster and for Lord Ongley, were richly and tastefully embellished with historical designs. In 1819, a service consisting of numerous bowls and dishes, for the Persian ambassador, was executed in a style of superior splendour: the ground was gold, chased and inscribed with Persian characters. These works are carried on with great credit under the superintendence of Mr. Thomason, for Mr. Blore ; and strangers who are desirous to inspect the works and show-rooms, receive the most polite attention.

The spar and marble works are situate at the corner of St. Helen's-street and King-street, on the site of the monastery of St. Helen. This manufactory was originally formed by Messrs. Brown and Son, but is now carried on by Mr. Joseph Hall, who has erected a steam engine to give motion to the very ingenious and novel machinery which he employs in the manufacture of the numerous elegant and ornamental articles which his show rooms contain.

Few strangers pass through Derby without paying a visit to this interesting establishment, where every operation is freely shown by the proprietor.

Captivating nature is here improved by art. A block of rude stone is converted into an elegant chimney-piece, or sculptured into a splendid monument. Here the various beautiful spars and marbles of the county are inlaid into chess and other ornamental tables, quite equal in appearance and durability to the celebrated *pietra dura.*

The plan adopted here for sawing and polishing marble is very interesting. A number of plates of soft iron, about the twelfth of an inch thick, four or five inches broad, and of sufficient length, are fixed in a frame at required distances ; this is called a set of saws ; it is placed upon the block of marble, and put in motion by the crank of the engine which produces a reciprocating horizontal movement ; sand and water are constantly dropping, which, getting under the saw plates, wear channels through the block, and it is by this means separated into a number of slabs: these slabs are then taken to the sweeping and polishing beds, which are equally ingenious, but would be difficult to understand by a mere description.

The lead mills, for the manufacture of white and red lead, of Messrs. Cox, Brothers and Co., Messrs. Goodale, and Mr. Holbrook, situate at Derby and its immediate neighbourhood, are extensive. Leaden pipes are manufactured by Messrs. Cox, Brothers and Co., and at Mr. Chatterton's, at their works in the Morledge, of any given bore or length.

The shot tower of Messrs. Cox and Co. is a curious and interesting object. This is a circular building, about fifty yards in height. The formation of the shot is an ingenious process, for which the proprietors of the works have a patent. The lead, in a state of fusion, is poured from a boiler at the top of the tower, and falls through sieves into a reservoir of water below. This tower suffered considerably by fire on the 13th of April, 1824, but was shortly afterwards repaired, and is now in full operation.

In 1734, the slitting, rolling and flattening mills were erected on the Derwent in the Morledge, to prepare iron for various uses, and for smelting, rolling, and preparing copper for sheathing the navy. These mills were the property of the late Thomas Evans, esq. who successfully worked them for many years.

Iron Foundries.—Among the numerous branches of trade carried on in Derby, the iron trade is not the least important; it combines strength, safety, utility, and beauty. Iron-foundries have been established in Derby half a century. The late Mr. Thomas Wheeldon who carried on the business many years, first, at the St. Peter's street foundry, and afterwards at the Derwent foundry, brought the cast-iron trade to great perfection. He was succeeded by his son-in-law, Mr. William Gibson, and it is now spiritedly and ably conducted by the Derwent Foundry Company, Exeter Street, who manufacture retorts and gas apparatus; wheels, rails, and all kinds of railway work; bridges, cast and wrought iron roofs, beams, and pillars; castings for steam engines; water, gas, and steam pipes; windows for churches, chapels, warehouses, or cottages of every order or design. Gates, palisading, ornamental balcony bars, and vases, made to model or dimension; spouts, mangers, and racks; boilers, grates, stove-pans, and every kind of shopgoods for furnishing Ironmongers.

In all these various works, this Foundry has now attained a degree of excellence equal to any in the kingdom.

In 1818, Messrs. Weatherhead, Glover, and Co. established the Britannia Foundry, in Duke Street, near to St. Mary's Bridge. At this foundry castings have been produced in superior workmanship and design to any previously made in this country. It has been distinguished not only for elegant castings for domestic purposes, but for its architectural works and ornamental vases. The Gothic church-windows and columns executed at this Foundry have been esteemed perfect specimens of this art, and are proofs of the capability of its being applied to the loftiest designs of the builder. The churches and chapels in which these Gothic window-frames, &c., have been affixed, are those of Portsea, Bordesley, near Birmingham; Walsall, Burton, and West Bromwich, Staffordshire; Kidderminster, in Worcestershire; Ashton-under-Lyne and Oldham, in Lancashire; and the new church of St. John's, in Derby. The elegant vases, and particularly the cast-iron temple for the Earl of Shrewsbury's Gardens, at Alton Towers, have been highly appreciated. This foundry is now the property of, and worked by Mr. Thomas Wright, who manufactures slide lathes, locomotive, tender, and carriage wheels, turn-tables, and all kinds of railway work; castings for steam engines; retorts for gas works; water and steam pipes, vats, pans, stoves, and spouts; Gothic and Grecian windows for churches and cottages; ornamental vases, gates, palisading, and every other sort of casting to model or dimension.

The *Union Foundry* was established by Messrs. Falconer and Peach in 1822. This company is in high repute for their domestic and engine castings. At this Foundry are manufactured all sorts of kitchen ranges, stove grates, patent mangles, furnaces, pans for bleachers, dyers and brewers' pots and kettles, plain and ornamental palisading and tomb railing, bookcases and garden-rollers, also castings for millwork and machinery ; water-wheels and engines, pumps, gas and water pipes, and spouting for factories and houses.

The *Phœnix Foundry*, Nottingham Road, Derby.—Mr. James Haywood the proprietor of these works, and a partner in the extensive ironmongery establishment in the Market Place, manufactures stove grates, kitchen ranges, Silvester's patent stoves for halls and churches, and other castings for ironmongers. Bridges, roofs, tanks, &c., for railways, columns, girders, palisading, and every description of ornamental castings, for architects and builders.

At these works were made the castings for the bridge over the Nottingham Road and other bridges on the North Midland Railway ; also a large proportion of the iron work for the erection of the Railway Station at Derby, and the whole of the girders, columns, and other castings required in the building of the Royal Exchange, London.

Messrs. Sandars and Haywood, Market Place, Derby, are furnishing ironmongers, iron, steel, and tin-plate merchants, brass and iron founders, manufacturers of every description of plumber's brass work ; bell-hangers, tin-plate workers, and copper-smiths, oil and colour-men, &c., &c.

Messrs. Weatherhead, Walters, and Co., Iron-gate, Derby, are general furnishing ironmongers, ironfounders, silversmiths, gunsmiths, bell-hangers, flax-dressers, rope-spinners, dealers in carpets, oil-cloth, matting, cutlery, plated copper, brass, tin, Britannia metal, and cast and wrought iron goods, oil, paints, colours, varnishes, soap, candles, vinegar, and British wines.

Messrs. Holmes, Rotten-row, Messrs. Ratcliffs, Corn Market, and Mr. Hunt, St. Peter's street, are also wholesale and retail ironmongers.

Connected with the iron trade we may notice the engine boiler manufactory of Mr. Harrison, near St. Mary's bridge, where water-tanks, boilers, railway-trucks, iron boats and all kinds of Smiths' work, are made to order.

The stranger who has a taste for examining excellent workmanship and ingenuity, would be much gratified by going through Messrs. Joseph and James Fox's manufactory, City-road ; these gentlemen manufacture the best lathes ever produced in any country, which are sent to all parts of the Continent.

At the manufactory of Mr. Smith, Liversage-street, London-road, who is the patentee for a portable steam engine, and a new invented printing machine, may be obtained slide lathes, planing machines, mill or engine work of the best description.

At the Nuns' Factory, Nuns' street, Mr. Duncan manufactures steam engines. In the same street, is Mr. Mosedale's factory, who has long been celebrated for his superior steam engines. He has recently put up a very powerful one at the original Silk Mill. At the Cavendish street Factory, Mr. Abell, makes excellent Machinery and Steam Engines.

The clock and watch manufacturers of Derby employ about sixty persons. Mr. John Whitehurst who conducts an extensive business in this line, is a relative of the celebrated geologist, natural philosopher and able mechanic, Mr. John Whitehurst, F. R. S. That eminent man settled at Derby about the year 1740, where he made the clock and chimes of All Saints' church and the clock of the Town Hall ; on which account the corporation presented to him the freedom of the borough. He was subsequently appointed inspector of weights and measures in London, where he died in February, 1788, in his seventy-fifth year. Mr. Whitehurst has made clocks for many of the halls belonging to the nobility and gentry of this and other counties, which are remarkable for their accuracy. He has also made a clock with chimes for Burton old church, and clocks for many churches in this and other counties which are universally admired. The watches of Mr. Brookhouse, Cooper, Woodward, Edwards, Holme and Smithard, Jolliffe and Son, Roberts, and other manufacturers, are highly appreciated.

In 1750, Mr. Abijah Mellor, established the jewellery business in Derby. There

g

are now six respectable establishments carried on in Derby. The articles manufactured here are esteemed equal to the best workmanship of London.

The principal Dyeing establishments are |those of Mr. Ward, Messrs. Tunaley, sen. and jun., and Mr. Henchley.

Roman cement was first manufactured in Derby by the Messrs. Brookhouse, who, for many years carried on an extensive business in that article and plaster. Great praise was due to the late Messrs. Thomas and John Brookhouse for discovering and producing to the country such a useful composition for buildings and ornamental work. The business is now conducted by Mr. Thomas Brookhouse. The Messrs. Brookhouse and the family of Simpson, are also eminent plasterers, and their superiority in that department is to be seen in many noblemen and gentlemen's mansions in this and other counties.

Many thousand tons of ground plaster are annually sent to London and different parts of the kingdom, from the mills of Messrs. Brookhouse, Messrs. Pegg and Co., and Mr. Woolhouse.

Printing and publishing establishments. The art of printing has been known and practised in Derby as long probably as in any other provincial town of the same extent. We do not, however, know that there is any copy of a work printed in Derby previous to the newspapers published by Hodgkinson at the commencement of the last century. The business of printing as wholesale publishers was introduced into Derby by Henry Mozley, esq. in 1815. A similar business is carried on by Messrs. Richardson and Son. The other printing offices are those of Mr. Burroughs, proprietor of the Derby Mercury, Messrs. Pike, proprietors of the Derby Reporter, Messrs. Wilkins and Son, Bemrose, Storer, Rowbottom, Chadfield, Horsley, Smith, Roberts, printer and news agent, Bamford, Hobson, and Glover and Son.

The circular and reciprocating saw mills of Messrs. Roe and Oakley, and Mr. Wait, are worthy of attention. At these mills a large quantity of timber is sawn for various uses.

Coach and harness manufactory.—In this department Derby can boast of one of the most extensive and respectable establishments in the kingdom.

The manufactory for fashionable carriages and harness, situate on the London road, and conducted by the Messrs. Holmes (who have lately been appointed coach makers to her Majesty Queen Adelaide, and his Royal Highness Prince Albert) gives employment to a great number of workmen, and justly merits the distinguished patronage with which it is honoured.

The spacious show rooms containing a variety of modern and elegant carriages on the most improved principles, are open for the inspection of visitors.

Messrs. Dagley and Smith have also a large establishment in London street, where they manufacture carriages of every description for the road and railway, and Mr. Moore, Curzon street, has for many years carried on the business of Coach builder.

During the last quarter of a century, the building department has been of considerable importance, having given employment to numerous stonemasons, bricklayers, labourers, plasterers, carpenters, joiners, plumbers and glaziers, painters, and a variety of artisans.

The most eminent builders are Mr. Thomas Cooper, who built the Church at Riddings, St. John's Church, the Martello towers at the county gaol, the Athenæum buildings, and several of the best houses in Derby. Mr. William Mansfield Cooper, the contractor for rebuilding the Guild-hall, enlarging the Congregational Chapel, Victoria street, the Carpenter's work at the Congregational Chapel, London road, and various public and private buildings. Messrs. Gascoyne and Son, who built the Shot Tower, the Congregational Chapel, and Liversage's Alms-houses, London road, and numerous public and private buildings. Messrs. Bridgart, who built the Town-hall, destroyed by fire, Oct. 21, 1841, Christ's Church, the New Methodist Chapel, King street, and the National School, Curzon street. Mr. John Wood, who built the Savings' Bank, Friar gate, and did the stone work for Christ's church, and is now restoring the beautiful tower of All Saints' Church. Mr. George Thompson, who built the Diocesan School, Friar gate. Mr. Edwin Thompson, built Trinity Church National School, and several handsome houses on the London road. Mr. Winterton, the contractor for converting St. Mary's-gate house into the New Baptist Chapel. Mr. Adin, Mr. Sowter, Mr. Swain, Mr. Moss, Mr. Slater, and others.

The Borough is divided into six wards, viz. Bridge ward, Becket ward, Castle ward, Derwent ward, Friar gate ward, and King's Mead ward. Six Councilmen are returned for each ward, who serve three years, and are eligible to be re-elected. The members returned at the last election to serve for the next three years, are inserted in page 137, with the exception of Mr. George Stevenson, in the place of Mr. Thomas Storer, for the Bridge ward, and Samuel Fox, jun. esq., instead of Mr. John Wright, Surgeon, for the Friar gate ward. The corporation consists of twelve Aldermen, out of whom the mayor is chosen, and 36 Councilmen. John Bell Crompton, esq., was appointed at Michaelmas, to serve the office of mayor for the ensuing year, 1843. There are 2087 electors entitled to vote for councilmen.

NAMES OF STREETS IN THE SIX WARDS.

Bridge Ward.—Amen alley, Bath street, Bold lane, Bridge gate, Corn market, west side of, St. James's lane, part of, College place, Darley lane, Duke street, Full street, west side, Iron gate, King street, north side, Market head, Market place, north side, North parade, Old shambles, Queen street, east side, Rotten row, St. Mary's gate, south side, St. Alkmund's churchyard, Victoria street, north side, and River street. 289 Electors.

Becket Ward.—Abbey barns, Abbott's hill, Babington lane, Back Sitwell street, Baker's lane, Becket-well lane, Britannia street, Burton road, Cannon street, Corn market, Cross lanes, Curzon street, Drewry lane, Dunkirk, Forester street, Green lane, Grove terrace, Grove street, Haarlem street, High street, Kensington street, Leonard street, Mill street, New Uttoxeter road, Normanton road, Osmaston road, Osmaston street, St. Peter's street, west side, Sacheverel street, Sitwell street, St. Peter's church yard, St. James's lane, Stockbrook field, Summer hill, Talbot street, Victoria street, south side, Wardwick, west side, Waterloo street, and Wilmot street. 400 Electors.

Castle Ward.—Albion street, Albion place, Bag lane, Borough's walk, Bloom street, Bourne street, Bradshaw street, Canal street, Canal side, Castle street, Castle place, Carrington street, Cockpit hill, Corn market, east side, Devonshire street, Eagle street, Hill street, Hope street, John street, Liversage street, London street, east side, Midland place, Morledge, part of, North street, Osmaston street, Osmaston road, Park street, Rivett street, Siddals' lane, St. Peter's street, east side, Thorn Tree lane, and Traffic street. 418 Electors.

Derwent Ward.—Chaddesden hill, Chester place, City road, Corn market, east side, Darwin terrace, Derwent street, Derwent row, Erasmus street, Exeter street, Exeter place, Full street, Mansfield road, Market place, south and east sides, Morledge, New market, Nottingham road, Old meadows, Old wharf, Queen street, part of, Silk mill lane, St. Michael's lane, Tenant street, and Walker lane, part of. 271 Electors.

Friar gate Ward.—Agard street, Ashbourn road, Bold lane, Brick street, Bridge street, part of, Brook walk, Cavendish street, Cheapside, Curzon street, Dog kennel lane, Ford street, Fowler street, Friar gate, George street, Large's street, Markeaton lane, Mill street, Old Uttoxeter road, Sadler gate, north side, Sadler gate bridge, Short street, South street, St. Werburgh's church yard, St. John's terrace, St. Mary's gate, part of, Vernon street, Wardwick, east side, and York street. 330 Electors.

King's Mead Ward.—Bridge gate, part of, Bridge street, part of, Brook street, Chapel street, Charles' street, Cherry street, Goodwin street, Green street, Jury street, Kedleston road, King street, Leaper street, Lodge lane, Lower Brook street, Mundy street, Nun's street, Orchard street, Parker street, Queen street, part of, St. Mary's gate, north side, St. Helen's street, Walker lane, William street, Willow row, and Wright street.　379 Electors.

Contested Elections.—But few contested Elections have taken place within the last 150 years. The Borough was contested in 1700, 1701, 1710, 1714, 1734, 1742, 1747, 1748, and 1774. After a lapse of 58 years, (during which period the interest of the noble house of Cavendish prevailed) the borough was contested in 1832; the candidates were the Hon. H. F. C. Cavendish, and Edward Strutt, Esq., in the Whig interest, and Sir Charles H. Colvile, in the Conservative interest. After a severe contest, the former members were again elected. At the close of the pole the numbers were, Strutt, 911, Cavendish, 744, Colvile, 445. On the 7th and 8th of January, 1835, a contest took place; the candidates were Edward Strutt, Esq., Hon. J. G. Ponsonby, and Hon. Francis Curzon, Barrister at Law, the latter in the Conservative interest. At the close of the Poll, the numbers were for Strutt, 903, Ponsonby, 724, Curzon, 525. On the 25th of July, 1837, a contest took place between Edward Strutt, Esq., Hon. J. G. Ponsonby, Hon. Francis Curzon, and Charles Robert Colvile, Esq., the two latter in the Conservative interest ; at the close of the poll the numbers were for Strutt, 836, Ponsonby, 791, Curzon, 525, Colvile, 456. In 1841, the present sitting members were opposed by Edward Sacheverel Chandos Pole, Esq., who came forward at the eleventh hour in support of the conservative interest. The contest was carried on with great spirit, but the whig interest again prevailed, at the close of the poll, the numbers were for Strutt, 891, Ponsonby, 789, Pole, 589.

Mayors of the Borough, see List in the History of Derbyshire, Appendix to vol. I. from 1637 to 1832.

1831.	Charles Matthew Lowe, Esq.	1837.	John Bell Crompton, Esq.
1832.	John Chatterton, Esq.	1838.	Douglas Fox, Esq.
1833.	Douglas Fox, Esq.	1839.	John Sandars, Esq.
1834.	Richard Wright Haden, Esq.	1840.	Francis Jessopp, Esq.
1835.	Joseph Strutt, Esq.	1841.	Stephen Gamble, Esq.
1836.	William Leaper Newton, Esq.	1842.	John Bell Crompton, Esq.

The most remarkable Floods on record, are extracted from Glover's History of Derbyshire.

1610.　This year, owing to a sudden rise of the Markeaton brook, three prisoners confined in the gaol, were drowned. The gaol was erected near to the brook, on the site where the Red Lion and White Lion Inns, Corn market, formerly stood, now occupied by the Post Office and Royal Hotel.

1611, May 14.　There happened such a land flood from the Markeaton brook, that in the memory of man the like was never seen.

1673.　A great flood upon the Markeaton brook, carried away the hay, filled the cellars as high as the Angel, Rotten row, and broke down three of the ten bridges. St. James's bridge was landed at the Sun Inn, St. Peter's street.

1698.　A great flood which washed down part of St. Werburgh's church, and the steeple fell.

1736.　A great flood on the River Trent.

1740, Dec. 11.　A great flood in Derby. On Tuesday last, we had the greatest inundation of water here that ever was known, occasioned by the falling of a great quantity of snow and rain, which began on Sunday, and continued (almost without intermission) till Tuesday morning, at which time several streets, and all the rooms upon the ground floor were laid a great depth under water. Great damage was done to the houses and furniture ; several walls were thrown down ; bridges and great quantities of wood carried away, and numbers of cattle swept from the pastures perished. The parish church of St. Werburgh received considerable damage, it having made so great a breach in the pavement throughout the church so as to require it to be new paved. At Alvaston a man attempting to save his cattle perished.

1770. Three several floods on the river Derwent, within a few days, which are more than the oldest man can remember to have happened in so short a space. The highest flood on the river Trent, owing to the late heavy rains, known since 1736.

1795. A great flood on the Trent, Swarkeston bridge washed down.

During the last half century there has been many heavy floods on the Markeaton brook, and the rivers Derwent and Trent. But it falls to our lot to record the most disastrous flood on the Markeaton brook that ever occurred in the memory of man, and one the least expected. On the night of March 31, 1842, the rain fell in torrents, and about 3 o'clock in the morning of the first of April, the Markeaton brook began to rise, and rose so suddenly and rapidly, that few of the inhabitants had timely warning of their danger. The sudden rise of the brook soon filled the cellars, laid many of the streets under water, and filled the houses and shops in the Corn market, Victoria street, part of St. Peter's street, St. James's lane, Wardwick, Curzon street, part of Sadler gate, Bold lane, part of St. Mary's gate, Jury street, Walker lane, Willow row, Ford street, Agard street, Friar gate, Bridge street, Brook street, and Morledge. In many of the streets the height of the flood was from 1 *ft.* 7 *in.* to 6 *ft.*, according to their levels, viz. Corn market, 5 *ft.* 6 *in.*, St. Peter's street, lower part, 4 *ft.* 6 *in.*, Victoria street, 4 *ft.* 7 *in.*, Becket-well lane, 5 *ft.* 2 *in.*, Wardwick, 4 *ft.* 3 *in.*, Curzon street, 3 *ft.* 4 *in.*, Cheapside, 4 *ft.* 5 *in.*, Friar gate, 3 *ft.* 9 *in.*, George street, 4 *ft.*, Sadler gate, lower part, 5 *ft.*, Bold lane, 5 *ft.* 6 *in.*, St. Mary's gate, lower part, 5 *ft.*, Jury street, 5 *ft.* 9 *in.*, Willow row, 6 *ft.*, Ford street, 4 *ft.*, Brook street, 4 *ft.* 6 *in.*, Bridge street, 3 *ft.*, Agard street, 3 *ft.*, Morledge, 2 *ft.* 10 *in.*, Tenant street, 3 *ft.* 6 *in.*, New market and Derwent street, 1 *ft.* 7 *in.*

About 120 tradesmen and gentlemen were considerable sufferers from this extraordinary flood. Amongst the heaviest losers by this great calamity may be enumerated, Joseph Strutt, esq., whose estimated loss was upwards of £1000. Mr. Sale, Messrs. Masseys, Mrs. Draper, and Mr. Hellaby, drapers; Mr. Wild, Mr. Cook, and Mr. Willder, grocers; Messrs. Ratcliff, and Messrs. Wheatcroft and Co., ironmongers; Mr. Goodall, Mr. Walton, Mr. Shaw, and Mr. Bryer, druggists; Mr. Cholerton, upholsterer; Messrs. Cox and Malin, wine merchants; Mr. Wallis, Mr. Huggins, Mrs. Taylor, Mr. Neale, Mr. Cantrill, Mr. Reeves, Mr. Lowe, Mr. Green, Mr. Wright, Mr. Dimock, Mr. Gover, Mr. Hollis, and Mrs. Johnson, innkeepers; Messrs. Holme and Smithard, jewellers, and watch manufacturers; Messrs. Moseley and Nephew, jewellers; Messrs. Mozley and Sons, Messrs. Pike, Mr. Storer, and Mr. Whittaker, booksellers; Mr. King, and Mr. Hawgood, smallware dealers; Mr. Lomax, and Mr. Eames, pawnbrokers; Mr. Forman, Hop merchant; Mr. Perkins, perfumer; Mr. John Brindley, Mr. Hatch, and Mr. Trusswell, cheesemongers; Mr. Rowbottom, and Mrs. Locker, confectioners; Mr. W. Brindley, clothier; Mr. Mellor, waste cotton manufacturer, and others; each varying from £5. to £500. The estimated total loss to the inhabitants amounted to about £15,000. One female was unfortunately drowned, besides several pigs, horses, and cows.

The Savings' Bank, is a handsome building, designed by Mr. H. J. Stevens. It is convenient in its plan, and striking in its appearance.

THE DERBY RAILWAY STATION.

Whether the tourist travels by the Midland Counties' Railway from Rugby, by the Birmingham and Derby Junction line, or by the North Midland Railway from Leeds, his journey will terminate at the same station. The Station at Derby is indeed the most spacious, convenient, and extensive structure of the kind yet erected. In perfect harmony and accordance with the magnitude of the three Railways forming a junction here, is the architectural design of this important station ; large in proportion, substantial in construction, simple and impressive in its features, it gives evidence of belonging to, and forming part of, a vast and gigantic work. It is built of brick, with but little ornamental work about it. It was erected by the North Midland Company with additional accommodations for the Midland Counties, and the Birmingham and Derby Companies, and is under the management of the North Midland Company ; the Proprietors of the two latter companies paying 6 per cent. annually, for those portions assigned to their own peculiar use. The entire area occupied, is 30 *a.* 0 *r.* 36 *per.* The length of the building is 1050 feet. The Station consists of entrance hall, offices for the booking of passengers and parcels, first class refreshment room, ladies' waiting room, offices for the directors, secretary, superintendent, and clerks. The basement is occupied by the second class refreshment room, larders, kitchens, ale and wine cellars, compartments for coal, and other conveniences. A shed of unequalled extent and beauty to cover in the landing places of the railway, and separate engine houses and workshops. The centre of the front over the principal entrance is lighted by a large handsome window, surmounted by an ornamental shield, on which are carved the Derby, Sheffield, and Leeds armorial bearings. The wings are also ornamented with shields, displaying the arms of Birmingham, Leicester, Nottingham, and York. The windows, doorways, and openings for carriages and passengers on the ground floor are camber or semicircular headed. The shed is so spacious as to cover nine lines of rails, being 140 feet in width, under three roofs. The centre one of 56 feet span, and the two exterior of 42 feet each, the principal carriage shed is 450 feet long, and the exterior roof contiguous to the building, extends 1050 feet in length, to the termination of each wing. The roofs are of very light, yet strong construction, containing an ample space of skylights, and supported by 60 fluted cast-iron columns, 22 feet high, the apex of the roof itself being 38 feet high. The platform or parade runs the whole length of the building. It is 31 feet wide along the principal carriage shed, and 16½ feet wide along each wing. This shed is splendidly lighted with gas ; two lamps are appended to each of the 60 columns, and there are 40 stone lamp columns along the parade ; there are also four iron tables, each having four gas lights appended ; the total number of lamps under the shed being 216.

The engine houses and workshops are separate for the three companies, and those of the North Midland are very tastefully and admirably constructed. The engine house is a polygon of sixteen sides, and 130 feet in diameter, and from the floor to the top of the lantern, 48 feet 10 inches, viz. the height of columns, 18 feet, roof 23 feet, and lantern, 7 feet 10 inches. The dome or conical roof is lighted by 48 windows. The exterior covering is of slate, laid upon boards, firmly screwed to the roof beams. Its spacious area will contain more than thirty engines, which may be moved with the greatest facility to any part of the building, by means of 16 lines of rails radiating from a central turn-table. To the right are the engine workshops, 184 feet 6 inches long, 70 feet 6 inches wide, the truss beams of the floor supported by 20 massive cast-iron columns ; the smithy attached is 42 feet long, of the same width. To the left are the carriage workshops, 191 feet 6 inches, by 70 feet 6 inches, the truss beams of the floor of the largest are supported by 16 cast-iron columns. These buildings form oblique wings to the polygon.

The Birmingham and Derby Junction Railway Company have erected a handsome engine shed of brick, 150 feet, by 48 feet, at a cost of from £3500. to £4000., built by the Messrs. Cooper. It is lighted by 36 semi-circular headed windows, with three carriage openings. The Midland Counties' Company have also erected a spacious engine shed, 134 feet by 52 feet, and workshops 200 feet, by 93 feet, the repairing shop is 93 feet by 88 feet; these are substantial brick buildings. The tank belonging to this Company is 56 feet by 26 feet. There are also two other tanks, 48 feet 6 inches by 27 feet, and every thing requisite for the three companies. About 300 men are employed in the repairs of the carriages, and in the various work done at this magnificent station.

The workshops, and every part of the station, were fitted with gas, under the superintendence of Mr. Crump. The lamps, 747 in number, are supplied by upwards of 1000 yards of 4 inch iron main piping. The Goods' warehouse is a handsome and lofty brick building of two stories, 165 feet by 90 feet, lighted by 36 windows and 9 carriage openings; to 7 of the openings, there are turn-tables. In the centre, there is a raised platform, for the convenience of loading and unloading the carriages. The plot of ground on which the Station is built, is in the form of a triangle, near to the London road, within a short mile of the Market place, and the principal Inns. The frontage extends about 2880 feet; the east or river side of the angle extends about 1120 feet; the south-west by west side extends about 1250 feet. The land has been raised considerably, many thousand tons of soil and gravel having been brought by railway for that purpose. This and all the beautiful stations on the North Midland line were designed by Francis Thompson, Esq., Architect.

The Reader may form some idea of the magnitude of this splendid Station, by its cost; viz. Office Buildings, Shed and Platform, £50,000. Engine House, Workshops, Locomotive, Store Offices, &c. £62,000. Goods' Warehouse and Office, £11,000. Earthwork, Permanent Way, &c. £5,000. Total £128,000.

Derby is become a great central point in the Railway communication of the country, and the directors of the three lines which form a Junction at this town have therefore acted wisely in adopting at once a large scale for their operations. No stronger or more decisive proof could be adduced of the energy and enterprise of the country, and the confidence of capitalists of its continued advancement, than the station and works which are here briefly described.

The Midland Hotel is a commodious establishment, fitted up in the first style, for the accommodation of passengers travelling by railway. It is elegantly furnished, and contains upwards of fifty superior bed rooms, and numerous dining and sitting rooms. Attached are excellent stabling and coach houses. Post horses and carriages are always in readiness. This Hotel, and the first and second class refreshment rooms are under the able management of Mr. Cuff.

The Brunswick Inn, is handsomely fitted up and very convenient for travellers by railway. This commodious house is well conducted by Mr. and Mrs. Lane.

The terms of the above establishments, are inserted in their advertisements, in the advertising sheet at the end of this work.

The North Midland Railway fares and trains are as under: Fares, First Class, 3d., Second, 2d., Third 1d. per mile. Trains, departure from Derby, December, 1842. Mail, 7 minutes before 3, $\frac{1}{4}$ p. 6, $\frac{1}{2}$ p. 9, Morning. $\frac{1}{4}$ before 4, and 6 o'clock, Afternoon. Sunday trains, 7, Morning, 3, Afternoon.

The Midland Counties from Derby to Rugby, Fares, First Class, 3d., Second, 2d., Third, 1$\frac{1}{4}d$. per mile. Trains, $\frac{1}{2}$ p. 8, $\frac{1}{2}$ p. 10, Morning. $\frac{1}{4}$ p. 1, 20 minutes before 5, Afternoon. $\frac{1}{2}$ p. 7, and 11 minutes to 11, Evening. Sunday Trains, $\frac{1}{4}$ p. 6, $\frac{1}{4}$ p. 12, Morning. 7, and 9, o'clock Evening.

The Birmingham and Derby Junction Fares, First Class, 3d., Second, 2d., Third, 1$\frac{1}{2}d$., per mile. Trains leave Derby 20 min. p. 8, $\frac{1}{4}$ before 12, Morning; $\frac{1}{2}$ p. 1, $\frac{1}{2}$ p. 4, Afternoon; $\frac{1}{4}$ p. 11, at Night. Sunday trains, 20 minutes p. 8, Morning, $\frac{1}{2}$ p. 5, and $\frac{1}{4}$ p. 11, at Night.

LINES OF RAILWAYS AND DISTANCES OF STATIONS.

LONDON AND BIRMINGHAM.

	From Lon.	Birming.
Harrow,	11½	101
Watford,	17¾	94¾
King's Langley,	21	91½
Boxmoor, for Hemel Hempstead,	24½	88
Berkhamstead,	28	84½
Tring,	31¾	80¾
Leighton Buzzard,	41	71½
Bletchley,	46¾	65¾
Wolverton, for Newport,	52½	60
Roade,	60	52½
Blisworth, for Northampton and Towcester,	62½	50
Weedon, for Daventry,	69¾	42¾
Crick,	75½	37
Rugby,	83¼	29¼
Brandon,	89¼	23¼
Coventry,	94	18½
Hampton,	103	9½
Birmingham,	112½	0

GRAND JUNCTION LINE.

Perry,	115¾	3¼
Newton,	119	6½
Bescot Bridge,	121¾	9¼
James's Bridge,	122½	10
Willenhall,	124¼	11¾
Wolverhampton,	126½	14
Four Ashes,	132¼	19¾
Spread Eagle,	133¾	21¼
Penkridge,	136½	23¾
Stafford,	141¾	29
Bridgeford,	145¼	32½
Norton Bridge,	147½	34¾
Whitmore Station,	155¾	43
Madeley,	158½	45¾
Crewe,	166½	53¾
Coppenhall,	167¾	55
Minshull,	171¼	58½
Winsford,	173¾	61
Hartford,	178¼	65½
Acton,	180¾	68
Preston Brook,	185	72½
Moore,	187½	74¼
Warrington,	190½	77¾
Newton,	195¼	82½
Liverpool,	211	98½

MIDLAND COUNTIES.

	Lond.	Derb.
Rugby,	83¼	49¼
Ullesthorpe,	91	41¾
Broughton Astley,	94¼	38½
Wigston,	99½	33¼
Leicester,	103	29¾
Syston,	107¾	25
Sileby,	110¾	22
Barrow,	113	19¾
Loughborough,	115½	17¼
Kegworth,	120¼	12½
Sawley,	125¼	7½
Borrowash,	128¼	4
Derby,	132¼	0

NORTH MIDLAND.

	Lond.	Leeds.	Derb.
Derby,	132¼	72¾	0
Duffield,	136¾	67½	4½
Belper,	139½	65½	7¼
Ambergate,	142¾	62¼	10½
Wingfield,	146¼	58¾	14
Stretton,	150	55	17¾
Clay Cross,	152¼	52¾	20
Chesterfield,	156¼	48¾	24¾
Staveley,	160	45	27¾
Eckington,	162	42½	30¼
Killamarsh,	164½	40½	32¼
Beighton,	167½	38¾	35¼
Woodhouse Mill,	168½	37½	40
Treeton,	170¾	36	41½
Masbro,	172¼	32¾	40
Sheffield,	177¼	37¾	45
Kilnhurst,	176¼	29	43
Swinton,	177¼	27¾	45
Wath,	179	25½	47

	From London.	Leeds.	Derby.
Darfield,	181½	23½	49¼
Barnsley,	185½	19¾	53¼
Royston,	188¾	16½	56½
Wakefield,	192½	12¾	60¼
Normanton,	194¾	9½	62½
Altofts,	196	8¾	63¾
Methley,	197¼	6½	65
Woodlesford,	200¼	4¾	68
Leeds,	204¾	0	72¾

YORK AND NORTH MIDLAND.

	From London.	York.	Derby.
Altofts	196	24	63
Castleford	199	21	66
Burton Salmon	203	17	70
Sherburn	207	13	74
Ulleskelf	211	9	78
Bolton Percy	213	7	80
Copmanthorpe	216	4	83
York	220	0	87

GREAT NORTH OF ENGLAND.

Shipton	226	6	93
Tollerton	230	16	97
Alne	231½	11½	98½
Raskelf	203½	13½	100½
Sessay	238	18	105
Thirsk	242	22	109
Ottrington	246	26	113
Northallerton	250	30	117
Danby Wiske	254	34	121
Cowton	258	38	125
Croft	261½	41½	128½
Darlington	264½	44½	131

MANCHESTER AND LEEDS.

	London.	Manchester.	Leeds.
Normanton,	194¾	51	9
Wakefield,	197¾	48	12
Horbury,	201¾	44	16
Dewsbury,	204¾	41	19
Cooper Bridge,	209¾	36	24
Brighouse,	211¾	34	26
Elland,	214¾	31	29
Sowerby Bridge,	217¾	28	32
Luddenden,	219¾	26	34
Hebden Bridge,	221¾	24	36
Eastwood,	224¾	21	39
Todmordon,	225¾	20	40
Littleborough,	231¾	14	46
Rochdale,	234¾	11	49
Blue Pits,	236¾	9	51
Mill's Hill,	239¾	6	54
Manchester,	245¾	0	60

BIRMINGHAM AND GLOUCESTER.

Lifford,	4	47
Blackwell,	10	41
Bromsgrove,	13	38
Stokeworks,	15	36
Droitwich,	18	33
Spetchley,	24	27
Worcester,	28	31
Defford,	31	20
Eckington,	33	18
Bredon,	35	16
Ashchurch,	37	14
Tewksbury,	39	16
Cheltenham,	44	7
Gloucester,	51	0

BIRMINGHAM AND DERBY.

Castle Bromwich,	4	37¼
Water Orton,	6¾	34½
Forge Mills,	8¼	33
Whitaker Junction,	10	31¼
Kingsbury,	11¾	29½
Wilncote and Fazeley,	15½	25¾
Tamworth,	17¼	24
Oakley and Alrewas,	23½	17¾
Barton and Walton,	26½	14¾
Burton,	30¼	11
Willington,	35	6¼
Derby,	41¼	0

DIRECTORY OF DERBY:

TAKEN

BY STEPHEN GLOVER,

IN

1842.

ABBREVIATIONS.—J *Journeyman.*—B *Burgess.*—Fr *Freeman.*—F *Freeholder.*

Abbott, Elizabeth	Vict., Cross Keys, and Permit and Excise Office	Corn market	
Abbott, Henry	Hairdresser and Perfumer	3, Sadler gate	B
Abell, John	Machinist	Parker street	
Abell, William	Engineer, Millwright, and Machinist	4, George street	F,B
Abney, Rev. Edw. H.	Vicar of St. Alkmund's	The Firs	F,B
Adams, Henry	Editor of the Derby Reporter	St. Peter's street	
Adams, Ann	Shoemaker	Burton road	
Adams, John	Farmer	Cowsley	B
Adams, Thomas	Shopkeeper	5, Parker street	B
Adcock, William	Cotton spinner	Full street	F
Adcock, William	Stonemason	Agard street	B
Adcock, John	Hosier	26, City road	F,B
Adcock, George	Shoemaker	Nottingham road	B
Adin, John	Carpenter and Builder	19, Friar gate	B
Adyman, Thomas	Cook's shop	Bridge gate	F
Albarn, James	Traveller	Duke street	F
Aldred, George	Lace dealer	Sacheverel street	
Aldridge, David	Farmer	Abbey Barns	
Aldridge, Hannah	Dressmaker	Albion place	
Aldridge, Richard G.	Schoolmaster Trinity School	Traffick street	
Allbutt, John T.		Leeds	F
Allcock, Walter		Allestree	F
Allcock, John	J. Watchmaker	Leonard street	
Allcock, William	J. Watchmaker	Leonard street	
Allcock, Richard	Farmer	Derby	
Alldam, Isaac	Gentleman	Eagle street	F
Alexander, Thomas	Tailor	Upper Brook street	

B

Allan, Alexander	Traveller	Osmaston road	B
Allen, George	Farmer	York street	
Allen, Henry	J. Whitesmith	Agard street	
Allen, John	Chairmaker	Hill street	
Allen, Charles	Beer seller	Bradshaw street	B
Allen, John	Whitesmith	3, St. Peter's Ch. yd.	B
Allen, John	Hair dresser	Bold lane	
Allen, James	Police officer	Ct. 2, Agard street	
Allen, George	Gardener and seedsman	12, Parker street	B
Allen, Richard	Shopkeeper	Spring gardens	F,B
Allen, George	Butcher	1, Green street	B
Allen, William	Tailor	Willow row	B
Allen, Joseph	Labourer	Hill street	
Allen, John	J. Joiner	Agard street	
Allen, John	Framework knitter	Bradshaw street	
Allen, William	Shopkeeper	Upper Brook street	
Allkin, Robert	House painter	9, Osmaston street	B
Allsop, Charles	Whitesmith	Kensington	
Allsop, James	Shopkeeper	Litchurch street	
Allsop, Joseph	Melancthon's Head	Park street	F,B
Allsop, Samuel	Vict., Sitwell Arms	Sacheverel street	F,B
Allsop, Richard	Baker and flour dealer	Ashbourn road	
Allsop, Isaac	Baker and flour dealer	Green lane	
Allsop, Sam. & Sons	Brewers, Burton-upon-Trent	Ale vaults, Corn mkt.	
Alton, James	Vict., Seven Stars, & contr. to carry mail bags to Rugeley	King street	F
Amatt, George	Joiner	Burton road	B
Ambrose, David	Milk seller	Larges' street	F,B
Ames and Co.	General Carriers to all parts of Staffordshire, Stourbridge, Kidderminster, Stourport, Worcester, Gloucester, and Bristol	Siddals lane	
Anderson, Richard	J. Smith	Eagle street	
Anderson, John,	Book-keeper	Agard street	
Anderson, John	Framework knitter	London road	Fr
Annable, Joseph	J. Millwright	Parker street	
Annable, William	Shopkeeper	25, Eagle street	
Anthony, Joseph	Beer seller, Ram	Normanton road	B
Anthony, George	Shoemaker	31, Duke street	
Appleby, John	Sawyer	Bridge street	
Appleby, John	Vict., Hawk and Buckle	27, Bradshaw street	B
Appleyard, John	Labourer	Traffick street	
Archer, John	J. joiner	Bridge gate	F
Archer, Henry	Butcher	25, London road	F,B
Argile, Samuel	Currier and leather cutter	11, Bridge gate	B
Argile, Edmund	J. Watchmaker	Leonard street	
Argyle, George	J. Colourman	Parker street	
Armstrong, George	Shopkeeper and Weaver	21, Burton road	B
Arnold, Henry	Cheesefactor	7, St. Alk. ch. yd.	F,B
Arnold and Orton	Cheesefactors	St. Alk. ch. yd.	
Ashby, Mrs. Thomas	Milliner and Dressmaker	Sacheverel street	

Ashby, Thomas	Accountant	Sacheverel street	B
Ashby, Abraham	Butcher, 7, Old shambles	Queen street	B
Ashby, George	Accountant	South street	
Askew, John	Gentleman	Kedleston road	B
Ashmole, Charles	Beer seller	Devonshire street	
Atherstone, Edward	Veterinary surgeon	Tenant street	B
Atherstone, Hugh	Veterinary surgeon	Sadler gate	B
Atkinson, George	Framework knitter	Brook street	
Atkinson, Robert	Railway coach builder	Liversage street	F
Atterbury, William	Dealer in bones	Ct. 9, Bridge gate	B
Atterbury, Charles	Works at Darley mill	25, Bath street	
Auckland, Bilberry	Compositor	19, Burton road	B
Auckland, John	Printing establishment	Curzon street	F
Ault, John	Timber merchant	21, London road	B
Ault, William	Vict., Stag and Thorn	Traffick street	B
Ault, Ann	Vict., Exeter Arms	Exeter place	
Ault, Samuel	Vict., Brown Bear	Green lane	B
Ault, Joseph	Tailor	Goodwin street	
Austin, Thomas	Shoemaker	25, Burton road	B
Austin, William	Beer seller	York street	B
Avery, Mrs.	Circulating library	King street	
Ayres, George	Warehouseman	Friar gate	
Ayrton, Rev. Samuel	Minister General Baptist Chapel and schoolmaster	Sitwell street	B
Bacon, Emma	Milliner and dress maker	Nun's street	
Bacon, Jeremiah	Locomotive department	At Station	
Bacon, Thomas	Shoemaker	St. Peter's street	F,B
Bacon, John	Tailor and draper	41, Bridge gate	B
Baddeley, James	Framework knitter	Leonard street	
Baggaley, John	Fishmonger	Market place	
Baggaley, Nathan	Joiner	22, Exeter street	B
Baggaley, William	Cooper	Castle street	
Bagley, John	Gentleman	South street	F
Baghurst, Edward	Shoemaker	Canal street	
Bagnall, George	Vict., Black Swan	Siddals lane	B
Bagshaw, Thomas	J. carpenter	Agard street	B
Bailey, Edward	J. lace weaver	High street	
Bailey, Thomas	Grocer and tea dealer	29, Iron gate	F,B
Bailey, Joseph	Labourer	Albion place	
Bailey, George	Shoemaker	Litchurch street	
Bailey, John	Accountant	38, Parker street	
Bailey, John	Tailor	Parker street	Fr
Bailey, Alice	Shopkeeper	Ashbourn road	
Bailey, John, sen.	Butcher	15, Queen street	F,B
Bailey, John, jun.	Butcher	52, St. Peter's street	B
Bailey, Thomas	Bookbinder	Parker street	B
Bailey, William	Vict., Eagle and Child	St. Alk. ch. yd.	F,B
Bailey, Robert	Eating house	16, Bridge gate	
Bailey, Edward	Librarian, county library	Amen alley	
Bailey, Hannah	Milliner and patent stay maker	19, Queen street	
Bainbrigge, Thomas Parker, esq.	Post master, and J. P. for the borough of Derby	Corn market	B

Bainbridge, Elizabeth	Shopkeeper	City road	
Baker, Sarah	Boot and shoe warehouse	Rotten row	
Baker, William	Framework knitter	Kensington	
Baker, Joseph	Boot and shoe warehouse, Corn market	Exeter place	F,B
Baker, William	Silk merchant	46, Friar gate	F, B
Baker, John	Weaver	Kensington street	B
Baker, William, esq.	Physician	79, Friar gate	B
Baker, John		Nottingham	F
Baker, John	Joiner	Nun's street	F
Baker, William	Shoemaker	19, Bag lane	
Bakewell, John	Grocer and tea dealer	Market head	Fr
Bakewell, Harriet, and Son	Wholesale and retail tea dealers and grocers	Market head	
Baldwin, Robert	Brushmaker	Dog kennel lane	B
Baldwin, David	Turner and chair maker	14, Friar gate	F, B
Balguy, Bryan Thomas, esq.	Town clerk, coroner, and clerk of the peace for the borough of Derby	Borrowash	Fr
Ball, James	Overlooker at Unsworth's mill	John street	
Ball, Henry	Guard on line of railway	Litchurch street	
Ball, William	Solicitor's clerk	1, Exeter place	Fr
Bamford, James	Glove maker	2, Wardwick	
Bamford, Robert	Baker	Market place	B
Bamford, William	Book-keeper	Osmaston road	B
Bamford, William	Breeches maker	2, Wardwick	B
Bamford, Robert	Butcher	Traffick street	B
Bamford, Wm., jun.	Book-keeper	Osmaston road	Fr, F
Bamford, John	Book-keeper	Bradshaw street	F
Bamford, Francis	J. Silk weaver	Short street	
Bamford, John	Framework knitter	Brook street	
Bancroft, Charles	Draper	Castle street	Fr
Bancroft, Gervase	Butcher	Castle street	Fr
Bancroft, Isaac	Watchmaker	40, Bridge gate	Fr
Bancroft, Wm., sen.	Tailor	15, Cheapside	F,Fr
Bancroft, William	Silk hand	3, Devonshire street	B
Bancroft, Wm., jun.	Tailor	Sadler gate bridge	Fr
Bancroft, Mrs.	Schoolmistress	Castle street	
Bancroft, Thomas	Carver and gilder	33, Devonshire st.	Fr
Bancroft, Abraham	J. Jeweller	Cheapside	Fr
Bancroft, John	Labourer	Castle street	Fr
Bancroft, Gilbert	J. Watchmaker	Borroughs's walk	Fr
Band, Edward	Silk hand	Searl street	Fr
Banister, Charles, James, and Robert	Linen and woollen drapers, silk mercers, and haberdashers	Rotten row	B
Bannister, William	Tailor	Cross lanes	
Bannister, Thomas	Cooper	49, Sadler gate	B
Bannister, James	J. Jeweller	Traffic street	
Bannister, John	Patten maker	Ct. 4, Full street	B
Bannister, Charles J.	Shoe warehouse	Sadler gate bridge	B
Bannister, William	Gentleman	Cherry street	F

Barber, William	Shopkeeper	19, Morledge
Barber, Samuel	Cheesemonger and provision warehouse	St. Peter's street and Siddals lane B
Barber, John, esq.	Alderman, clerk of the general meetings of lieutenancy, agent to his grace the duke of Devonshire, and deputy clerk of the peace for the county	8, Queen street F, B
Barber, Robert	J. Cabinet maker	39, London road L
Barber, Ann	Beer seller	8, Jury street
Barber, Henry	Shoemaker	Castle street
Barber, John	Baker and flour dealer	23, Queen street F, B
Barber, Mary	Straw hat maker	39, London road
Barker, Miss		Vernon street
Barker, Mrs.	Lodging house	Traffick street
Barker, Charles	Porter at Station	Canal street
Barker, Elijah	Shoemaker and shopkeeper	48, Burton road B
Barker, Charles, & Son	Tailors	52, Bridge street B
Barker, John	Grocer	1, High street, F, B
Barker, John	Boot and shoemaker	Union buildings
Barker, William	Butcher	Sadler gate bridge B
Barker, James	Tailor	Traffick street
Barker, Charles	J. Tailor	Bag lane
Barker, William	Baker	18, Morledge Fr
Barker, Sarah	Milliner and dress maker	Grove street
Barker, Benjamin	Tailor	Normanton road
Barker, Stephen	Shoemaker	Agard street Fr
Barker, Edward	Joiner, clock case, and cabinet maker	St. Mary's gate
Barlow, Benjamin	Shoemaker	Agard street Fr
Barlow, Matthew	Shoemaker	Cross lanes F
Barlow, James	Works at china factory	42, Erasmus street
Barlow, Joseph	J. Tailor	Agard street Fr
Barlow, George	Potter at china factory	Erasmus street
Barlow, James		Belper Fr
Barnes, Thomas	Shoemaker	St. Peter's street
Barnes, John	Gentleman	Albion place F
Barnes, William	Woollen draper, hosier & hatter	18, St. Peter's street
Barnes, John	Hairdresser	Burton road
Barnes, William	Carrier to Nottingham	Green lane B
Barnes, John	Labourer	Devonshire street
Barnsby, John Edwd.	Compositor	Wilmot street B
Barnett and Son	Upholsterers	7, Market place
Barnett, Joseph	Shopkeeper	Walker lane B
Barnett, William	Upholsterer	Market place F, B
Barnett, George	Upholsterer	Market place F, B
Bartlett, John	Shoemaker and Vict., Fox and Grapes	27, Castle street B
Bartlett, John	Vict., Spread Eagle	St. Peter's street F
Barton, Andrew	J. Brushmaker	Bag lane
Barton, William	Modeller and sculptor	11, Parker street B

Barton, James	Galloon manufacturer, and dealer in woollen cloths and lastings	Parker street	
Barton, William	Gentleman, commissioner in the court of requests	9, Full street	F, B
Barraclough, Isaac	Cutler	King street	
Barrett, Charles	Silk framework knitter	Eagle street	
Basford, Robert, sen.	Plasterer	24, Morledge	
Basford, Robert, jun.	Plasterer	25, Morledge	B
Basford, John	House painter	Parker street	Fr
Basford, George	Foreman at Gamble and Co's.	41, Parker street	F, B
Bassano, John	Shopkeeper	4, Darley lane	B
Bassano, Thomas	Silk framework knitter	34, Willow row	
Bassano, Francis Matthias	Gentleman	9, Pickering terrace, Bayswater, Midsx.	F
Bassano, Walter	Gentleman	73, Queen street, Cheapside, London	F
Bassano, Philip	Gentleman	Ocean row, Stepney, Middlesex	F
Bassano, Anthony	Shopkeeper	19, Nottingham road	B
Bassendine, George	Boot and shoe maker	5, Cheapside	B
Bateman, George	Shopkeeper	Morledge	B
Bateman, George	Coach and coach wheel maker	Morledge	
Bateman, Mrs.		Osmaston road	
Bateman, Thomas Osborne	Esquire	Osmaston road	F
Bateman, William	Stonemason	Brook street	
Bateman, Henry	Working jeweller, herald chaser, and dealer in toys	12, Sadler gate	
Bates, John	Vict., Fountain Inn	Osmaston street	B
Bate, Henry	Baker and flour dealer, warehouse St. Michael's lane	St. Peter's street	F, B
Bates, William	Twist hand	Canal street	
Bates, Edward	Engineer	Park street	F, B
Baxendale, Joseph	Gentleman	Whetstone, Midsx.	F
Battelle, Robert D.	Gentleman	Alrewas	F
Baxter, Mrs.	Dyer	Bloom street	
Baxter, William	Framework knitter	Union buildings	
Baxter, William	Stay maker	Haarlem street	
Baxter, Robert	Wine and spirit merchant, Globe Tavern	34, Iron gate	F, B
Baxter, John	Shoemaker	Bloom street	
Baxter, Harvey	Dyer	Bloom street	
Bayley, Mrs.	Large's alms houses	Friar gate	
Bayne, Kenneth	Gentleman	South street	C, B
Bazene, Francis	J. Painter	Brook street	
Beard, John	Gentleman	Hanley, Staffordsh.	F
Beardmore, John	Coal higgler	9, Cannon street	
Beardsley, Edmund	J. Joiner	Parker street	
Beardsley, William	Butcher	9, Brick street	
Beardsley, John	Framework knitter	Ct. 5, Agard street	
Beasley, Edward	Butcher	Bridge gate	

Beasley & Champion	Ale and porter brewers, Carrington brewery, Nottinghamshire, store rooms	Full street	
Beal, Thomas	Warehouseman	Leonard street	
Beal, Joseph	J. Chandler	Leonard street	
Beard, George	Gentleman	John street	F
Beck, William	Tea dealer	Osmaston street	
Bedford, William	Shoemaker	Union buildings	
Beeland, Wm., jun.	Woollen draper and tailor	23, Iron gate	B
Beeland, Wm., sen.	Silk mercer, linen and woollen draper, and haberdasher	23, Iron gate	F,Fr
Beeland, Mary	Millinery and dress rooms	Iron gate	
Beer, Richard	Baker and flour dealer	38, Bath street	B
Beer, James	Baker and flour dealer	49, Nun's street	B
Beeson, Alfred	Accountant	Litchurch lane	
Beeson, Thomas, jun.	Shoemaker	Eagle street	Fr
Beeson, John	Silk hand	Siddals lane	Fr
Beeson, William	Brazier and tin plate worker, work-shop, Corn market	17, Iron gate	F,B
Beeson, Thomas, sen.	Shoemaker	Eagle street	Fr
Beeson, Thomas	Maltster & Vict.,Star & Garter	24,St.Mary's gate	F,B
Beeson, Thomas	Twist hand	Leonard street	
Belfield, John	Shoemaker	Castle street	
Belfield, Simon	Dealer in coals	Eagle street	
Bellamy, John	J. Joiner and cabinet maker	Sacheverel street	F
Belfin, William	Higgler	Devonshire street	
Bell, James	Foreman to the North Midland Railway Company	Wilmot street	B
Bell, Horace	Gentleman	Duffield road	
Belsham, Edw.		Duffield	Fr
Bembridge, Eliz.	Shopkeeper	City road	
Bembridge, James	Tailor and Woollen Draper	36, London road	B
Bembridge, George	Tailor	32, Nun's street	
Bembridge, William	Horse Trimmer	South street	
Bemrose, William	Bookseller, stationer, printer, bookbinder, patent medicine warehouse, licensed to sell stamps, and Derby Mercury Office	Iron gate	F,B
Benfield, Thomas		Spondon	F
Bennett, Miss		Friar gate	
Bennett, Benjamin	Frying-pan and shovel manufacturer	Osmaston street	
Bennett, Francis	Labourer	Green street	
Bennett, William	Surgeon	12, Friar gate	B
Bennett, Paul	Butcher	33, Friar gate	F,B
Bennett, William	Joiner, cabinet maker, and beer seller	St. Helen's street	F,B
Bennett, Edward	Police officer	16,Orchard street	F,B
Bennett, George	Frying-pan manufacturer	Ct. 2, Morledge	
Bennett, Thomas	Brickmaker	OldUttoxeter rd.	F,B
Bennett, Joseph	Gent's. boarding & day school	2, Parker street	B

Bennett, Charles	Joiner, and printer's furniture manufacturer	Curzon street	B
Bennett, Robert	Linen and woollen draper, and agent to the West of England Life and Fire Assurance Office	13, Iron gate	B
Benson, William	Labourer	Markeaton lane	
Bent, Thos. esq. M.D.	Magistrate and alderman	68, Friar gate	F, B
Bentley, William	Shoeing smith, farrier, and vict., Golden Fleece, workshop, 15, Sadler gate	South street	B
Bentley, Richard	J. whitesmith	19, Bridge gate	
Bentley, John	Sinker maker	13, Duke street	
Bentley, Samuel	Shoeing smith and beer seller	Old George yard	B
Bentley, James	Shoeing smith	Thorntree lane	B
Berrey, Edward	Silk hand	Leonard street	
Berrey, John	Framework knitter	Litchurch street	
Berrey, Francis	Framework knitter	Sacheverel street	
Berresford, William	Straw hat manufacturer, and stay maker	8, King street	B
Bestwick, J.	Shoemaker	4, Lodge lane	
Bestwick, William		Drakelow	F
Biggs, Benjamin	Shoemaker	Grove street	
Bilbrough, William	Footman	3, Exeter place	B
Billett, Henry	J. Nail maker	Duke street	
Bingham, Miss		Vernon street	
Bilson, John	Distiller of herbs	Bridge gate	
Binger, J. O. esq.	Superintendent of Railway coaching department	Litchurch Terrace	
Bingham, Thos. esq.		Lincolnshire	F
Bingham, John, esq.	Gentleman	Rose cottage	Fr
Bingham, Miss M. A.		Vernon street	
Birch, Joseph	Labourer	Ct. 7, Sadler gate	
Birch, Charles	Beadle to St. Alkmund's	Ct. 9, Bridge gate	Fr
Birch, Benjamin	J. tape weaver	Cannon street	
Birch, Richard	Liversage Alms houses	London road	Fr
Birch, Richard Wm.	Solicitor, high constable for the Hundred of Morleston and Litchurch, and clerk to the subdivision meetings and borough magistrates	20, Wardwick	F, B
Birch, William	J. clock and watchmaker	Litchurch street	
Birch, William	Twist hand	Sitwell street	
Birch, William	J. weaver	Short street	
Birch, Lewis		Cheadle	F
Birchall, Minshull	Coal merchant and farmer	Duke street	F, B
Birchillo, Ralph	Dyer	Cuckold's alley	
Birkin, Henry	Higgler	13, Mansfield rd.	F, B
Birkin, William	Boy's day school	18, Full street	B
Birkin, Elizabeth	Furniture calenderer	Chester road	
Birkin, John	Labourer	Devonshire street	
Birkin, James	Gardener	Ct. 3, Bridge gate	B

Birks, Benjamin	Moulder	River street	
Blackwall, Richard	Works at silk factory	Canal street	
Blackwall, Mary	Schoolmistress	Burton road	
Blackwall, Henry	Upholsterer & cabinet maker, furniture warehouse	13, Queen street	B
Blackwall, James	Vict., Black-boy	Old George yard, Sadler gate	B
Blackden, John	Labourer	Leonard street	
Blackstone, Joseph	Silk weaver	Hill street	
Blake, William	Framework knitter	4, Duke street	B
Blake, John	Porter at Station	Bag lane	Fr
Blake, Daniel	Professor and composer of music and tuner of piano fortes	George street	
Bland, John	Overlooker at Madeley's mill	Eagle street	
Bland, John	Vict., the Cossack	Bag lane	B
Bland, William	Boot and shoemaker	Ct. 3, Friar gate	
Bland, John	J. tailor	Erasmus street	
Bland, James	Shoemaker	Ct. 6, Bold lane	
Bland, Mary	Dressmaker	Bradshaw street	
Blood, William	Shoemaker	1, Osmaston road	B
Blood, J.	Book-keeper	Ford street	
Blood, Thomas	Cornfactor	15, Darwin row	B
Blood, Robert		Hartshorn	F
Bloor, William	Framework knitter	Devonshire street	Fr
Bloor, Joseph	Vict., Britannia	4, River street	F,B
Bloor, Robert	China manufacturer, London warehouse at 34, Old Bond st., corner of Stafford st.	Nottingham road	F
Bloor, Mrs.	Schoolmistress	Fingal street	
Blore, Joseph	Spar ornament manufacturer and marble mason	68, Bridge gate	B
Blore, Thomas	Vict., Druid's Arms	Traffick street	F
Blount, James	Labourer	Markeaton lane	
Blundstone, Samuel	Hairdresser	St. Peter's street	B
Blundstone, William	Shopkeeper	35, Osmaston st.	F,B
Blundstone, Fanny	Milliner	Osmaston street	
Blythe, Thomas	J. jeweller	Siddals lane	
Boam, Francis	Currier and leather cutter	Kensington	
Boam, George	Moulder	Devonshire street	
Boam, Christopher	Butcher	Burton road	Fr
Boam, Daniel	Butcher	45, Burton road	Fr
Boam, John	Butcher	4, Castle street	Fr
Boam, Thomas	Pavier and Sougher	Traffick street	F,B
Boam, George	Framework knitter	13, Normanton road	
Boden, Thomas	Gentleman	Fishpond house, Curzon street	F,Fr
Boden, Francis	Baker and flour dealer	St. Leonard street	B
Boden, Richard	Cornfactor, 10, corn market	Green hill lane	F, B
Boden, Henry	Gentleman	Grove terrace, Osmaston road	F, B
Boden, George	Hairdresser and perfumer	43, Corn market	B

Boden and Morley	Lace manufacturers and merchants	Traffick street and Castle street	F
Boden, George	Framework knitter	Normanton road	
Boden, William		Milford	F
Boden, Isaac	J. weaver	Talbot street	
Bolsover, Samuel	Spar & ornament manufacturer	Osmaston road	B
Bolton, Charles	Rake maker	Ossian street	
Bolton, John	Bookbinder & treasurer to the Wesleyan tract society	103, Friar gate	B
Bolton, Alice	Straw bonnet maker	Friar gate	
Bolton, William	Bookbinder	39, St. Mary's gate	
Bolus and Co.	Hat manufacturers	Market head	
Bonam, Elizabeth	Straw bonnet maker	St. Peter's street	
Bond, Joseph	Grocer	Traffick street	B
Bond, William	J. joiner	Ct. 6, Full street	
Bonell, John	J. millwright	Burton road	
Bonsall, Isaac	Porter at Station	Siddals lane	
Bonsor, Alexander	Carver and gilder	Ford street	B
Booth, John	J. joiner	St. Mary's gate	
Borrey, Francis	Framesmith	Sacheverel street	B
Borman, Allen	Surgeon	London road	
Borrington, James	Plumber and glazier	Friar gate	Fr
Borough, Charles	Surgeon	St. Peter's street	B
Borough, William	Solicitor, office, 26, Corn mrkt.	Normanton terrace	B
Borrows, James	Shoemaker	Green lane	
Bostock, Mrs.		Grove terrace	
Bostock, W. & Sons	Boot and shoe makers, 8, Sadler gate, & 22, Queen st.	20, South street	B
Bostock, William	Framework knitter	Ct., Kensington st.	B
Boswell, Clement	J. coach trimmer	Liversage street	
Boswell, William	J. coach painter	Wilmot street	B
Bosworth, William	Letter carrier	Uttoxeter road	
Bosworth, Mrs.		Ford street	
Botham, Robert	Upholsterer & cabinet maker	48, Friar gate	F,B
Botham, Henry	Blacksmith	Ct., Queen street	
Botham, Mary	Dressmaker	24, St. Helen's street	
Bourne, Robert	Foundry man	Exeter street	
Boultbee, Thomas	Silk framework knitter	10, Burton road	
Boulton, William	Vict., Lord Nelson	Wardwick	B
Bottom, John	Shoemaker	Bag lane	
Bowcock, Eli & Bart.	Ribbon Weavers	Bloom street	
Bowden, Joseph		Wolverhampton	F
Bowden, Richard	Painter	53, St. Peter's street	
Bowring, John	Warehouseman	9, Erasmus street	
Bowring, C. and M.	Tea dealers	Osmaston road	
Bowring, Charles	Accountant	St. John's terrace	
Bowler, John	Cheesemonger & bacon dealer	Albion street	
Bowler, Jacob	Coal dealer	Parker street	B
Bowler, Joseph	J. engineer	14, Bath street	
Bowler, Joseph	Joiner and cabinet maker	10, Jury street	F,B
Bowler, Thomas	Labourer	Sacheverel street	
Bowler, William	Joiner	Willow row	Fr

Bowman, Edward	J. brickmaker	Litchurch street	
Bowman, Ebenezer	Farmer	One Ash grange	F
Bowmer, James	Butcher	28, Willow row	
Bowmer, Joshua	Butcher and beer seller	Ashbourn road	
Bowmer, Benjamin	Labourer	12, Talbot street	
Boyce, John	Labourer	Ct. 4, Bold lane	
Bradbury, Thomas	Shoemaker	Sadler gate	Fr
Bradbury, John	Joiner	61, Devonshire st.	F
Bradbury, Joseph	Farmer	Spondon	F
Bradbury, Edward	Vict., Tailor's Arms	20, Green lane	F,B
Bradbury, John	J. jeweller	Ct. 7, Willow row	Fr,F
Bradbury, James	Hostler	Bag lane	
Bradbury, Sarah	Shopkeeper	Erasmus street	
Bradley, Joseph	Solicitor's clerk	15, Normanton road	B
Bradley, Thomas L.	Gent.	Clinton st., Nottm.	F
Bradley, Thomas	Agent to Thomas Bostock	22, Queen street	B
Bradshaw, John	Framework knitter	14, Uttoxeter road	B
Bradshaw, Mrs.		Friar gate	
Bradshaw, Edward	Shoemaker	Eagle street	Fr
Brailsford, William	Pensioner	Devonshire street	
Brailsford, John	J. colourman	Duke street	
Brain, Thomas	Shopkeeper	Burton road	
Bramwell, John	Bailiff	Ct., St. Mary's gate	
Brandreth, Thomas	J. tailor	Leonard street	
Branton, Thomas	Grocer and tea dealer	37, Queen street	B
Branton, William	Grocer and tea dealer	37, Queen street	B
Brassington, John	Portrait painter	87, Friar gate	
Brassington, James	Vict., Half Moon	30, Sadler gate	F,B
Brassington, Thomas	Plasterer	Brook street	
Bratby, William	Shoemaker	Nottingham road	F,B
Brearey and Son	Auctioneers	Victoria street	
Brearey, Thomas	Auctioneer, land and general agency office	Victoria street	F,Fr
Brearey, Rowland Amcotts	Auctioneer and valuer, agent to the Church of England Insurance Company and the Family Endowment Society	Corn market	F,Fr
Brearey and Eyre	Auctioneers	13, Corn market	
Brearey, Geo. Norman	Farmer	Victoria street	Fr
Brearley, Thomas	Cabinet maker	Wilmot street	
Brearley, Joseph	Cabinet maker	Upper Brook street	B
Breawood, Thomas	Traveller	Sacheverel street	
Bregazzi, Mary	Thermometer and barometer maker, and carver & gilder	2, Cheapside	
Brentnall, Mrs.		Sacheverel street	
Brentnall, Charles	Warehouseman	Sitwell street	F,B
Brentnall, William	Boot lace manufacturer	Exeter street	
Brentnall, Francis	Book keeper	Sacheverel street	B
Brentnall, James	Baker and confectioner	30, Iron gate	B
Brentnall, Hannah	Ladies' boarding school	St. Mary's gate	
Brentnall, John	Shopkeeper & vict., Earl Grey	13, Old Uttox. road	B

Brentnall, Mark	Weighing machine	Bridge gate	F
Bretnor, Thos.	Bailiff	Sacheverel street	B
Bretnor, Bernard & Co.	Grocers and tea dealers, and agents for Birmingham Fire, and Eagle Life, offices	10, Friar gate	B
Brewer, Elizabeth	Milliner and dressmaker	St. Mary's Gate	
Brewer, George H.	Plumber and glazier	1, Agard street	B
Briand, Thomas	Wheelwright	Parker street	
Bridgart, John & R.	Builders and carpenters	Friar gate	F, Fr
Bridgart, George	Builder and carpenter	29, King street	Fr
Bridgart, William	Artist's repository, varnish, oil, and colour warehouse	14, Sadler gate	B
Bridgart, Thomas	Plasterer	17, South street	B
Bridgart, William	Carpenter and builder	Leicester	F
Bridgart, Samuel	J. Joiner	Siddals lane	
Bridgart, Robert	Builder and carpenter	Friar gate	F, Fr
Bridgeford, James	Silk hand	Full street	Fr
Bridges, Richard	Butcher	Goodwin street	Fr
Bridgett, Thos. & Co.	Silkmen & silk manufacturers	Bridge street	F, B
Bridgett, Thomas	Gentleman		F, B
Brierley, Richard	Shoemaker	Willow row	
Brierley, Thomas	Compositor	Wilmot street	B
Briggs, William	Confectioner	Traffick street	B
Briggs, Thos. James	Gentleman	Litchurch	F, B
Briggs, Amos	Shopkeeper	Sitwell street	B
Briggs, John	Gentleman	Litchurch	F
Briggs, Thomas	Gentleman	Litchurch	F
Briggs, Joseph	Livery stables, licensed to let post horses	Osmaston street	F, B
Briggs, Benjamin	Shoemaker	Grove street	F
Briggs and George	Wholesale and retail woollen drapers	St. Peter's bridge	F, B
Briggs, John	Silk weaver	Short street, near Leonard street	
Briggs, William	Framework knitter	Litchurch street	
Briggs, Walter	Bookbinder	Sacheverel street	Fr
Briggs, William	Coachman and chaise driver	Sacheverel street	
Brindley, John	Cheesemonger, bacon dealer, and provision warehouse	44, Corn market	F, B
Brindley, Joseph	J. bookbinder	Ashbourn road	
Brindley, William	Clothier and woollen draper	7, Tenant street	B
Brinsley, William	Butcher	Brook street	
Britt, David Caleb	Beer seller	Hope street	
Brittain, James	Framework knitter	High street	
Brittain, James	Shopkeeper	Bag lane	
Britton, William	Shoemaker	Bridge street	
Britton, Alexander	Master of Lancastrian school	Ashbourn road	B
Broadhurst, George	Vict., Red Lion	74, Bridge street	B
Brocklesby, Joseph	Vict., Roebuck	35, Bridge gate	B
Brocklesby, John	Clerk at Messrs. Mozley & Sons	16, Parker street	B
Brocklesby, Robert	Flour, bacon, & cheese dealer	Sitwell street	
Brocklesby, Joseph		Duke street	Fr

Brocksop, John	Book-keeper	St. Peter's street	Fr
Brodhurst, George	Brazier and tin plate worker	Victoria street	B
Brodhurst, George	Patent mangle	24, Bridge street	
Bromley, William	Fishmonger	Eagle street	
Bromley, Robert	Agent and land surveyor	47, London road	F,B
Bromley, Job	Moulder	Cockpit hill	
Bromley, John	Land surveyor and agent to the Economical Life and Fire Assurance Company	41, St. Mary's gate	B
Brookes, Samuel	Currier and leather cutter	31, Queen street	B
Brookes, John	Beer seller & clerk at gas works	Parker street	B
Brookes, Francis	Beer seller	Kensington street	B
Brookes, Rev. Leigh		Full street	B
Brookes, Philip	Chemist, druggist, & grocer	3, Cheapside	F,B
Brookes, Samuel	Sawyer	Grove street	
Brookfield, John	Gentleman	London road	F
Brookhouse, James	Plasterer	Thorn tree lane	Fr
Brookhouse, Thomas	Gentleman	28, Morledge	F, Fr
Brookhouse, Robert	Original Roman cement and plaster manufactory	Morledge and Eagle street	Fr
Brookhouse, Milicent	Gardener and green grocer	Friar gate	
Brookhouse, Thomas	Plasterer	Park street	
Brookhouse, John	Plasterer	Ford street	F,Fr
Brookhouse, Joseph	Watch manufacturer	5, St. Peter's street	B
Brookhouse, Joseph	Roman cement and plaster manufacturer, St. Mary's gate	Morledge	Fr
Broomhead, E. & G.	Plumbers and glaziers	4, Bridge gate	Fr
Broomhead, William	Baker and shopkeeper	29, Queen street	B
Broughton, Thomas	Framework knitter	Ashbourn road	Fr
Broughton, Henry	Shoemaker	Bridge gate	Fr
Broughton, William	Framework knitter	Drury lane	Fr
Broughton, Henry	Framework knitter	Ashbourn road	Fr
Broughton, Edward	Framework knitter	Green lane	Fr
Broughton, Edward	Framework knitter	Spa	Fr
Broughton, Joseph	China painter	Nottingham road	Fr
Broughton, Robert	Framework knitter	Bridge street	Fr
Broughton, John	Policeman	Hope street	Fr
Broughton, Thomas	Shoemaker	Bridge gate	Fr
Broughton, Edwin	Framework knitter	Ashbourn road	Fr
Broughton, Griffith	Framework knitter	Ashbourn road	Fr
Broughton, Daniel	Framework knitter	Ashbourn road	Fr
Broughton, Thomas	Livery stables & horse breaker	Siddals lane	B
Broughton, Ann	Dressmaker	Green lane	
Brown, Thomas	Cabinet maker & upholsterer	41, Osmaston st.	B
Brown, Philip	Vict., Green Man	21, Kensington st.	B
Brown, Joseph	J. joiner	Kensington	
Brown, William	Basket maker	Brook street	
Brown, Samuel	Gentleman	Uttoxeter road	
Brown, Samuel	Wagoner	37, Morledge	
Brown, William	Jeweller	St. Peter's street	B
Brown, Thomas	Warehouseman	South street	B
Brown, William	Labourer	32, Erasmus street	

Brown, Thomas	Blacksmith and beer seller	8, Talbot street	B
Brown, Joshua	Framework knitter	Brook street	
Brown, Francis	Milk seller	Burton road	B
Brown, Richard	Gentleman	2, St. Helen's st.	F, Fr
Brown, John	Tailor	17, Agard street	B
Brown, George	Plumber and glazier	19, London road	F, B
Brown, William	Joiner and builder	Larges' street	B
Brown, John	Labourer	Bradshaw street	
Brown, Joseph	Draper	4, Green street	
Brown, Richard	Hawker	Park street	
Brown, William	Shoemaker	St. Michael's lane	
Brown, Joseph	Town crier, & furniture broker	Victoria street	B
Brown, Thomas	J. corn miller	Rivett street	
Brownsword, William	Beer seller	Brook street	
Brownsword, Joseph	Framework knitter	Ct. 1, Burton road	
Brownsword, Peter	Watchmaker	Bourne street	F
Brownsword, Thos.	Framework knitter	Union buildings	F
Brunsley, William	Labourer	Upper Brook street	
Bryan, William	Cooper	Parker street	
Bryan, Samuel	Shoe warehouse	46, Queen street	B
Bryan	Sawyer	Parker street	
Bryan, John	Serjeant in cavalry	Talbot street	
Bryer, Benjamin	Butcher, Old shambles	14, St. Mary's gate	B
Bryer, Richard	Chemist & druggist, Corn mkt.	26, Friar gate	B
Brunt, William	Beer seller	Darley lane	
Brunt, John	J. blacksmith	Chester place	
Buckland, Francis		Wraisby, Bucks.	F
Buckley, Francis	Flour, cheese, and bacon dealer	John street	
Buckley, Francis	Clerk at Mr. Hackett's	Kensington	
Buckley, Elizabeth	Haberdasher	49, St. Peter's street	
Buckley, John	Excavator	Leonard street	
Buckley, William	Tape Weaver	South street	
Buckley, Charles	Jeweller	49, St. Peter's st.	F, B
Buckley, Elizabeth	Milliner and dressmaker	Friar gate	
Budworth, Samuel	Framework knitter	Talbot street	Fr
Budworth, William	Shoemaker	Ct., Queen street	
Bull, Mary Anne	Milliner and dressmaker	14, Morledge	
Bull, James	J. silk throwster	Brook street	
Bull, Benjamin	Labourer	Bag lane	
Bull, John	Shopkeeper	10, Albion street	B
Bull, John	Pavier and sougher	Bloom street	
Bull, James	Vict., Noah's Ark	Morledge	
Bull, William	Chip seller	46, Willow row	
Bull, John	Vict., Greyhound	Market head	F, B
Bull, Samuel	Register office for servants	4, Friar gate	F, B
Bull, George	Collector of taxes	35, Bridge street	B
Bull, Samuel	Joiner and vict., Noah's Ark	14, Morledge	B
Bull, Miss	Milliner and dressmaker	Normanton terrace	
Bull, Thomas	Vict., Lamb Inn	Park street	
Bullivant, Joseph	Framework knitter	Burton road	
Bullock, Joseph & Son	Tailors and woollen drapers	3, Wardwick	B
Bullock, Joseph	Framework knitter	5, Drury lane	

Bullock, James	Woollen draper and tailor	26, Sadler gate	B
Bullock, Richard	Silk hand	Siddals lane	
Bullock, John	Works at Darley mill	Chester place	
Bullock, William	Blacking manufacturer	Bath street	
Bullock, George	Tobacco manufacturer, whole-sale and retail	Full street, and 6, Iron gate	B
Bullock, James	House and sign painter	Upper brook st.	F,B
Bullock, Charles	Framework knitter	Parker street	
Bullock, Joseph	Huckster	Albion street	
Bullock, John	Labourer	Bag lane	
Bullock, Joseph	China painter	Leonard street	Fr
Bullock, Joseph	House and sign painter	Nun's street	
Bulmer, James	Plumber and glazier	Corn market	F, B
Bunting,Lydia&Jane	Milliners and dressmakers	St. Peter's bridge	
Bunting, Samuel	Fireman at Bridgett's mill	30, City road	
Bunting, James	Labourer	Chester place	
Bunting, Samuel	Labourer	River street	
Burnett, Elizabeth	Dressmaker	11, Friar gate	
Burnett, William	J. corn miller	Duke street	
Burnett, John	Gardener and seedsman	11, Friar gate	B
Burroughs, Thomas	Proprietor and publisher of Derby Mercury, office Iron gate	Osmaston road	F,B
Burres, William	Labourer	Hill street	
Burrows, John	J. shoemaker	Eagle street	
Burrey, Francis	Frame smith	Sacheverel street	
Burton, Joseph	Cooper	King street	
Burton, Thomas	Wheelwright	Morledge	
Burton, Job	J. currier	Spring gardens	
Busher, Joseph	Locksmith	King street	
Busher, William	Whitesmith	30, Goodwin street	
Butler, Thomas	Grocer and tea dealer	28, Grove street	B
Butler, Herbert	Higgler and Coal dealer	St. Mary's bridge	
Butler, Joseph	Surgeon	Bridge street	
Butterworth, Thomas	Manager at Bridgett's mill	Bridge street	B
Buxton, Thomas	Surgeon and silk manufac-turer, mill Wardwick	St. Alk. ch. yard	B
Buxton, Thomas	Bricklayer	Parker street	
Buxton, John	Stonemason	Devonshire street	
Buxton, Thomas		Allestree	F
Buxton, Anthony	Joiner	Duke street	F
Buxton, Thomas	Boat builder	17, Nottingham rd.	B
Buxton, James	House, sign & furniture painter	Nottingham road	F,B
Buxton, John	Silk dyer	Liversage street	F,B
Buxton, John	Bricklayer	Brook street	
Buxton, James	Cow keeper	Nottingham road	
Byatt, Thomas	Stonemason	Bloom street	
Bysh, John	Traveller	Parker street	
Cadman, John	Wholesale and retail grocer and tea dealer	47, Sadler gate	
Cain, Richard	Clerk at Mr. Peet's	Parker street	
Cain, Edward	Blacksmith	Canal street	

Caldwell, James	Draper	Sacheverel street	F,B
Calladine, Mrs.	Furniture calenderer	Agard street	
Calladine, Geo. Malin	Cont. for conveying mail bags to Ashbourn	8, Agard street	B
Calladine, Robert	Labourer	Sacheverel street	
Calladine, William	Labourer	Siddals lane	
Calladine, Samuel	Labourer and pensioner	50, Willow row	
Calladine, John	Boatman	Castle street	
Calladine, Geo.	Collector of poor's rates and market tolls	Corn market	
Calow, Joseph	Gardener	John street	B
Calow, John	Gentleman	John street	
Calliner, Eliza	Milliner and dressmaker	Castle street	
Calvert, Edward	Gent., Agent to the Guardian Fire office, and cashier at Messrs. Smith & Co's. bank	10, Full street	F, B
Camp, William	Beer seller	Chester place	B
Camp, John	Labourer	Leonard street	
Camp, Robert	Framework knitter	44, Burton road	B
Camp, Thomas		Leicester	F
Campion, John	Bell Inn	Sadler gate	F
Campion, George	Gentleman	Eagle street	F
Campion, Robert	Plumber and glazier	Hope street	
Campion, Thomas	J. corn miller	28, Bath street	
Campion, Thomas	Baker and flour dealer	16, Eagle street	F,B
Cantrell, Mrs.		St. Peter's street	
Cantrell, William	J. carpenter	Liversage street	
Cantrell, Henry	Nag's Head Commer. Inn and posting house	St. Peter's street	B
Cantrell, Mrs.	Genteel lodgings	Ford street	
Cantrell, Thomas	J. engineer	High street	
Carson, Robert	Wine and spirit merchant and vict., Sir Walter Scott	Wardwick	B
Carson, John	Draper and vict , City Arms	17, Osmaston st.	F,B
Carr and Smith	Engineers and millwrights, manufacturers of patent printing presses, steam engines, &c.	Liversage street	B
Carter, William	Labourer	Liversage street	
Carter, James	Tea dealer and draper	Wilmot street	
Carter, Thomas	Gentleman's servant	Park street	
Cartlich, Thomas	Broker, upholsterer, general furniture dealer & appraiser	43, Sadler gate	F,B
Carrington,Rich.,jun.	Baker and flour dealer	Bag lane	
Carrington,Rich.,sen.	Vict., Bird-in-hand	21, Morledge	B
Cartwright, Daniel	Bookseller	Loughborough	F
Cartwright, Mrs.		Osmaston street	
Carroline, Thomas	J. brewer	Bag lane	
Carvill, Samuel		Outwood, Staffords.	F
Castledine, John	J. maltster	Traffick street	
Cash, William	Gardener	Cheapside	B
Cash, Thomas	Silk twister	Brook street	

Cash, Stephen	Gardener,fruiterer&seedsman	Queen street	F,B
Cash, Thomas	Gardener and seedsman	32, Morledge	F,B
Cattell, Joseph	Druggist	4, Burton road	B
Cave, Mary	Vict., Fox and Goose	11, Friar gate	
Cay, George	Shopkeeper	Ashbourn road	
Cay, Joseph	J. jeweller	Wilmot street	
Cay, George Nichols.	Brushmaker	Brook street	
Chadfield, Joseph	Bookseller, printer, stationer, paper hanging warehouse, and musical repository	Friar gate	F,B
Chadfield, Charles	J. printer	Dunkirk	B
Chadwick, Samuel	Milk seller	Normanton road	F
Chadwick, William	Gardener and green grocer	35, London road	B
Chadwick, Samuel	Shopkeeper	Normanton road	B
Chadwick, Robert	Wholesale stationer	25, Queen street	B
Challinor, William	Oil and colourman, City road	15, North Parade	F,B
Challinor, William	Tailor	Green lane	
Challinor, Mrs.		North Parade	
Challinor, Josiah	Colour manufacturer	City road	B
Chambers, John	Gentleman	Tibshelf	F
Chambers, Joseph	Shoemaker	Morledge	
Chambers, Jarvis A.	Butcher	5, Burton road	F,B
Chaplain, Jonathan	Shoemaker	65, St. Peter's street	B
Chaplin, Samuel	Shoemaker	Brook street	
Chaplin, Joseph	Tailor	Mill street	Fr
Chapman, Frederic	Twist hand	Devonshire street	
Chatterton, John, sen.	Gentleman, 1, Amen Alley	Alvaston	Fr
Chatterton, John, jun.	Plumber and glazier, wholesale and retail manufacturer of sheet lead, patent lead and tin pipe, &c., and agent to the Manchester Plate Glass company	Morledge,Full st.	F,Fr
Chatterton, Samuel	Framework knitter	City road	
Cheetham, John, jun.	Joiner	Ashbourn road	B
Chawner and Blurton	Ladies' boarding and day sch.	London street	
Chawner, Henry	J. glazier and plumber	At Station	
Cheetham, Mrs.		Wilmot street	F
Cheetham, John	Joiner	Parker street	
Cheetham and Son	Builders and joiners	King street	
Chell, John	Wine and spirit merchant	9, Parker street	F,B
Chell, Thomas	Gentleman	1, Brook street	F,B
Cheshire, William	J. shoemaker	Parker street	
Chester, Thomas	Works at Fox's, engineers	Cockpit hill	
Chester, Richard	Engine driver	Canal street	B
Chisholme, Daniel	Pensioner	7, Exeter street	
Cholerton, William	J. cabinet maker	Fowler street	
Cholerton, Thomas	Moulder	Morledge	Fr
Cholerton, Edward		Littleover	Fr
Cholerton, Joseph	J. jeweller	Devonshire street	
Cholerton, Sarah	Vict., Black Swan	London road	
Cholerton, John	J. joiner and cabinet maker	Fowler street	

c

Cholerton, Robert	Almshouses	Bridge gate	F
Cholerton, H. & Co.	Coach timber benders	Albion street	B
Cholerton, Thomas	Joiner	Back Sitwell st.	F,B
Cholerton, Matthew	Upholsterer, cabinet maker, and paper-hanger	21, Victoria st.	Fr,B
Cholerton, Francis	J. currier	2, Fowler street	Fr,B
Cholerton, Francis	Joiner	26, Osmaston st.	F
Cholerton, John	Framework knitter	Ct, 1, St. Helen's st.	
Cholerton, Edward	Shopkeeper	Eagle street	F,B
Cholerton, Thomas	Framework knitter	Parker street	
Cholerton, John	Grocer and tea dealer	23, Willow row	F,B
Cholerton, Thomas	Framework knitter	Court, Lodge lane	
Cholerton, Samuel	J. brushmaker	Liversage street	F
Church, John	Needle maker	18, St. Helen's st.	B
Clapp, Edward	Turner and chairmaker	Kensington	
Clarke, Thomas	Framework knitter	Green street	
Clarke, Michael	Cooper	49, Willow row	
Clarke, Frederic	Hairdresser and perfumer	St. Peter's street	
Clarke, William	Weaver	Brook street	Fr
Clarke, John	Framework knitter	Green lane	Fr
Clarke, John	Wine merchant, and agent to the Royal Exchange Life Assurance Company, wine and spirit vaults, 8, Tenant street	80, Friar gate	F,B
Clarke, Edward	Framework knitter	Short st.,Leonard s.	Fr
Clarke, Benjamin	Spar turner	Leonard street	Fr
Clarke, Thomas	Framework knitter	Kensington	
Clarke, William	Framework knitter	Leonard street	Fr
Clarke, James	Shoemaker	Bath street	Fr
Clarke, Alfred	Hairdresser and perfumer	St. Peter's street	B
Clarke, Mary	Baker and flour dealer	44, Bridge gate	
Clarke, Mary & Thos.	Maltsters and corn factors	Nottingham road	
Clarke, Thos.	Corn factor	Nottingham road	F
Clarke, Samuel	Tarpawling manufacturer	Morledge	
Clarke, John	Framework knitter	Willow row	
Clarke, Charles	Bookbinder	37, Willow row	B
Clarke, Joseph		Sadler gate	Fr
Clarke, James	Maltster	30, Sadler gate	
Clarke, John	Earthenware dealer	17, Bridge street	
Clarke, Richard		Chaddesden	Fr
Clarke, Joseph	Guard on Railway	John street	B
Clavey, Edward	J. cabinet maker	Sitwell street	B
Clavey, Philip	Dealer in glass & earthenware	31, Sadler gate	F,B
Clay, Miss		Tenant street	
Clay, John, jun.	Butcher	Traffick street	
Clay, Thomas, jun.	Butcher	Leonard street	
Clay, John, sen.	Butcher	Leonard street	
Clayson, Mary	Beer seller	Willow row	
Cleever, William	Pipe maker	34, Nun's street	B
Clifford, Sam.	Gentleman	Shardlow	F
Clifford, Wm.	Gentleman	Wilne	F

Clifford, John	Blacking manufacturer	Thorn-tree lane	
Clements, Robert	Framework knitter	Kensington	
Cluer, Mary	Milliner and dressmaker	Market place	
Clulow, William	Shopkeeper	Osmaston road	
Clulow, Edwin	Policeman at Station	Hope street	
Coape, Joseph	Shoemaker	Devonshire street	
Coates, John	Works at Britannia Foundry	Duke street	
Cobbard, Thomas	Works at silk factory	Canal street	
Cockayne and Slack	Coal merchants	London rd. & Not. rd.	
Cockayne, George	Collector of rents	89, Bridge street	
Cockayne, Thomas	Weaver	Brook street	
Cockayne, Caleb	Dealer in British lace	16, Notting rd.	F, Fr
Cockayne, Edward		Chellaston	Fr
Cockayne, Charles	Shoemaker	Duke street	Fr
Cockayne, William	Silk dyer	3, Silk-mill lane	B
Cockayne, Joseph	J. butcher	23, Full street	
Cockayne, William	J. joiner	Siddals lane	
Cockayne, Jesse	Framesmith	45, Bridge gate	F, Fr
Cockayne, John	Needlemaker & collect. of rents	1, Parker street	Fr
Cockayne, Mary	Shopkeeper	Duke street	
Cockayne, Thomas	Framesmith	Bridge gate	Fr
Cocker, John	Stonemason	Back Parker street	F
Cocker, Christopher	Shoemaker	Litchurch street	
Cocker, Reuben	J. engineer	Cannon street	Fr
Cock, John Henry	Currier and leather factor	104, Friar gate	F, Fr
Coggan, Thomas	Compositor	Uttoxeter road	B
Coke, D'Ewes, esq.		Brookhill hall, Notts.	F
Coke, Thomas	Gentleman	Wilmot street	B
Cole, William	Broker, upholsterer, and general furniture warehouse	St. Peter's street	B
Colburne, John	Shoemaker	Ct., Mill street	
Colborne, Samuel	Labourer	8, Ashbourn road	
Coleburn, George	Shopkeeper	23, Bridge gate	B
Coleman, John	Carver and gilder	3, King street	B
Coleman, Thomas	Postboy, King's Head	St. James's lane	
Collard, John	Framework knitter	47, Burton road	
Collier, John	Beer seller	Leaper street	B
Collier, James	Farmer	Dunkirk	
Collier, William	Labourer	63, Eagle street	B
Collins, Richard	Fishmonger	Summer hill	
Collis, Philip	Framework knitter	Burton road	
Collinson, John	Farmer	Litchurch	
Collumbell, David	Tailor	21, Darley lane	
Collumbell, William	Gentleman	Duffield road	
Collumbell, John	Relieving officer	1, King street	F, B
Collumbell, Sarah	Grocer and tea dealer	1, King street	
Collumbell, Richard	Tailor	Goodwin street	B
Collumbell, Charles	Butcher	Kensington	
Collumbell, Edmund	Parish clerk of St. Alkmund's, and deputy registrar for St. Alkmund's district	Kedleston road	
Compton, James	Gentleman	Wilmot street	B

Cooke, John		St. Peter's street	F
Cooke, John	J. Printer and shopkeeper	Jury street	
Cooke, Thomas	Tea merchant, coffee dealer, and general grocer	Corn market	B
Cooke, Thomas	Butler	Wilmot street	
Cook, John	Plasterer	Sitwell street	B
Cooke, John	Naturalist, and proprietor of natural museum	Market place	B
Cook, James Chris.	Clock and watchmaker	St. James's lane	B
Cooke, James	Hatter	31, Exeter street	B
Cooling, Edward	Gardener	Uttoxeter road	B
Cooper, Thomas	Shoemaker	St. Helen's street	
Cooper, Thomas	Beer seller	Darley lane	
Cooper, John, jun.	Tanner	Green street	B
Cooper, Thomas, and Son	Woolstaplers, fellmongers, and glue boilers	Slack lane, and 31, Full street	B
Cooper, John	Framework knitter	Brook street	
Cooper, Thomas	Gentleman	St. Peter's bridge	F,B
Cooper, William Mansfield	Carpenter, cabinet maker, builder, and surveyor	St. Mary's gate	F,B
Cooper, Thomas	Stone and marble mason, and builder	Brook street	F,B
Cooper, William	Framework knitter	Ct. 4, Brook street	
Cooper, Mary	Plumber and glazier	Thorn tree lane	
Cooper, John	Gentleman	Traffick street	F,B
Cooper, William	Watchmaker	31, London road	B
Cooper, Joseph	Gardener	Darley lane	
Cooper, George	Baker and flour dealer	Bridge street	B
Cooper, Samuel	J. printer	Ct. 4, St. Mary's gate	
Cooper, Elizabeth	Straw bonnet maker	Bridge street	
Cope, John	Shoemaker	Devonshire street	
Cope, Matthew	Smith	Bath street	Fr
Cope, James	Looker over at mill	Brook street	B
Cope, Mrs. Martha		Lodge lane	
Cope, John	Fishmonger and poulterer, oyster rooms and beer seller	48, Sadler gate	B
Cope, Henry	Dyer of silk	St. Michael's lane	B
Cope, William	Dealer in game	48, Sadler gate	
Cope, John	Silk dyer	Brook street	
Cope, Josh. James	Smith at Britannia foundry	Duke street	Fr
Copeley, Matthew		Hanley, Staffordsh.	
Copestake, John	Shopkeeper	Talbot street	Fr
Copestake, Sarah	Shopkeeper	20, Burton road	
Copestake, George	Farmer	Stockbrook lane	B
Copestake, Mrs.	Milliner and dressmaker	Wilmot street	
Copestake, John	Shoemaker	62, Willow row	
Copestake, Esther	Shopkeeper	5, Nun's street	
Copestake, Charles	Baker and flour dealer	33, Morledge	B
Copestake, James	Gentleman	Old Uttoxeter road	B
Copestake, John	Gentleman	Wilmot street	
Copestake, John	Labourer	Fingal street	
Copley, James	Mr. Mason's colour works	Derwent street	

Copson, Thomas	Silk weaver	Parker street
Corber, Stephen	Silk weaver	Parker street
Corbin, Rev. J.	Minister of Congregational chapel	36, Friar gate
Corden, John	Auditor and surveyor to the Derby Poor Law Union	14, Osmaston st. F,B
Corden, William	Labourer	15, Morledge
Corden, Samuel	Framework knitter	Ct. 1, King street
Corden, Joseph	Shoemaker	38, Friar gate B
Corden, Joseph	Farmer	Dunkirk B
Corden, Francis	Bookbinder	Ct. 1, King street
Core, Henry	Gas fitter	Kensington street
Corner, William	Joiner	Devonshire street
Corn, John	Gentleman	Wilmot street B
Cotteral, Thomas	Joiner	Hope street
Cotton, John	Silk framework knitter	18, Fowler street Fr
Cotton, John	Moulder	Duke street
Cotton, John	Beer seller	78, Devonshire st. B
Cotton, James	Framework knitter	New st. Uttox. rd. Fr
Cotton, William	Shoemaker	Ashbourn road Fr
Coulson, William	Labourer	Erasmus street
Coulson, Nathaniel	Slater and grave-stone cutter	Nottingham road B
Coulson, Robert	Slater	Siddals lane B
Coulson, George	Cashier at Messrs.Evans's bank	6, St. Mary's gate B
Cowlishaw, Rich. P.	Grocer and confectioner, clerk at Trinity Church	John street, London road B
Cowlishaw, James	Builder, and clerk of works at Railway station	Traffick street
Cowlishaw, Joseph	Stonemason	Bag Lane
Cowlishaw, John	Joiner and beerseller	Traffick street F,B
Cowlishaw, Thomas	Joiner and surveyor	Park street
Cowlishaw, Thomas		Mayfield F
Cowlishaw, John	Book-keeper	South street
Cowlishaw, James	Whitesmith	London road F,B
Cowpe, William T.	J. currier	16, Devonshire street
Cox, George Henry Richardson	Solicitor, Tenant street res.	Spondon B
Cox, Brothers & Co.	Lead merchants, manufacturers of white lead, lead pipe, and patent shot, Derby and Nottingham works	Morledge and Mill Hill
Cox, George, esq.		5, Grove Terrace Fr
Cox, Roger, esq.	Counting house, Tenant street	Spondon Hall F,B
Cox, Haden, and Pountain	Wine and spirit merchants and importers	Market place
Cox, Edward Soresby, esq.	Counting house, 38,Morledge	Culland Hall and Brailsford B
Cox, William Thos.	Gentleman	Spondon Cottage F,B
Cox, Wm. Sons & Co.	Cheesefactors	17, Tenant street F
Cox, Samuel Walker	Gent., Counting house, 17, Tenant street	Brailsford Lodge B
Cox, Thos. esq.	Counting house, 38, Morledge	Nun's green house F,B

Cox, Henry, esq.	Counting house, 16, Market place	Park field house, Kedleston road	F,B
Cox, John	Gentleman	Burton road	F,B
Cox, Harriet	Milliner and dressmaker	5, Tenant street	
Cox, William	Wine merchant	31 & 37,Cornmkt.	F,B
Cox and Malin	Wine, spirit, porter, and cider merchants	Corn Market	F
Cox, William	Higgler	Thorn-tree lane	B
Cox, Samuel	Eating house	Bridge street	B
Coxon, John	Framework knitter	Brook street	
Coxon, Robert Eaton	House & furniture painter	Curzon street	B
Coxon, Jacob	White and blacksmith, shop, Osmaston street	Devonshire street	B
Coxon, John	J. engineer	Albion place	
Cragg, William Preston	Schoolmaster of Dr. Bell's school	South street	
Cramond, William	Manufacturer of silk hosiery and gloves	2, George street	B
Cramp, James	Ribbon weaver	Brook street	
Craycraft, Miss Diana		Ashbourn road	
Cresswell, William	Gentleman	Cross lanes	
Crooks, Paul	Moulder	36, Erasmus street	
Crompton, Newton, and Co.	(Old Bank) draw on Smith, Payne, & Smith, London	Iron gate	
Crompton, William		Burton-upon-Trent	F
Crompton, Mrs. Eliz.		Mill Hill house	
Crompton, John Bell, esq.	J. P. and alderman for the borough of Derby, J.P. for the county, Iron gate	Milford House	G,Fr
Crooks, Thomas		Rugby, Warwicksh.	
Cross, Sophia	Milliner and dressmaker	St. Helen's street	
Crosby, Matthew	Labourer	Kensington	
Crosby, Henry	Framesmith	Traffick street	B
Crosby, William	Farmer	Dog-kennel lane	
Crowley, Hicklin, Batty, and Co.	Carrriers by water from Lister's wharf, Tuesday and Friday, to Birmingham, Warwick, Coventry, Banbury, and Oxford	Siddals lane	
Crossly, Matthias	Clerk at Weatherhead, Walters, and Co.	Normanton road	B
Crump, Thomas	Engineer, plumber, and gas fitter, superintendent of Gas Works	Friar gate and Cavendish street	F,B
Crump, William	Officer of excise	Burton road	
Cubley, Mrs.		5, Amen alley	
Cubley, William	Painter and gilder	Queen street	B
Cubley, Anne	Fancy repository and baby linen warehouse	34, Queen street	Fr
Cubley, William	Weaver	Cannon street	
Cunliffe, Henry	Cabinet maker	Siddals lane	B
Curshaw, Richard	Stonemason	Brook street	

Curzon, John, esq.	Solicitor, agent to the Earl of Harrington	3, Full street	Fr,B
Curzon, John	Framework knitter	Litchurch street	
Curzon, Henry, Hon. Admiral		19, Ashbourn road	B
Dagley and Smith	Coach builders	London road	B
Dagley, Herbert	Coach builder	London road	B
Dagley, Thomas	Coach builder	London road	F
Dakin, William	Shopkeeper	33, Eagle street	F,B
Dakin, John	J. blacksmith	Traffick street	
Dakin, John	Gardener	Burton road	B
Dakin, John	Works at factory	Cannon street	
Dakin, Charles	Tape weaver	Large's street	
Dakin, Joseph	J. plasterer	Eagle street	
Dakin, Thomas	Foundry man	Traffick street	
Dalby, Mrs.		Wilmot street	
Dalby, Samuel	Butcher	Osmaston road	F,B
Dale, Henry	Traveller	Osmaston street	B
Dallison, Robert	Framework knitter	William street	Fr
Dallison, John	Butcher	Hill street	Fr
Dallison, Thomas	Twist hand	Devonshire street	
Dallison, Richard	Shopkeeper	William street	B
Dallison, Wm., jun.	Hosier	Eagle street	F,B
Dallison, Wm., sen.	Hosier	75,Devonshire st.	F,B
Dallison, William	J. jeweller	New buildings, Nun's street	Fr
Dallison, Daniel	Milk seller	Friar gate	
Dallison, Thomas	Straw hat and bobbin net manufacturer	38, Sadler gate	Fr
Dallison, Gilbert	Butcher	Corn market	Fr
Dallison, Ann	Milliner and dressmaker	38, Sadler gate	
Darby, Thos. & Sons	Woollen drapers and tailors	23, Market place	F,B
Darby, John Thos.	Woollen draper and tailor	23, Market place	F,B
Darby, Henry	Woollen draper and tailor	23, Market place	F,B
Darby, Thomas, sen.	Gentleman	4, Wilmot street	F,B
Daulby, John	Dealer in hay	Sacheverel street	
Davenport, Joseph Launcelot	Silk throwster, warehouse, Queen street	14, Full street	B
Davenport & Humpston	Silk throwsters	Full street	
Davenport, Fletcher	Draper	Bath street	
Davenport, Jedediah	Gentleman	11, North parade	
Davenport, Thomas	Farmer & framework knitter	Abbey barns	Fr
Davidson, Mrs.	Secretary to John Stephenson, esq.	Osmaston street	
Davis, William	Vict., Three Jolly Butchers	Traffick street	
Davis, James	Maltster	Uttoxeter road	
Davis, Thomas	Vict., Neptune	5, Osmaston street	B
Davison, John	Hawker	Bath street	
Davis, John	Optician and mathematical instrument maker	St. Mary's gate	
Dawson, Thomas	J. watchmaker	Grove street	

Dawson, Gregory	Coach proprietor	Chapel street	F,B
Dawson, Thomas	Parish clerk at St. Peter's ch.	St. Peter's ch. yd.	F,Fr
Dawson, George	Hair dresser	St. James's lane	
Dawson, John	J. jeweller	Grove street	
Dawson, John	Vict., George the Fourth	36, Leonard street	B
Dawson, Edwd., esq.		Whatton house, Kegworth	F
Dawson, Joseph	Pig jobber and vict.	Grove street	Fr
Dawson, John	Pig jobber and vict.	Morledge	Fr
Day, Thomas	J. tanner	84, Friar gate	
Day, George	J. printer	Hill street	
Day, Joseph	Overlooker at Amb. Moore and Co's. mill	Grove street	
Dean, Rev. James		Grove terrace	B
Dean, Thomas	Collector of rents	Eagle street	F,B
Dean, William	Gardener	13, Cannon street	
Dear, John	J. engineer	Sitwell street	
Denham, William	Horse dealer	Siddals lane	B
Denman, William	Baker and grocer	Osmaston street	B
Denstone, James	Watchmaker	Talbot street	
Denstone, William	Baker and grocer	Sacheverel street	B
Denstone, James	Policeman	Drury lane	
Denstone, Joshua	Baker maltster, & miller	Cheapside	F,Fr
Denstone, James	Vict. and maltster	Huffin heath	F
Derby Canal Comp.		Cockpit hill	
Derby & Derbyshire Banking Company	Draw upon Williams, Deacon, and Co., bankers, London, Robt. Ronald, esq. manager	Corn market	
Derwent Foundry Co.	Iron founders	Exeter street	
Dewar, David	Librarian, Mechanics' Institu.	Wardwick	
Dewe, Charles Thos. Reynolds	Solicitor and commissioner of bankruptcy, office Iron gate	Grove terrace	F,B
Dewe and Fox	Solicitors	Iron gate	
Dewick, John	Framework knitter	Sacheverel street	
Dexter, George	Policeman at Station	Hope street	F
Dexter, Samuel	Beer seller	Osmaston street	B
Dexter, Francis	Labourer	Litchurch street	
Dicken, George	Framework knitter	Dunkirk	
Dicken, Francis	Tailor	13, Darwin row	
Dicken, William	Sawyer	Osmaston road	
Dicken, Edward	Sawyer	St. Peter's street	
Dilkes, George	Farmer	Spa lane	B
Dilkes, William	Gentleman's servant	Siddals lane	
Dimock, Thomas	Vict., Old Spot, & maltster	21, St. Helen's st.	B
Dimock, James	Beer seller	Victoria street	B
Dixon, Capt. Francis		2, Cherry street	F,B
Dix, Richard	House surgeon at Infirmary	London road	
Dobb, Joseph	Hatter	Sacheverel street	
Dobson, J. Thompson		Liverpool	F
Dobson, Thomas	Engineer	Wilmot street	B
Dobson, Ralph	Bookseller, bookbinder, and printer	Traffick street	

Dobson, N.	Grocery and provision wareh.	Canal street	
Docker, Thomas	Gentleman	Osmaston street	B
Docker, Mark	Manufacturer of curled hair	Osmaston street	
Docker, Henry	Gentleman	Leonard street	F
Dolman, John	Vict., Jolly Toper	Nottingham road	
Dolman, Samuel	Sawyer	St. Peter's ch. yd.	
Dovey, John	J. joiner	Kensington street	
Downing, James	Weaver	High street	
Downes, Charles	Earthenware dealer	Canal street	
Douge, Philip	Beer seller, Forester's Arms	Park street	B
Doyle, William	Shoemaker	South street	
Doxey, Charles	Stoker and patten maker	Erasmus street	
Dowdeswell, Edw.	Gentleman's servant	York street	
Drabwell & Benson	Milliners	Sadler gate	
Draper, Mary	Linen and woollen draper	Corn market	
Draycott, Joseph	Tailor	Old Uttoxeter road	B
Dreher, John Fred.	Pork butcher	Morledge	
Drew, Isaac	Boot and shoemaker	10, St. Mary's gate	B
Drew, William	Shoemaker	Osmaston street	B
Drewry, John esq.		Melbourn	F
Drewry, Edward	Gentleman Trevor square,	Knightsbridge	F
Dudley, Charles	Turner and chairmaker	Ct., Willow row	B
Dudley, William	Wood turner	47, Willow row	
Dudley, Sarah	Dress maker	Osmaston street	
Duesbury, William	Bloomsbury, near	Birmingham	F
Duesbury, Francis	Jeweller	Traffick street	F, B
Duesbury, Wm. H.	Cheesefactor and confectioner	Cheapside	B
Duesbury, John		Quorndon	Fr
Dukes, John	J. upholsterer	Grove street	
Duncan, William	Shopkeeper, and foreman to D. Duncan	Parker street	
Duncan, David	Engineer	Nun's street	B
Duncan, John	Foreman to D. Duncan	Grove street	
Dunn, Bryan		9, Charles street	B
Dunnicliff & Severne	Solicitors	Office, St. Mary's gate	
Dunnicliff, John	Solicitor, and perpetual commissioner for taking acknowledgements of deeds by married women	6, Burton road	B
Dunnicliffe, John	Butcher	St. Peter's street	B
Dunnicliffe, William	Butcher, shop Market place	Green lane	B
Dunnicliffe, John	Butcher	Bridge street	B
Dunnicliffe, William	Butcher	Dunkirk	
Dunstone, William	J. engineer	Bradshaw street	
Durden, Joseph	Moulder	Castle place	
Dwyer, William	Shoemaker	Normanton road	
Dyche, Joseph & Rob.	Timber merchants	Cockpit hill	F, B
Dyche, William,	Beer seller	Bag lane	B
Dyche, Charles	Tailor	Sadler gate	
Dyche, Samuel	Coal dealer	Bag lane	
Dyche, Robert	Timber merchant	Cockpit hill	F, B
Eames, Francis	Pawnbroker & gen. salesman	Victoria street	B

Earp, Samuel	Proprietor of Dr. Camm's medicines	Osmaston street	B
Earp, Thomas	Canal and land agent	London st.&Corn m.	B
Earp, George	Baker	Curzon street	B
Easom, James	Framework knitter	St. Helen's street	Fr
Easom, Joshua	Shopkeeper & letter carrier	26, Kensington st.	B
Eaton, George	Gentleman	Corn market	
Eaton, Joseph	Brazier	Bag lane	
Eaton, Richard, sen.	Gentleman	Ashover	F
Eaton, Francis	Grocer	49, Friar gate	B
Eaton, Thomas	Dyer	27, Exeter street	B
Eaton, Richard, jun.	Attorney's clerk	Nottingham	F
Eaton, Sophia	Milliner and dressmaker	33, Queen street	
Eaton, Robert	Dyer	33, Queen street	B
Eaton, John	Shoemaker	13, Parker street	B
Eaton, Joseph	Carpenter	Chapel street	B
Eccleshare, Joseph	Straw bonnet manufacturer	40, Willow row	Fr
Edge, Thomas	Agent to Beasley and Champion, brewers	Large's street	
Edmonds, Joseph	Officer of excise	York street	
Edwards, W. jun.	J. painter	Sitwell street	Fr
Edwards, William	Watchmaker	10, Rotten row	Fr
Edwards, William	Clerk at Evans's bank	Wilmot street	F
Edwards, Joseph	Labourer	Bag lane	
Edwards, Thos. jun.	Tailor	York street	
Edwards, William	Framework knitter	Eagle street	
Edwards, Henry	J. bricklayer	Devonshire street	
Edwards, Thos. sen.	Tailor and woollen draper	24,Queen st.York st.	B
Edwards, John	Wine and spirit merchant	St. Alkmu. ch. yd.	B
Edwards & Hallam	Wine and spirit merchants	Iron gate	
Edwards, William	Framework knitter	Talbot street	Fr
Edwards, Pet. Turner	Draughtsman & accountant	Agard street	
Egard, Charles	Butcher	Ashbourn road	
Eggleshaw, Edward	Works at china factory	Brook street	
Eggleston, Matthias	Confectioner and tea dealer	33, Iron gate	B
Eggleston, William	Cow keeper	Becket well lane	
Eley, John	Vict., White Hart	Bridge gate	
Eley, William	Nail maker	Lodge lane	Fr
Eley, John, jun.	Blacksmith	Bold lane	Fr
Eley, William	Petrifactioner	Brook street	
Eley, William	Cooper	St. Michael's lane	Fr
Eley, Samuel	Nail manufacturer	36, Bridge gate	B
Eley, Samuel	Higgler	Bold lane	Fr
Eley, Michael	Labourer	Ashbourn road	
Eley, Francis	Printer	Upper Brook st.	Fr
Eley, John, sen.	Hawker	Bold lane	Fr
Eley, William	Weaver	Borough's walk	
Eley, George	Nail maker	Bridge gate	
Eley, Joseph		Belper	Fr
Ellaby, William	J. engineer	Brook street	B
Ellam, William	Paint and colour manufacturer, Markeaton mills	Cherry street	B

Ellerington, William	J. engineer	Bradshaw street	
Ellicock, Samuel	Dealer in cutlery	John street	
Elliott, Francis	Currier and leather cutter	27, Sadler gate	B
Elliott, James	Currier and leather cutter	22, Sadler gate	B
Elliott, Leonard	Dealer in toys	13, St. Alk. ch. yd.	B
Ellis, Robert	Moulder	Erasmus street	
Ellis, Rev. J.	Minister, Primitive Methodist chapel	Babington lane and Albion street	
Elsam, William	Gymnastic master	Traffick street	
Elsons, Robert	J. baker	Litchurch street	
Emerson, Robert	Carpenter and builder	Park street	
Emerson, John	Joiner	Park street	
Emerson, Thomas	House and sign painter	Sacheverel street	B
Emberry, John	J. bookbinder	Parker street	
Endsor, Thomas	Shoemaker and beer seller	Siddals lane	B
England, George	Dealer in flour and bacon	Brook street	F,B
Etches, Sam. sen.	Labourer	Bag lane	Fr
Etches, Samuel	Labourer	19, Albion street	B
Etches, Wm. Jeffrey	Cheese factor	St. Peter's bridge	B
Etches, Charles	Gentleman	Wilmot street	F,B
Etches, John	Boot and shoemaker	Bold lane	B
Evans, William, esq.	M. P.	Allestree Hall	F,Fr
Evans, Samuel, esq.	Banker	Darley Hall	F,B
Evans, William and Samuel	Bankers, draw. on Jones, Lloyd, and Co. London	St. Mary's gate	F,B
Evans, Sam. & Co.	Paper makers and merchants	Queen street	B
Evans, Walter & Co.	Cotton spinners	Darley	F
Evans, William	Olefiant gas manufacturers	9, Kensington st.	B
Evans, George	J. joiner	Litchurch street	
Evans, Joseph	Dyer and scourer	St. Michael's lane	B
Evans, Rev. Richard	Curate of St. Werburgh's	Normanton road	B
Evans, George	Shoemaker	15, Bloom street	
Evans, John	Shopkeeper	Sadler gate bridge	B
Evans, Daniel	Officer of excise	Bath street	
Ewin, Alexander	Petrifactioner	Court 7, Bold lane	
Eyre, Timothy	Butcher	20, Queen street	B
Eyre, James	Artist	Derwent street	Fr
Eyre, Vincent, esq.		Highfields	F
Eyre, Thomas	Hatter and hosier	54, Sadler gate	F,Fr
Eyre, Beebe	Law stationer and accountant, varnish & colour manufac.	28, Piazza, Mrkt. pla. 7, Island place	B
Eyre, James	Whitesmith	Full street	
Eyre, Timothy	Works at lead mill	Albion street	
Eyre, Samuel	Auctioneer, accountant, and valuer, agent to the York and London Fire and Life Assurance company, and Plate Glass company	15, Full street	F,Fr
Eyre, Sarah	Milliner and dressmaker	Derwent street	
Fagen, Owen	Lodging house	St. Michael's lane	
Fairbanks, James	Farmer	Nottingham road	
Falconer, Thomas	J. smith	6, Mansfield road	B

Falconer, Abraham	Moulder and beer seller	City road	B
Falconer, Peach & Co.	Iron founders, Union Foundry City road		
Falconer, Edward	Iron founder	14, City road	B
Falconer, Joseph	Moulder	5, City road	Fr
Falconer, Ann	Dress maker	6, Mansfield road	
Falkner, Thomas	Compositor	Erasmus street	Fr
Falkner, John Giles	Compositor	Sadler gate	Fr
Falkner, Ralph	Sawyer	19, Erasmus street	
Falkner, William	Tape weaver	High street	
Falkner, John	Painter	Union buildings	
Fallows, John	Shoemaker	Cockpit hill	F,B
Fantum, John	Chimney sweeper	Ct. 1, Willow row	
Farnsworth, Wm.	Labourer	Brook street	
Farnsworth, Samuel	J. jeweller	Normanton road	
Farnsworth, Mrs.		Liversage street	
Farnsworth, Mary	Milliner and dressmaker	26, Bold lane	
Farnsworth, Abrm.	Framework knitter	Ct. 1, Burton road	
Farnsworth, Charles	Framework knitter	Kensington	
Farnsworth, Isaac	Framework knitter	Bold lane	
Farnsworth, James	Corn cutter	Bold lane	
Farnsworth, John	Tape weaver	Large's street	
Farrels, William	Lodging house	Bag lane	
Farrell, James	Shoemaker	Willow row	
Farrington, John	Labourer	Albion street	
Faulkner, John	Timber merchant & carpenter	Nottingham road	B
Feaks, Robert	Blacksmith	Markeaton	F
Fearn, John	Shopkeeper	William street	B
Fearn, Henry	Woollen draper and tailor	St. Peter's street	B
Fearn, Richard	Gardener and seedsman	Upper brook st.	Fr
Fearn, John	Traveller	William street	
Fearn, James	Sawyer	Castle street	
Fearn, Richard		Ford street	F
Fearn, Mrs. R.	Milliner and dressmaker	Ford street	
Fearn, George	Hat manufacturer	5, St. Helen's street	
Fearn, Mrs. George	Milliner and dressmaker	St. Helen's street	
Fearn, Samuel	Surgeon	6, St. Peter's street	
Featherstone, C. W.	Law stationer	Amen Alley	
Ferguson, Geo. esq.	Physician	London road	B
Fernyhough, Wm.	Woollen draper and tailor	Sadler gate	
Field, Mrs. M. C.	Mistress of Trinity school	Liversage street	
Fields, Thomas	Painter, provision warehouse, and dealer in game	London road	F,B
Fielding, Thomas		Barnsbury prk. Lon.	F
Finlayson, John	Coach builder	22, London road	B
Finlayson, Captain	Superinten. of stores at Station	Normanton road	
Fisher, Jonathan	Gentleman	Lodge lane	F
Fisher, John	Gentleman	Foremark hall	F
Fisher, John	Carver and gilder	35, Sadler gate	B
Fisher, Isaac	Book-keeper	Traffick street	B
Fisher, Thomas	Surgeon, and proprietor of private asylum	Cross lanes	B
Fisher, Rev. William	Curate at St. Peter's	3, Grove terrace	B

Fitchett, Samuel	J. upholsterer	Ashbourn road	B
Fitchett, Thomas	Bookbinder	7, Bridge street	Fr
Fitchett, Thomas	Beer seller, Rainbow	6, Green street	F,B
Fitchett, Robert	Gentleman	Mount Carmel	F,B
Flack, Edward	Solicitor	Friar gate	Fr
Fleming, Charles	Furrier	Queen street	
Fletcher, Joseph	Manufact. paper ribbon blocks	38, Goodwin st.	B
Fletcher, George	J. jeweller	London road	
Fletcher, Jethro	J. joiner	Normanton road|	
Fletcher, Wm. Vickers	Gentleman	Nun's street	
Fletcher, Eliza		Wilmot street	
Fletcher, Rev. Wm.	M.A., Head master of the Free Grammar school, Gent's. boarding school, and lecturer at All Saints' church	St. Peter's street	B
Fletcher, Joyce	Dyer	London road	
Fletcher, William	Gardener and seedsman	Bold lane	B
Fletcher, Thos. W.		Dudley	F
Fletcher, William	Baker and flour dealer	23, Willow row	F,B
Fletcher, Hannah	Milliner and dressmaker	Ford street	
Fletcher, John	Gardener and seedsman	52, Willow row	B
Fletcher, John M.	Tailor and draper	Victoria street	
Fletcher, Joseph	J. tailor	Albion place	
Fletcher, Brothers	Sole inventors and manufacturers of paper ribbon blocks, hosier's boxes made to order	Goodwin street	
Flewker, John	Solicitor	16, Wardwick	F,B
Flewker, Mrs.		Burton road	
Fley, Richard	Tobacconist, & dealer in snuff and cigars	13, Rotten row	B
Flint, John	Gentleman	Osmaston road	F,B
Flitcroft, Richard	Silk weaver	Grove street	
Flour company		St. Michael's lane	
Flower, Henry	Chemist and druggist	43, Queen street	F,B
Flude, Thomas	Vict., Anchor Inn	St. Peter's street	B
Fogg, John	Tailor	27, Bold lane	B
Footit, Richard	Joiner & cabinet maker	London road	B
Ford, William	J. shoemaker	Eagle street	
Ford, John	Painter	20, Devonshire st.	Fr
Ford, Robert	J. stonemason	Burton road	
Ford, George	J. bricklayer	Talbot street	
Ford, John	Shoemaker	Kensington street	
Ford, Benjamin	Labourer	Agard street	
Ford, John	Tailor	23, Friar gate	Fr
Ford, Thomas	Chair and basket maker	2, King street	F,B
Ford, Thomas	Shoemaker	21, Green street	Fr
Ford, Thomas	Shoemaker	Bloom street	Fr
Ford, George	Wheelwright	Nottingham road	B
Ford, James	Vict., brickmaker's arms, and brickmaker	Ashbourn road	F,Fr

Ford, James	Maltster	Agard street	B
Ford, Rev. J.	Minister, Particular Baptist ch.	Agard street	
Ford, George	Brush manufacturer	Victoria street	B
Ford, Sarah	Dressmaker	Chapel street	
Ford, Joshua	Shoemaker	Kensington	Fr
Ford, Joseph	Coal dealer	Short street	
Forman, Robert	Gentleman	13, Wardwick	F,B
Forman, Elijah	Plumber and glazier	Wardwick	F,B
Forman, Robert, sen.	Hop and seed merchant	Corn market	F,B
Forman, Robert, jun.	Maltster	Curzon street	
Forester, Richard Forester, esq.	M.D., F.L.S., J.P., and alderman	Abbott's Hill	F,Fr
Foss, William	Shoemaker	Darley Abbey	
Foster, Thomas	Vict., Marquis of Anglesey	10, Cheapside	B
Foster, John	J. bricklayer	Litchurch street	
Foster, William	Gardener and seedsman	26, St. Peter's st.	B
Foster, William	Gardener and seedsman	50, Sadler gate	B
Foster, Edward	Painter	5, St. John's terrace	B
Foster, Michael	Labourer	Litchurch street	
Fotherby, Joseph	J. corn miller	Duke street	
Foulds, Samuel	Framework knitter	4, Brook walk	
Fowell, George	J. ribbon weaver	Normanton road	
Fowler, J. Coke, esq.		Temple, London	F
Fox and Rudkin	Surgeons	Ford street	
Fox, Samuel, sen.	Esquire		F,Fr
Fox, Mrs.		Wardwick	
Fox, Joseph	Labourer	Burton road	
Fox, James	Engineer	City road	F,B
Fox, Henry Wm.	Solicitor	8, Grove street	
Fox, James and Joseph	Engineers, and manufacturers of lathes	City road	B
Fox, Charles	Engineer	Mansfield road	
Fox, John	Labourer	Upper Brook street	
Fox, Mrs. Sophia	Dealer in perfumery	Osmaston road	
Fox, Joseph	Engineer	Nottingham road	B
Fox, Samuel	Labourer	Green lane	
Fox, William	Milk seller	Mundy street	
Fox, Edward	Gentleman	21, Green lane	F,B
Fox, Samuel, jun. esq.	Justice of Peace, silk & cotton hosiery warehou. Wardwick	14, North parade	F,Fr
Fox, Benjamin	J. weaver	Brook street	
Fox, Rev. Samuel	Vicar of Horsley, and curate of Morley	Morley Rectory	F
Fox, Wm. Darwin R.	esquire	Delamare, Cheshire	F
Fox, Francis, esq.	M.D. Physician	Wardwick	Fr
Fox, Douglas, esq.	Justice of Peace, member of council for Castle ward, alder.	Wardwick	F,Fr
Fox, Archibald	Engineer	Wardwick	Fr
Freake, J. F.	Auctioneer and appraiser	Market place	
Freckleton, John	J. smith	Ct. 1, Willow row	
Freckleton, John	Whitesmith	45, Bridge street	
Freckleton, John	Baker, flour dealer, & shopkr.	London road	

Frear, Benjamin, esq.	Solicitor, steward of the Duffield Rectory court, and Sawley Provincial court, and clerk to the court of Requests for the borough of Derby, and to the Nutbrook Canal company	22, Friar gate	F,B
Freeman, William	Carpenter and joiner	Brook street	F
French, Miss		Ashbourn road	
Fritche, Geo, jun.	Organist at All Saints' church, music master, and professor of dancing	Rose Hill cottage	B
Fritche, Geo. sen.	Gentleman	Victoria street	Fr
Fritche, Froude	Professor of dancing, and organist at St. Alkmund's ch.	8, North parade	B
Frost, Charlotte	Milliner and dressmaker	Traffic street	
Frost, Mrs.		Osmaston road	
Frost and Stevenson	Silk double, galloon, and silk manufacturers	Chester road	
Frost, Joseph	Framework knitter	Ct. 7, Bold lane	
Frost, Ralph	Silk ferret manufacturer	Duffield road	F,B
Frost, John	Framework knitter	Brook walk	
Frost, John	Beer seller	Ashbourn road	B
Frost, William	Millwright & machine maker	City road	B
Frost, William	Vict., Greyhound	Friar gate	B
Fryer, William	Straw bonnet manufacturer	6, Friar gate	B
Fuller, Mrs. Maria		Wilmot street	
Fulton, Andrew	Gentleman	Sacheverel street	B
Furniss, Alfred W.	Tea dealer, grocer, and provision warehouse	London street	B
Furniss, William	Grocer and tea dealer	27, Bridge street	B
Furniss, William	J. coach builder	Sitwell street	
Gadsby, Peter	Shoemaker	Grove street	F
Gadsby, John	Solicitor	Office, Victoria st.	
Gadsby, Thomas	Carpenter and builder	21, Wardwick	F,B
Gadsby, William	Grocer and tea dealer	42, St. Peter's st.	F,B
Gadsby, Enoch	Boot and shoe warehouse	22, Wardwick	B
Gadsby, John	Gentleman	Large's street	F,B
Gallimore, Richard	Police officer	No. 5, Castle street	
Gallimore, John W.	Resident dispenser at charitable and parochial Dispensary	Bridge gate	
Gamble, Stephen&Co. lateGamble&Bridgen	General furniture warehouse and upholsterers	15, Iron gate	
Gamble and Cubley	House & ornamental painters	Queen street	B
Gamble, Stephen, esq.	Alderman, and Mayor of the borough, 1841-2.	Duffield road	F,B
Gamble, Joseph	General carrier by boat and wagon to all parts of the north and west	St. Peter's street	
Gamble, John, sen.	Gentleman	4, Full street	F,Fr
Gamble, William	Joiner	79, Friar gate	F,B

Gamble, William	Shoemaker	9, River street	
Gamble, Thomas	Upholsterer	Queen street	Fr
Gamble, John, jun.	Painter	North parade	B,Fr
Gardiner, William	Gentleman, cheese agent	London road	
Garforth, John	Wood engraver	Fox's Cottage, New Uttoxeter road	
Garforth, Alfred	Compositor	15, Kensington street	
Garratt, John	J. joiner	4, Chester place	
Garratt, William	Framework knitter	78, Bridge street	
Garratt, William	Gentleman's servant	Osmaston street	B
Garner, Robert	Saddler & harness maker	7, Victoria street	B
Garner, Mrs.		Sacheverel street	
Garner, William	Framework knitter	Brook street	
Garner, William	Book-keeper	Ashbourn road	
Garrick, Thomas	Livery stable keeper and silk dyer	Victoria street	
Garton, Stephen	Milk seller	Burton road	B
Garton, Thomas	Milk seller	37, Burton road	
Gascoyne, Mrs.	School mistress	Eagle street	
Gascoyne, Jos.& Son	Builders	St. Peter's street	F,B
Gascoyne, Joseph	Builder	St. Peter's street	F,B
Gascoyne, George	Builder	Osmaston street	F,B
Gaskell, James	Lead works	Grove street	
Gaskill, Samuel	Gentleman	Etwall	F
Gaunt, Mary	Straw bonnet maker	St. Peter's street	
Gaunt, Joseph	Gardener and seedsman	St. Peter's street	B
Gaunt, Francis	Labourer	High street	
Gaunt, Joseph	Gardener	16, Bridge street	
Gawthorne, Wm. R.	Commercial boarding house	St. Mary's gate	B
Gawthorne, Rev. James	Minister of Congregational chapel	Becket-well lane	B
Gee, Henry	Gentleman	Old Uttox. road	B
Gee, William	Police Officer, No. 4	Upper Brook street	
Gee, Thomas	Framework knitter	31, Burton road	B
Gee, Thomas	Shoemaker	Union buildings	
Genn, William	Jeweller	Sacheverel street	
George, John	Wholesale draper	St. Peter's street	B
German & Holmes	Linen and woollen drapers, silk mercers, & haberdashers	Corn market	B
German, George	Draper	Corn market	F,B
Gell, Thos. esq.		Friar gate	B
Gell, James	J. weaver	Hill street	
Gell, Rev. Philip	M.A., minister of St.John's ch.	Friar gate	F,B
Gibson, Wm.	Locomotive department	Wilmot street	
Gibson, William	Farmer	Spa	Fr
Gibson, John	Framework knitter	Bloom street	
Gibson, John	Blacksmith	Parker street	
Gibson, Henry	Whitesmith	Parker street	
Gibson, Miss	Judge's lodgings	St. Mary's gate	
Gibson, Thomas		London	F
Gibson, Richard	Silk stocking manufacturer	Exeter street	
Gibson, William	Nail maker and shopkeeper	26, Bridge street	B

Gibson, William	Gentleman	Exeter place	F
Gilbert, Elizabeth	Straw hat maker	Traffic street	
Gilbert, Thomas	Labourer	Bag lane	
Gilbert, S. R.	Gentleman	Matlock	F
Gilbert, John	Sawyer	Bloom street	
Gilbert, Josiah	Butcher	Old shambles	B
Gilbert, George	Collar and harness maker	42, Bridge gate	B
Gilbert, Richard	Shoemaker	Bag lane	
Gilbert, William	Twist hand	Sitwell street	
Gilbert, Francis	Warehouseman	Unsworth's mill	
Gillam, William	Boot maker	24, Iron gate	F,B
Gilroy, Matthew	Newton moor, near Alnwick, Northumberland		F
Gisborne, Rev. T.		Yoxall Lodge	F
Gisborne, Hen. F.	Surgeon	15, Tenant street	B
Gisborne, John, esq.			F
Glazebrook, Paul	Cabinet maker, appraiser, and general furniture dealer	30, Eagle street	B
Gleadah, Thos. O.	Managing clerk to Wm. Eaton Mouseley, esq.	Ashbourn road	
Glue, Henry	Butcher	Hope street	B
Glew, Isaac	Bricklayer		
Glue, Joseph	Vict., Talbot Commercial Inn, and Nottingham house	Iron gate	F
Glover, Stephen	Auctioneer, valuer, house, land, commission, & general agent, accountant, and collector of debts—Publisher of the History of Derbyshire, &c.	Derby	B
Glover, Joseph	Framework knitter	Bridge gate	F
Glover, Thomas	Managing clerk for Derwent foundry company	Eagle street	B
Glover, William	Whitesmith	Bradshaw street	
Glover, Thomas	Brush manufacturer	London road	F,B
Glover, George	Clerk at Evans's bank	Wilmot street	B
Godwin, Rich. Bennett, esq.			F,B
Godwin, Geo. Wm.	Gentleman	Australia	F
Godwin, Thomas	Shoemaker	10, King street	B
Gold, Benjamin	Pensioner	Grove street	
Goodale, John	Solicitor	Corn market	B
Goodale, Wm.&John	Tanners	Friar gate	B
Goodale, John	Tanner	Friar gate	B
Goodall, Henry	Chemist and druggist	Victoria street	B
Goodall, George	Painter	20, River street	
Goodson, John	Shopkeeper	Walker lane	
Goodwin, Th. & Fr.	Cheese factors	Cockpit hill	F,B
Goodwin, Thomas	Cheese factor and agent	Devonshire st.	F,B
Goodwin, Francis	Cheese factor and agent	Cockpit hill	F,B
Goodwin, Thomas	Farmer	Brailsford	F
Goodwin, Thomas	Shoemaker	Bloom street	
Goodwin, William	Shopkeeper	38, Friar gate	B

D

Goodwin, William	Broker and general salesman	Piazza, mrkt. place, & Burton road F,B
Goodwin, Hannah	Lodging house	Bloom street
Gordon, Eliz. & G.	Dealer in rags and hardware	23, Walker lane B
Gorse, Joseph	Wood turner	Ashbourn road
Gough, John	Coal higgler	Cockpit hill B
Gould, Thomas	J. carpenter	Litchurch street
Gould, Thomas	Farmer	Ashbourn road B
Goulding, Thomas	Hairdresser & dealer in toys	14, Bridge gate F,B
Gover, William	Professor of music and pianoforte tuner, vict., Apollo tavern	8, Ford street
Gover, Edward Wm.	Professor of music, and organist at St. Werburgh's church	32, Friar gate
Gover, Wm. Edward	Professor of music & dancing	King street
Grace, Robert	Surveyor of buildings	Sitwell street
Grafton, John	Porter at Station	Ct. 4, Bridge gate B
Graham, Robt. Ch.	Book-keeper at Station	Union Buildings
Graham, John	Agent to Mr. Hunt, brewer	Erasmus street
Gratian, Joseph		Belper F
Gray, George	Shoemaker	Bridge street Fr
Gray, Walter, jun.	Shoemaker	Agard street Fr
Gray, Walter, sen.	Shoemaker	Agard street Fr
Gray, John	Shoemaker	26, Goodwin st. F,Fr
Gray, Thomas	Shoemaker	Agard street Fr
Gray, James	Shoemaker and beerseller	Walker lane B
Greatorex, Francis	Farmer	Litchurch street
Greatorex, William	Labourer	Liversage street
Greatorex, William	Butcher	Osmaston road F,B
Greatorex, Jeremiah	Grocer and tea dealer	46, St. Peter's st. B
Greatorex, Joseph	Butcher	21, Friar gate B
Greatorex, Joseph	Cow keeper and joiner	South street
Greatorex, William	Cow keeper and higgler	Spa
Greatorex, Edward	Butcher, Iron gate	Agard street B
Greatorex, Luke	Beer seller, White Hart	John street B
Greatorex, William	J. jeweller	Litchurch street
Greatorex, William	J. weaver	South street
Greaves, Augu. Gor.	Surgeon	Friar gate B
Greaves, John	Works at factory	Siddals lane B
Greaves, John	Butcher	Goodwin street
Greaves, William	Gardener	Castle street
Greaseley, Charlotte	Schoolmistress	Exeter street
Green, Thomas	Bricklayer	Devonshire st. Fr
Green, William	J. engineer	Chester road B
Green, Thomas	Vict., Queen's Head	Victoria street B
Green, Miss	Dress and straw hat maker	1, George street
Green, Joseph	Hair dresser	Queen street Fr
Green, Thomas	Spar manufacturer	Upper Brook st. Fr
Green, William	J. tailor	Bridge street
Green, Edward	Spar manufacturer	Upper Brook st. F,Fr
Green, James	J. brewer	33, Burton road

Green, John	Solicitor	York street	
Green, John	Hair dresser	Mundy street	Fr
Green, William	J. engineer	9, Exeter street	
Green, Bernard	Spar manufacturer	Nun's street	F,B
Green, Lawrence	Linen draper	City road	F
Green, Benjamin	J. joiner	Lodge lane	
Green James	Watch manufacturer	Liversage street	
Green, William	Spar manufacturer	Parker street	Fr
Greeves, Rev. J.	Minister, Wesleyan chapel,	King street	
Gregg, William	Framesmith	Ct. 1, Sadler gate br.	
Gregory, John, jun.	Vict., Milton's Head	Osmaston road	F,B
Gregory, Frances	Milliner and dressmaker	17, Victoria street	
Gregory, William	Stay, glove, foreign lace, baby linen, and Scotch embroidered muslin warehou.	17, Victoria street	B
Gregory, Thomas	Beer seller, Acorn, & maltster	36, Queen street	F,B
Gregory, James	Vict., Wheat Sheaf	30, Walker lane	B
Gregory, John	Agent to James Sutton and Co's. wharfs, Cockpit hill, Old wharf	Hill street	F,B
Gregory, Robert	J. blacksmith	Eagle street	
Gregory, Peter	Warehouse man	Cockpit hill	
Gregson, George	Works at tape factory	Cannon street	
Gretton, John	Butcher	Osmaston street	
Grey, John	Rag dealer	Walker lane	B
Gribble, Mrs.	Lodging house	Osmaston street	
Griffin, James	J. blacksmith	Castle street	
Griffin, John	Agent to James Sutton & Co.	8, Bridge gate	
Griffiths, Edward	Stoker	Park street	B
Griffiths, T.	Shoemaker	41, Willow row	
Grime, Thomas	Gent., agent to Sir George Crewe, bart.	Osmaston road	B
Grimshaw, John	J. carver and gilder	Normanton road	
Grosvenor, Gilbert	Managing clerk to J.Barber,esq.	Sitwell street	
Growcock, William	Silk weaver	Albion street	
Grundy, Rev. G.	Minister, Methodist New Connexion	London road	
Gunn, Thomas	Plumber and glazier	35, Devonshire st.	Fr
Gutteridge, Thomas	Butcher	Park street	B
Guylee, Joseph	Woollen draper and tailor	46, Full street	B
Hackett, John	Smallware&tape manufacturer	Talbot street	F,B
Hackett, John & Son	Smallware and tape manufacturers	27, Talbot st., Wirksworth & Tansley	B
Hackett, Thomas	Linen and woollen draper, mercer, hosier, and haberdasher	20, Market place	F,B
Hackney, Joseph	Earthenware dealer	Albion street	
Haden,Rich.Wr.,esq.	Magistrate	St. Mich. ch. yard	F
Hadfield, Mary	Beer seller	21, Willow row	
Hadfield, Francis	J. cabinet maker	Osmaston road	
Hadfield, Mary	Schoolmistress	Albion street	
Hadfield, William	Labourer	Litchurch street	

Hadfield, George	Higgler	Becket well lane	B
Hadfield, Mrs. S.		Ashbourn road	
Halbard, John	Gunsmith and bell hanger	Sitwell street	
Hagen, Benjamin	Ale and porter brewer	15, South street	B
Hage, Mary	Shopkeeper	Traffick street	
Hague, Edward	Schoolmaster and surveyor	South street	
Hales, Richard	Weaver	High street	F
Hall, Frederic		Swanwick	F
Hall, John	J. joiner	Albion place	
Hall, Richard	Framework knitter	Ct. 3, Bridge street	
Hall, Richard		Manchester	F
Hall, John	Framework knitter	Ct. 3, Bridge street	
Hall, William	Needle maker	Parker street	
Hall, John	68, South Audley	street, London	F
Hall, Mrs. Esther		North parade	
Hall, William	J. watchmaker	Traffick street	B
Hall, William	Broker	Willow row	
Hall, Richard		Derby	Fr
Hall, Joseph	Hot, cold, shower, and vapour baths ; sculptor, and manu- facturer of spar ornaments	King street	F,B
Hall and Goodwin	Pawnbrokers and general salesmen	Piazza, mrkt. pl.	F,B
Hall, John	Gardener	Burton road	F
Hall, William	Pawnbroker	Green lane hill	B
Hall, William	Framework knitter	Markeaton lane	
Hall, Samuel	J. coach spring maker	Bridge street	F
Hall, Lorenzo Kirk- patrick, esq.	Justice of Peace	Milford	F
Hall, Henry	J. clockmaker	Siddals lane	F
Hall, Thomas	J. shoemaker	Bloom street	
Hall, Elizabeth	Milliner and straw hat maker	15, Bridge street	
Hallam, George	Wine merchant	Iron gate	B
Hallam	Silk weaver	South street	
Hallam, Michael	Agent to District Society for promoting Christian know- ledge	17, Sadler gate	F,B
Hallam, John	Broker	39, Walker lane	
Hallam, George	Hawker	Sadler gate	
Hallam, Richard	J. colourman	Bag lane	
Halton, Thomas	Brass founder	Parker street	
Ham, John	Shoemaker	Green street	
Hampton, Joseph	J. weaver	Brook street	
Hancock, John	China painter	Exeter street	
Hancocck, Sampson	China painter	Liversage street	
Hancock, S. W.	Manufacturer of hosiery	St. Alkmund's ch. yd	
Hand, Richard	Cooper	Talbot street	
Hand, Joseph	Beer seller, Speed the Plough	Nottingham road	B
Hand, William	Joiner	St. Mary's square	
Handford, Joseph	Gentleman	Osmaston street	F,B
Hannible, John	Grocer	Liversage street	
Hanson, William, esq.	Superintendent of coaching department at Station		

Hanson, Joseph	Milk seller	28, Sadler gate	B
Hanson, Thomas	Baker and flour dealer	39, Sadler gate	B
Hanson, William	Gentleman's servant	36, Full street	B
Harcourt, Joseph	Lint maker	Price's ct., St. Ma. gat.	
Harding, Thomas	Shoemaker	Friar gate	F
Hare, John	Temperance coffee house	Bag lane	
Hardy, Thomas	China painter	Hill street	
Hardy, James	Baker	St. Peter's ch. yard	
Hardy, Thomas	Labourer	Spring gardens	
Hardy, Richard	J. joiner	Erasmus street	
Hardy, Thomas	Shoemaker	45, Brook street	
Hardy, Michael	Works at flour mill	1, River street	
Hardwick, Francis	Framework knitter	32, Burton road	B
Harley, William	Blacksmith	Sacheverel street	
Harlow, John	Labourer	25, Green lane	
Harlow, Mary	Milliner and dressmaker	Green lane	
Harlow, Charles, sen.	Bricklayer	Mundy street	
Harlow, John	Bricklayer	Brook street	
Harlow, John	Shoemaker	Leaper street	
Harlow, James	Porter at Station	Sitwell street	
Harlow, Charles	Bricklayer	Brook street	
Harpur, John	Brickmaker	Talbot street	F,B
Harpur, Joseph	Brickmaker	Uttoxeter road	F,B
Harper, William	Shopkeeper	Parker street	F,B
Harper, Thomas	Sawyer	32, Parker street	
Harper, William	J. weaver	Upper Brook street	
Harper, William	Traveller	Parker street	B
Harris, William	Tailor	Chester road	Fr
Harris, Benjamin	J. joiner	Litchurch street	
Harris, Joseph	Tailor	Friar gate	
Harris, George	J. weaver	Hill street	
Harris, James	Framework knitter	Uttoxeter road	
Harris, John	Framework knitter	Duke street	
Harris, William	Works at china factory	Parker street	
Harris, Thomas	Lapidary	Grove street	
Harrison, Thomas	Baker	York street	F,B
Harrison, Mary	Shopkeeper	1, Agard street	
Harrison, Mrs. Wm.		St. Mary's gate	F
Harrison, James	Beer seller	Duke street	B
Harrison, James	Hostler	Ct. 4, Full street	
Harrison, David	Vict., Old Crown	No. 20, Morledge	B
Harrison, John	Corn factor & flour dealer	17, Morledge	B
Harrison, John	Shoemaker	17, Morledge	B
Harrison, John	Joiner	Lodge lane	B
Harrison, Mrs.		Friar gate	F
Harrison, Charles	Shoemaker	Kensington	
Harrison, Hannah	Milliner and dress maker	St. Peter's street	
Harrison, John	Sexton at All Saints' church	8, Full street	
Harrison, Joseph	Draper	Grove street	
Harrison, William	Vict., George and Dragon	50, Walker lane	B
Harrison, John	J. cabinet maker	Agard street	
Harrison, Joseph	Wood turner	27, Nun's street	

Harrison, Hannah	Shopkeeper	Burton road
Harrison, Samuel	Tea dealer	Sacheverel st. F,Fr
Harrison, William	J. watchmaker	Hope street F
Harrison, Miss	Dress maker	38, St. Mary's gate
Harrison, John	Hosier	8, Cherry street B
Harrison, Thomas	Labourer	9, Britannia street
Harrison, William	Gentleman	Sitwell street F
Harrison, Robt. Thos.	Shoe warehouse	Victoria street B
Harrison, Miss		Osmaston terrace
Harrison, William	Grocer and draper	Swarkestone Fr
Harrison, John	Engineer, manufacturer of steam engine boilers, iron boats, barges, and ferries, gas tanks and gas holders, steam and kitchen apparatus, all kinds of buildings warmed by hot water, steam, or hot air, and smith's work in general	46 & 47, Bridge gate, and 1½, Mansfield road Fr, F, B
Hart, Edward	Chemist and druggist	7, Sadler gate B
Hart, Mary	Lodging house	London road
Hart, James	Shopkeeper	Castle street
Hart, William	Gentleman	St. John's terrace B
Hartley, Mrs.	Lodging house	King street B
Harwood, Thomas	Surgeon	St. Peter's street F,B
Harvey, William	Framework knitter	Ct. 3, Queen street
Harvey, Thomas	Gentleman	Parker street F
Harvey, William	Gentleman	10, Parker street F,B
Harvey, George	Framework knitter	St. Michael's lane
Harvey, Samuel	Joiner, and clerk at St. Werburgh's church	10, George street B
Harvey, Francis	Works at lead mill	Bag lane
Hasard, Joseph	Farmer	Melbourn F
Haslam, George	Works at china factory	Sadler gate Fr
Haslam, Eleanora	Ladies' boarding & day school	North parade
Haslam, W. Canaway	Gentleman	5, North parade
Haslam, Henry	Huckster	Bag lane
Haslam, William	Milk seller	Willow row F
Haslam, John	Cow keeper	36, Willow row F, B
Haslam, Francis	Lace manufacturer, hosier, and haberdasher	Cheapside B
Haslam, William	Whitesmith, bell hanger, and brass founder	St. Helen's street B
Haslam, John	Gentleman	Leonard street F,Fr
Haslam, William	Farmer	Little Chester Fr
Haslam, Benjamin	Plumber and glazier	Queen street
Hastie, William	Compositor	York street
Hatch, Samuel	Cheese and bacon dealer	Victoria street B
Hatfield, Samuel	Book-keeper and cashier	Unsworth's mill
Hatter, Mary	Milliner and dressmaker	Tenant street
Haughton, William	Traveller	Exeter street

Hawgood, Henry	Dealer in smallware, toys, japan goods, hardware, and rag merchant	Cheapside	B
Hawkes, Thomas	Framework knitter	Spring gardens	
Hawkridge, John	Shoemaker	31, Waterloo street	Fr
Hawkridge & Sons	Tailors and woollen drapers	St. Mary's gate	
Hawkridge, T., sen.	Tailor and woollen draper	St. Mary's gate	B,Fr
Hawkridge, Henry	Tailor	Bridge street	Fr
Hawkridge, Samuel		Derby	Fr
Hawkridge, T., jun.	Tailor	St. Mary's gate	Fr
Hawksworth, Sam.	J. tailor	Brook street	
Hawksworth, Matt.	Cook	Fingal street	
Hawksworth, John	J. jeweller	Grove street	
Hawley, William	Needle maker	Parker street	Fr
Hawley, Joseph	Labourer	Canal street	
Hawley, Anthony	Blacksmith	Bloom street	Fr
Haworth, John	Fitter-up at foundry	Devonshire street	
Haynes, Richard	Milk seller	18, Bridge street	B
Haynes, Thomas	Milk seller	23, Brook street	
Haynes, William	Butcher and beer seller, Dog and Pheasant	Normanton road	B
Haynes, Thomas	Vict., White Swan	St. Peter's street	F,B
Haynes, Richard	Framework knitter	Nun's green	Fr
Haynes, Charles	Whitesmith	Cheapside	Fr
Haynes, Henry	Baker	Queen street	
Haynes, Henry	Vict., Peacock	Nottingham road	B
Haynes, Joseph	Framework knitter	Brook walk	Fr
Haynes, John	Whitesmith	St. Werb. ch. yd.	Fr
Haynes, Joseph	Labourer	Bag lane	
Haynes, Thomas	Butcher	Green street	
Haynes, William	Butcher	Bag lane	
Haynes, George	Butcher	Parker street	
Haynes, John	Milk seller	Mundy street	F
Haywood, Joseph	J. silk weaver	Short street	
Haywood, John	J. broad silk weaver	Lodge lane	
Haywood, Thomas	J. plumber and gas fitter	Friar gate	Fr
Haywood, James	Ironmonger, Phœnix brass and iron foundry	10, Market place and Exeter street	F,Fr
Haywood, George	Brass and iron founder	Willow row	B
Hays, Richard	Framework knitter	High street	
Hazledine, Thomas	Shopkeeper	Leonard street	
Hazledine, William	Gardener	29, Willow row	F,B
Hazledine, William	Clerk of the market	Upper brook street	
Headley, George	Framework knitter	Walker lane	
Heald, John George	Solicitor's clerk	Sacheverel street	F
Heason, Richard	Gentleman's servant	Normanton road	
Heathcote, Mary		Normanton road	
Heathcote, Thomas	Shoemaker	Hill street	
Heathcoat, Thomas	Draper	36, Brook street	B
Heathcoat, John	Shopkeeper	William street	B
Heathcote, Joseph		Breadsall	F

Heath, Nicholas	Cheesefactor	Osmaston street	B
Heath, Thomas	J. bricklayer	High street	
Heath, John	Bookbinder	Drewry lane	
Heath, George	J. bricklayer	Cannon street	
Heath, Thomas		Needwood Forest	F
Hefford, John	Shoe warehouse	Queen street	
Hegg, Thomas	J. tobacco cutter	Sitwell street	
Hellaby, Edward	Linen and woollen draper	Corn market	B
Hellaby, William	Clock maker	Brook street	
Hemingway, Benj.	House painter	18, Full street	F,B
Hemingway, George	Shoemaker	Erasmus street	
Hemsley, Etham	J. weaver	Grove street	
Heming, John	Shoemaker	32, Agard street	B
Henley, John	Marble mason	Parker street	
Henchley, Samuel	Dyer	2, Derwent street	F,B
Henchley, Thomas	Farmer	Nottingham road	B
Henchliffe, Luke	Framework knitter	William street	Fr
Henchliffe, William	Tailor	Leonard street	
Henshaw, Henry	Cornfactor	Bridge gate	B
Heskett, Thomas	Shoemaker	27, Bag lane	B
Hesketh, William	Labourer	23, City road	
Hewett, Benjamin	Hawker	Sacheverel street	
Hewitt, John	J. joiner	Sitwell street	
Hewitt, Joseph	Joiner and wheelwright	Normanton road	F,B
Hewitt, James	Farmer and beer seller	10, Nun's street	F,B
Hewitt, Thomas	Beer seller	Willow row	B
Hewitt, Benjamin	Gentleman	30, St. Helen's st.	F,B
Hewitt, James	Farmer	10, Ashbourn road	B
Hewitt, Geo. Alex.	Chemist and druggist	Iron gate	
Heygate, James	Physician, the College	Full street	B
Hibbert, Eliz.& Mary	Straw bonnet manufacturers	Sitwell street	
Hibbert, James	J. painter	Sitwell street	Fr
Hicken, John	J. watchmaker	15, Orchard street	
Hicken, Thomas	Superintendent at Station	Friar gate	
Hickham, Thomas	Gardener	Siddals lane	B
Hickinbottom, John	Watchman	Bloom street	
Hicklin, Alfred	Framework knitter	Brook street	B
Hickson, Thomas	Coal merchant	7, Exeter place	B
Hickton, Samuel	J. engineer	Bradshaw street	
Hies, Thomas	Framework knitter	Grove street	
Highton, Isaac	Farmer	Dunkirk	Fr
Highton, William	Farmer	Dunkirk	Fr
Hill, James	Policeman at Station	Park street	B
Hill, George	Labourer	Bloom street	
Hill, John	Shopkeeper	Morledge	B
Hill, Thomas	Broker	18, Willow row	B
Hill, Isaac	Labourer	Ct. 4, Morledge	
Hill, John	Vict., Brick and Tile	1, Brick street	F,B
Hill, John	Surgeon	20,St.Alk.ch.yd.	F,Fr
Hill, Daniel	Labourer	Albion place	
Hill, George	Painter	St. Peter's ch. yd.	B
Hill, James	China painter	26, Parker street	Fr

Hill, Thomas	Grocer and flour dealer	High street	
Hill, Thomas	Hostler at Fox and Owl	41, Bridge gate	B
Hill, Joseph	Moulder	City road	
Hill, William	J. tape weaver	High street	
Hill, Isaac	Cupola tenter	13, City road	
Hill, Robert	Train time keeper	Hope street	
Hill, William	Milk seller	Castle street	
Hill, William	China painter	19, Bath street	
Hill, William	Works at china factory	Parker street	
Hill, Samuel		Houndsgate, Nottingham	F
Hill, John, jun.	Cooper	Brick street	F
Hill, Joseph	Grocer and baker	Park street	B
Hillsley, William	Sawyer	Bag lane	
Hilton, Joseph	Gentleman's servant	Etwall	F
Hind, Thomas	Gentleman	Burton-on-Trent	F
Hind, Joseph	Tailor	Eagle street	B
Hind, Robert	Horse dealer	Traffick street	B
Hinkley, E.	Milliner and dressmaker	Full street	
Hinkley, Rupert		Upper Thurvaston	F
Hipworth, Robert	Draper	Wilmot street	B
Hirst, John	Framesmith	Devonshire street	F
Hirst, William	Moulder	7, Mansfield road	Fr
Hirst, William	Jeweller		
Hitchcock, Richard	Gentleman	Bold lane	F
Hobday, Solomon	Porter at Station	Canal street	
Hobson, Edmund	Clerk at Kenworthy & Co's.	Nottingham road	B
Hobson, William	Bookseller, printer, book-binder, and circulating library	Iron gate	B
Hobson, James	Cabinet maker	19, South street	B
Hobson, George	J. cabinet maker	South street	
Hodges, Wm. Henry	Clerk to the New market, high constable, and billet master	New market	F
Hodgkinson, George	Plumber, glazier, and beer seller, Elephant and Castle	Bold lane	B
Hodgkinson, John	Butcher	St. Peter's street	B
Hodgkinson, F.& Co.	Linen and woollen drapers	1, Iron gate	B
Hodgkinson, Henry Vicars	Grocer & provision warehouse	Brook street	F
Hodgkinson, Thos.	Shopkeeper	Nottingham road	
Hodgkinson, George	Wheelwright	Friar gate	B
Hodgkinson, Joseph	Cornfactor	Brook street	
Hodgkinson, Charles	Wheelwright	78, Friar gate	
Hodgkinson, Thos.	Grocer and tea dealer	42, Queen street	F, B
Hodgkinson, Thos.	J. maltster	Nottingham road	
Hodgkinson, John		Findern	F
Hodgkinson, Rich. E.	Baker and flour dealer	2, Lodge lane	B
Hodgkinson, John	Works at factory	Litchurch street	
Hodgson, William	Gentleman	Normanton terrace	B
Hodson, William	Sheriff's bailiff	St. Mary's gate	F, B
Hogg, John	Tailor	Bag lane	

Holbrook, Edward	Grocer	Green lane	Fr
Holbrook, Chas., esq.	White lead and paint manufacturer, works St. Peter's street	Boulton	B
Holbrook, Joseph	Framework knitter	Bridge street	B
Holehouse, Benjamin	Labourer	Willow row	Fr
Hoggatt, William	Shopkeeper	Sitwell street	B
Holland, Joseph	Gardener	31, Grove street	B
Holland, George	Joiner	Devonshire street	
Holland, John	Gardener	23, Green lane	F,B
Holland, Frederick	Framework knitter	Bridge street	
Hollester, Isaac	Labourer	15, Erasmus street	
Hollingshead, Edmd.	Confectioner and biscuit baker	20, Iron gate	F,B
Holder, John, esq.		Ashbourn road	
Holloway, Thomas	Butcher	Victoria street	F,B
Holloway, Gilbert		Tamworth	F
Hollingworth, James	Chemist and druggist	St. Peter's street and Queen street	F,B
Hollingworth, F. S.	Woollen draper and tailor	St. Peter's street	B
Hollins, Sarah	Brass founder	Cavendish street	
Hollins, John	Brass founder	London road	B
Hollis, Robert	Warehouseman	Thorn tree lane	B
Hollis, William	Vict., Coach and Horses	St. James's lane	B
Holme and Smithard	Jewellers and watch manufacturers	Corn market	B
Holme, George	Boot and shoe warehouse	Market head	B
Holmes, Herbert and Alfred	Coach builders and harness manufacturers by appointment to her Majesty Queen Adelaide and his Royal Highness Prince Albert	London road	F,B
Holmes, George	Cutler and ironmonger	1, Rotten row	F,B
Holmes, Henry	Cutler and ironmonger	1, Rotten row	F,B
Holmes, William	Cutler, ironmonger, and brickmaker	Uttoxeter road and Rotten row	F,B
Holmes, John	Brickmaker	Uttoxeter road	F,B
Holmes, Samuel		Duffield	Fr
Holmes, John	Book-keeper	Wilmot street	
Holmes, Henrietta	Beer seller	24, Eagle street	
Holmes, Thomas	Shoemaker	Orchard street	
Holmes, Godfrey, sen.	Wharfinger agent to Wheatcroft's	Eagle street	Fr
Holmes, Godfrey, jun.	Warehouseman and grocer	Eagle street	Fr
Holmes, Sarah	Schoolmistress	River street	
Holmes, James	Bobbin manufacturer	Leonard street	
Holmes, William	Baker and flour dealer	Osmaston street	B
Holmes, Joseph	Shopkeeper	Grove street	Fr
Holmes, Thomas	Stonemason	Eagle street	Fr
Holmes, Jonathan	Haberdasher	100, Friar gate	B
Holmes, Thomas	Vict., Vine Inn	Ford street	B
Holmes, William	Plumber and glazier	Ct. 3, Sadler gate	Fr
Holmes, James	Horse breaker	Canal street	

Holmes, Edward	Shopkeeper	Walker lane	Fr
Holmes, Matthew	Framework knitter	Duke street	
Hood, George	Plumber and glazier, agent to the County Fire and Life Insurance Office	George street	F, Fr
Hood, Samuel	Book-keeper	York street	
Hoon, Isaac	Shoemaker	Bloom street	
Hoose, John	Coal dealer	Ford street	F
Hooton, William		Little Chester	F
Hope, Rev. R. Mellor	Curate of Little Eaton	Duffield	Fr
Hope, Miss		North parade	
Hope, Rev. C. Robert			F, Fr
Hope, William	Vict., Golden Lion	Bridge gate	B
Hope, Robert John	Gentleman	London road	Fr
Hopkin, Thomas	Works at china factory	Bridge gate	Fr
Hopkin, George	Framework knitter	Darley lane	Fr
Hopkins, Thomas	Framesmith	Bridge gate	
Hopkinson, John	J. maltster	Siddals lane	B
Hopkinson, Eliz.	Schoolmistress	Erasmus street	
Hopkinson, Edward	China painter	8, Bath street	
Hornshaw, Lewis	General broker & whitesmith	Middle Brook street	
Hornshaw, John	Whitesmith and vict., Nottingham Arms	21, Bridge gate	F, B
Horrocks, John	Solicitor	29, Friar gate	F, B
Horsley, Nathaniel	Gentleman	17, Queen street	F, Fr
Horsley, John		Beeston, Notts.	F
Horsley, John	Basket maker	Grove street	
Horsley, William	Bookseller, stationer & printer	Sadler gate	F, B
Horsley, Charles	Bookbinder	York street	F, B
Horton, Benj., sen.	Model maker	Park street	F
Horton, Benj., jun.	Model maker	Liversage street	F
Horton, Samuel	Labourer	3, Bath street	
Horton, Thomas	J. brass founder	Parker street	
Hough, Thomas	J. joiner	Eagle street	
Hough, George	J. bricklayer	Eagle street	
Hough, Henry	J. carpenter	Litchurch street	
Hough, Robert	Framework knitter	Becket well lane	Fr
Hough, James	Fitter-up at foundry	Bridge gate	Fr
Hough, William	Moulder	Derby	Fr
Houghton, John	Butcher	Bloom street	Fr
Houghton, Henry	Framework knitter	Brook street	
Houghton, David	Pensioner	Morledge	Fr
Houghton, Henry	Labourer	Chester place	Fr
Houghton, William	Labourer	Bag lane	Fr
Hoult, Jacob	Baker and flour dealer	3, Brook street	B
Howard, Rev. John G.	Vicar of St. Michael's	Lodge lane	F, B
Howe, John	Joiner	Back Sitwell street	B
How, Thomas	J. cabinet maker	Market place	Fr
How, John Wood	J. cabinet maker	Talbot street	Fr
Howkins, Samuel	Butcher	26, Ford street	F, B
Hoyes, Thomas	Framework knitter	30, Grove street	B
Hudson, William	Butcher	Park street	

Hudson, James	Whitesmith	Bath street	
Hudson, Joseph	Net manufacturer	Bloom street	
Hudson, John	Gent's. boarding school	36, Full street	B
Hudson, William	Beer seller and raff yard	London road	
Hudson, Moses	Shopkeeper	Eagle street	
Hudson, William	Basket maker	Green lane	
Huff, John	Framework knitter	Kensington	
Huggins, Francis	Vict., Royal Hotel and Commercial Inn	Victoria street	B
Hughes, Duke	Painter	36, St. Peter's street	
Hughes, John	Butcher	45, London road	B
Hughes, John	Cabinet maker, and archery warehouse	30, King street	F,B
Hughes, John	Miniature painter	King street	B
Huish, J. & M.	Solicitors	St. Michael's ch. yd.	B
Hulme, James	Gentleman's servant	Ct. 4, Nottingham rd.	
Humber, Richard	Joiner and builder	Leonard street	Fr
Hume, David	Dyer	Wilmot street	
Humphreys, John	Clerk at Smith's bank	Osmaston street	B
Humphries, Ellen	Glass warehouse	Full street	
Humpstone, Samuel	Tobacco manufacturer	Cross lane	B
Humpstone, Joseph	Agent to Curtis and Harvey, gunpowder manufacturers	Wardwick	F,B
Hunt, Joseph	Baker and flour dealer	Green lane	B
Hunt, Edward	Baker and flour dealer	Park street	B
Hunt, Samuel	Baker and flour dealer	Old Uttoxeter road	
Hunt, James	Labourer	Litchurch street	
Hunt, George	Whitesmith	Duke street	F,B
Hunt, John	Confectioner	St. Peter's street	B
Hunt, John	Whitesmith	Nottingham road	
Hunt, Henry	Ale and porter brewer, Navigation Brewery	Nottingham road	B
Hunt, Francis	Vict., Black Horse	Nun's street	B
Hunt, Joseph, sen.	Whitesmith, bell-hanger, manufacturer of iron fencing	St. Peter's street and Normanton rd.	F,B
Hunt, Hannah	Beer seller and shopkeeper	Osmaston street	
Hunt, Joseph, jun.	Furnishing ironmonger, oil and colour man, &c.	St. Peter's street	B
Hunt, John	Shoemaker	37, Goodwin st.	F,B
Hunt, Joseph	Baker and flour dealer	Nun's street	B
Hunt, William	Glove&breeches maker&tailor	13, Friar gate	B
Hunt, G.	Boot lace and trimming manufacturer	City road	
Hurd, William	Pork butcher	Bold lane	
Hurd, William	Vict., Robin Hood	Ct. 1, Iron gate	B
Hurst, William	Purse weaver	Grove street	
Husbands, William	Joiner	34, Exeter street	F,B
Huss, Samuel	Tailor	Bridge street	B
Hussey, Rev. Walter	Wesleyan minister	Cherry street	B
Hutchinson, Thos.	J. lace manufacturer	Albion place	Fr
Hutchinson, William	Agent to Messrs. Allsop, brewers, Burton	Friar gate, store room, Corn market	Fr

Ingham, Thomas	Beer seller, British Arms	48, Bridge gate	B
Ingham, Henry	Brazier and tin-plate worker	Brook street	
Ingham, John	Framework knitter	64, Bridge street	
Inott, John	Perfumer and hair cutter	Rotten row	B
Inwood, John	Sawyer	Litchurch street	
Ironmonger, Eli	Shopkeeper	Friar gate	B
Jackson, Charles	Needlemaker	27, Bridge gate	
Jackson, Charles	Framework knitter	Albion street	
Jackson, William	Twist hand	Brook street	
Jackson, John	Agent to the Tutbury Glass works	5, St. Peter's street	
Jackson, Benjamin	J. joiner	Kensington	
Jackson, John	Medicine dealer	Talbot street	B
Jackson, Henry	Framework knitter	Bradshaw street	
Jackson, Samuel	Framework knitter	Kensington st.	Fr
Jackson, Daniel	Blacksmith	Ashbourn road	
Jackson, William	Fishmonger	45, Full street	
Jackson, William	J. joiner	Kensington street	
Jackson, Henry	J. silk weaver	South street	
Jackson, Francis	Joiner and cabinet maker	St. Peter's ch. yd.	B
Jackson, William	Grocer	Grove street	
Jackson, Thomas	Labourer	77, Bridge street	
James, John	Schoolmaster	Parker street	Fr
James, Henry W.	Professor of music	5, Bridge gate	B
James, Thomas	Fellmonger	St. James's lane	B
James, William	Smith	Parker street	
James, Thomas	Parish clerk at St. Michael's	Parker street	
Jankinson, John	Hostler	10, Orchard street	
Jankinson, Berrisford	Labourer	Friar gate	
Jankinson, Joseph	Beer seller	58, Bridge street	B
Jankinson, James	Earthenware dealer	High street	
Jarvis, A.	Milliner and dressmaker	Sadler gate	
Jarvis, Charles		Chichester	F
Jay, John	Joiner and cabinet maker	Bradshaw street	
Jay, James	Schoolmaster and registrar	Becket well lane	B
Jeffery, John	Gentleman's servant	York street	F,B
Jefferies, Thomas	Hosier	Parker street	F,B
Jefferies, William	Framework knitter	Parker street	
Jelks, John	Porter at Station	Park street	B
Jennings, Mrs.		Darwin terrace	
Jennings, James	Gardener	Leonard street	F
Jennings, Miss	Milliner and dressmaker	Parker street	
Jerram, Thomas	Baker and flour dealer	Leonard street	B
Jessopp, Fras. & Son	Solicitors	Wardwick	
Jessopp, Francis, esq.	Alderman	Wardwick	F,Fr
Jessopp, Fr. Johnson	Solicitor	Wardwick	F,Fr
Jepson, John	Mechanical chimney sweeper	St. Peter's street	
Jepson, Joseph	Labourer	Devonshire street	
Jepson, Ellen		Wilmot street	
Johnson and Pratt	Schoolmasters	Agard street	
Johnson, Thomas	Plasterer	Morledge	Fr
Johnson, William	Pig jobber	Kensington street	F,B

Johnson, John	Gentleman	4, St. John's terrace B
Johnson, Thomas	Watchmaker	London road
Johnson, John	Surgeon	11, St. Alk. ch. yd. F, B
Johnson, John Whitaker	Surgeon	St. Mary's gate B
Johnson, John	Shoemaker	City road
Johnson, William	Plasterer	Devonshire street Fr
Johnson, Joseph	Hostler	30, Erasmus street Fr
Johnson, John	J. brewer	New street
Johnson, William	Gentleman	York street
Johnson, Joseph	Shopkeeper	Willow row
Johnson, William	Boot maker, shop King street	Grove cottage F, B
Johnson, Joseph	Beer seller	Mill street B
Johnson, John	Alderman	Albion street F, B
Johnson, Charles	Baker and flour dealer	5, Charles street B
Johnson, Wm. Henry	Baker and flour dealer	Siddals lane
Johnson, Joseph	Labourer	30, Nun's street
Johnson, Isaac	Plasterer	Cockpit hill Fr
Johnson, Joseph	Agent to John Harrison, esq.	Osmaston road F, B
Johnson, Thomas	Twisthand	Bradshaw street
Johnson, Samuel	Coal dealer	Cockpit hill F, Fr
Johnson, William	Coal dealer & dealer in tiles	11, Cockpit hill, F, B
Johnson, William	Labourer	Parker street F
Johnson, John	Dealer in glass and china	14, Tenant street B
Johnson, Mary	Vict., The Bird	Jury street
Johnson, James	Tollgate keeper	Kedleston road F
Jolley, William	Vict., Tap House	4, Rotten row F, B
Jolley, John	Farmer and milkseller	Ashbourn road B
Jolley, Samuel	Hair cutter	6, Bag lane
Jolliffe, Robert	Watch manufacturer	St. Peter's street
Jolliffe, Simon	Watch manufacturer	St. Peter's street B
Jolliton, Thomas	Framework knitter	Parker street
Jones, Thomas	Vict., Checquers	Willow row
Jones, Dorothy	Shopkeeper	Walker lane
Jones, David	J. clock and watchmaker	Devonshire street
Jones, Rev. Noah	Unitarian minister	North parade B
Jones, Wm. Henry	Jeweller	5, Green lane B
Jones, John	Surgeon	43, Friar gate B
Jones, Richard	Chemist and druggist	12, Iron gate B
Jones and Hewitt	Dispensing chemists	Iron gate
Jones, William		60, Friar gate F
Jordan, John		Kedleston F
Joyce, Thomas	J. joiner	High street
Joynes, Edward	Labourer	Litchurch street
Julian, William	J. coach builder	Leonard street
Kay, George	J. brushmaker	Upper Brook street
Kay, Robert	J. brushmaker	40, Brook street B
Kay, George	Bookbinder	Ashbourn road
Kearsley, Josiah	Painter	2, Amen Alley B
Keeling & Tomisson	Milliners, dress makers, and straw bonnet makers	St. Alkmund's ch. yd.
Keeling, Francis	Architect	Ashbourn road

Keeling, Thomas	J. joiner	Leonard street	
Keeling, John	Gentleman	Osmaston street	F,B
Keeling, Thomas	Plumber and glazier	Market place	Fr
Keeling, William	Stone mason	15, Bath street	F
Keeling, John		Sutton-on-the-Hill	F
Keeling, George	Plumber and glazier	St. Mary's gate	
Keeling, Thomas	J. millwright	28, Nun's street	
Keeling, Rev. R.	Minister of Wesleyan chapel	King street	
Keene, Richard	Book-keeper	Brook street	F,B
Keenan, Thomas	Grocer and register office	Victoria street	B
Keetley, Jonathan W.	Conveyancer, St. Peter's st.	Wilstrop	F
Keeton, Thomas	Vict., Duke of York	Burton road	F,B
Keeton, Henry	Vict., Dog and Hare	Alvaston	F
Keeton, Francis	Shopkeeper	49, Friar gate	
Kelley, James	Labourer	Agard street	
Kempton, James	J. weaver	Brook street	
Kempton, John	J. weaver	Brook street	
Kendrick, William	Wool comber	Normanton road	
Kendrick, Samuel	Musician	Leaper street	
Kendrick, William	Gentleman	1, St. John's terrace	B
Kent, Henry	Works at lead mill	Bag lane	
Kent, James	Joiner	Leaper street	F
Kent, Ann	Farmer	Brook street	
Kent, William	Joiner	Leaper street	F
Kent and Askew	Linen and woollen drapers	Iron gate	
Kenworthy & Co.	General carriers by canal and railway	Cockpit hill	
Kerry, Joseph	Shoe warehouse	9, Cheapside	B
Kerry, Jonathan	Wagoner	Duke street	
Kersham, Mrs.		Wilmot street	
Kershaw, Richard	Stonemason and beer seller	Upper Brook st.	B
Key, James	Shoemaker	Old Uttoxeter rd.	Fr
Key, William	Shoemaker	2, Willow row	Fr
Key, Thomas	Shoemaker	Brook street	Fr
Key, William	Shoemaker	William street	Fr
Keys, Samuel	Painter	Sheepy,Leicestersh.	F
Keys, Sam. sen.	China painter	Bridge street	Fr
Keys, Simeon	Hair dresser	Goodwin street	Fr
Keys, William	Shoemaker	Full st. alms hou.	Fr
Khars, J. Nich.	Solicitor	St. Mary's gate	
Kidney, John	Gardener	Bag lane	
Kramer, Frederick	Pork butcher	Iron gate	
Killer, John E., esq.		Friar gate	F, B
Kimberlain, Thomas	Joiner	Castle place	F
Kimpton, Edward	J. riband weaver	Castle street	
King, Samuel	Architect	Queen street	B
King, Isaac	Hair dresser	56, Bridge street	B
King, Charles, jun.	Dealer in smallware	St. Peter's street	F,B
King, Hannah	Vict., Bull's Head	Queen street	F
King, Charles, sen.	Sergeant at mace	St. Peter's street	B
King, Ann	Poulterer and eating house	Queen street	
Kinsey, Francis	Vict., Nottingham Castle	Queen street	F, B

Kirk, Samuel	Artist and animal painter	St. Peter's street	F
Kirby, William	Basket maker	8, London road	
Kirby, Thomas	Higgler	High street	
Kirby, Henry	Attorney's clerk	Castle street	
Kirk, William	Draper	Green lane	B
Kirk, William	Framesmith	Ct., Bridge gate	
Kirk, Thomas	Horse breaker and trimmer	Summer hill	B
Kirk, William	Needlemaker	St. Helen's street	
Kirk, William	Vict., Horse and Trumpet	43, Full street	B
Kirk, Valentine	Stamp distributor & hawker's license office	St. Mary's gate	
Kirkland, Mrs.	Schoolmistress	Green street	
Kirkland, Joseph	Glass manufacturer	Sacheverel street	
Kirkland, John	Stonemason	Upper Brook street	
Kirkland, Thomas	Grocer and flour dealer	Mansfield road	B
Kirkland, Mary	Shopkeeper	Brook street	
Knight, William	Upholsterer	Friar gate	B
Knight, James	Hair dresser	Bridge street	B
Knight, R. V.	Draughtsman and foreman to Mr. Wright, Britan. foundry	Duke street	B
Knight, John	Framework knitter	Mundy street	
Knight, Joseph	Gentleman	Ashbourn road	F,B
Knight, Robert	Wagoner	River street	
Knight, Elizabeth	Milliner and dressmaker	Duke street	
Knight, John	Framework knitter	Brook street	
Knight, Thomas	Shopkeeper	1, Bridge street	B
Knight, Rev.	Minister of New Jerusalem Temple	King street	
Knighton, Robert	Labourer	Kensington	
Kniveton, Robert	Maltster, Siddals lane	8, Parker street	B
Kniveton, Joseph	J. weaver	Short street	
Knowles, John	Cook shop	Canal street	
Knowles, John	Shoemaker	Bridge street	
Labon, John	Chair turner	Ct. 3, Morledge	
Labon, Thomas	Chair turner	Ct. 3, Morledge	
Lacey, John	Foundryman	Exeter street	
Lackington, John	House and land agent	Osmaston road	F,B
Lakin, Robert	Warehouseman	Devonshire street	
Lakin, George	Labourer	Large's street	
Lakin, William	Warehouseman	Devonshire street	
Lakin, Sarah	Milliner and dress maker	St. Mary's gate	
Lallemands, the Misses	Ladies' boarding school	Green lane	
Lamb, George	Land agent and surveyor, office Corn market	Osmaston road	
Lamplough, John W.	Clerk at Smith's bank	Nottingham road	
Lander, Mrs.	Confectioner	Ford street	
Lander, John J.	Stonemason	Siddals lane	
Lancashire, George	Grocer and druggist	Carrington street	
Lark, Walthall	Tailor	Bag lane	
Larrard, Thomas		Kingston-on-Hull	F
Larrard, Edward	Framework knitter	Green street	F
Lassells, Sarah	Straw bonnet and dressmaker	Bold lane	

Lathbury, Thomas	Framework knitter	Ct. 8, Bold lane	Fr
Latham, John	Labourer	Brook street	
Latham, Rev. John	Minister of St. John's church	The Elms, Duff. rd.	B
Lawrence, Edward	J. riband weaver	Parker street	
Lawton, Benjamin	J. weaver	Brook street	
Leacroft, Richard Beecher, esq.		Osmaston road	F,Fr
Leadbrook, William	J. weaver	Normanton road	
Leadbiter, Alfred	Traveller	Exeter street	
Leech, Elizabeth	Grocer and tea dealer	Bag lane	
Leech, Ann & John	Vict., Fox & Owl commer. inn	Bridge gate	F
Leech, John	Vict., Fox & Owl commer. inn	Bridge gate	F,B
Leech, John		Holbrook	F
Leech, Joseph	J. jeweller	Canal street	
Leech, Robert	Solicitor	Queen street	F,B
Leedham, Ann	Basket maker	Bradshaw street	
Lee Hunt, Peter Bainbrigge, esq.		Ashbourn	F
Lee, George	Moulder	Duke street	
Lee, John	Higgler	Parker street	
Lee, George	Boot and shoe warehouse	Sadler gate	B
Lees, William	Beer seller, White Hart	John street	
Lees, Alfred	Baker, flour dealer, and provision warehouse	37, Walker lane	F,B
Lees, George	Stoker	2, Canal street	Fr
Leese, William	Woollen draper and tailor	St. Mary's gate	B
Legg, John	Shoemaker	Grove street	
Leeson, Thomas	Labourer	Grove street	
Lewis, Josiah	Gentleman (mill, Bridge st.)	Parsonage house, Osmaston	F,B
Lewis, Samuel & Co.	Hosiery wareho., Willow row	Ivy Lodge	B
Lewis, William	Labourer	Albion place	Fr
Lewis, John	Butcher	Canal street	
Levills, Joseph	Dyer	Brook street	
Levy, Thomas	Framework knitter	Litchurch street	
Levy, David	J. weaver	Nun's street	
Lilley, George	Shopkeeper	London road	B
Lilley, John	Vict., Royal Oak inn	24, Market place	B
Lillingston, Rev. E.	Perpetual curate of All Saints	15, Ashbourn road	F
Lindley, John	Surgeon	6, St. Mary's gate	B
Lindley, James	Sadler and harness maker	15, St. Peter's st.	B
Lindley, Richard	Bookseller, printer, & stationer	14, Rotten row	B
Lindley, William	Moulder	Erasmus street	
Linfoot, Isaac	Gentleman	Kedleston road	B
Lister, Thomas	Book-keeper	Exeter street	
Lister, William	J. engineer	Erasmus street	
Lister, Sarah	Carrier to Alfreton, Chesterfield, Sheffield, Barnsley, Wakefield, Leeds, and all parts of the north, also to Loughborough, Leicester, and all parts of the south, by wagon	Siddals lane	

E

Lichfield, John	Shoemaker	Sadler gate	F,B
Littlewood, William	Joiner	11, Osmaston st.	B
Livesay, John	J. weaver	Traffic street	B
Livesey, Robert	J. weaver	Traffic street	
Lloyd, J.	Boot and shoe maker	Bold lane	
Loats, Charles	Shoemaker	York street	B
Locker, William	Warehouseman at china manufactory	26, Exeter street	Fr
Locker, Joseph	Bookseller and circulating library	9, Jury street	B
Locker, John	Hostler at New Inn	11, Orchard street	
Locker, John	Blacking manufacturer	Devonshire street	
Locker, Ann	Baker and confectioner	Green lane	
Lockett, William, esq.	Magistrate	Wardwick	Fr
Lomas, Samuel	Locomotive department	Green lane	
Lomas, Henry	Locomotive department	Green lane	
Lomas, Ralph	Gentleman, commissioner in the Court of Requests	Curzon street	F
Lomax, William	Pawnbroker, silversmith, jeweller, and general salesman	35, Corn market	B
Lomax, George	Beer seller	Walker lane	B
Longbottom, Thos.	Bookbinder	Ashbourn road	
Longdon, Robert	Silk glove manufacturer and hosier	32, Friar gate	B
Longdon, Mrs.	Lodging house	Bag lane	
Longdon, William	Vict., Old Tiger, & maltster, malthouse Friar gate	35, Queen street	B
Longdon, Thomas	Painter	Ashbourn road	B
Longdon, Henry, jun.	Butcher, Queen street	St. Michael's lane	F,B
Longdon & Basford	House and sign painters	Talbot yard	
Longdon, William	China painter	16, Exeter street	Fr
Longdon, William	Grocer	Bridge street	
Longdon, Roger	Vict., Seven Stars	Upper Brook st.	B
Longdon, Henry, sen.	Vict., Old Dolphin	6, Queen street	F,B
Longdon, John	Officer of police	No. 25, Canal street	
Longdon, Luke		Dog Inn, Chester gate	F
Lord, Joseph	Plumber and glazier	Iron gate	B
Lovegrove, John	China painter	43, Erasmus street	
Lovick, Samuel	Glass and china warehouse	22, Market place	B
Lowe, John	Wood turner	Star & Garter yard	
Lowe, Samuel	Wholesale & ret. draper & hosier	St. Peter's bridge	B
Lowe, Joseph	Vict., Old Flower Pot	8, King street	B
Lowe, Edward	Wood turner	Talbot street	
Lowe, Richard	Gardener	New street	F
Lowe, Mary	Straw bonnet manufacturer	Talbot street	
Lowe, Thomas	Shoemaker	Ashbourn road	
Lowe, Mrs. Ann		Burton road	
Lowe, George	China painter	27, Bath street	
Lowe, William	Maltster & vict., Ram inn	29, Bridge street	F,B
Lowe, Rev. Henry		Hornby, Yorkshire	F
Lowe, Richard	Butcher	Sadler gate	B
Louis, John	J. joiner	Litchurch street	

Lucas, Daniel	China painter	10, Erasmus street	
Lucas, William	Shopkeeper and china painter	20, St. Helen's st.	B
Ludlam, Henry	Coal merchant & vict., Castle and Falcon	Cockpit hill	B
Ludlam, Isaac	Stonemason	Park street	B
Lynn, Rev. Andrew	Methodist New Connexion	London road	
Lyon, Peter	Muffin baker	18, Osmaston st.	B
Macconnell, Richard	Gentleman	24, King street	F,B
Mackenzie, Henry	General salesman	Corn market	F,B
Macintyre, James	Engineer	Bradshaw street	
Macklin, Rev. Rose-ingrave	Minister of Christ church	Wardwick	F,B
Maclocklin, Thos.	Works at silk mill	Albion street	
Maddox, Joseph	Shoemaker	Ashbourn road	
Maddox, William	Labourer	Brook walk	
Maddox, Richard	Butcher	Osmaston street	
Maddocks, Joseph	Vict., Bay Horse	Uttoxeter road	
Madeley, Thos. & Co.	Manufacturers of silk & cotton small wares	Cavendish street	
Madeley, Thomas	Manufacturer	3, Wilmot street	B
Magalgin, George	J. shoemaker	Wright street	
Maggay, Charles	Tailor	Hill street	
Malin, Thomas	Twist hand	Grove street	
Malin, William	Wine merchant	Osmaston road	B
Malin, James	Carpenter and builder	Green lane	F,B
Mallinder, John	J. shoemaker	Ct. 9, Bridge gate	
Maloy, William	Lodging house	31, Walker lane	
Mango, Joseph	Compositor	John street	
Manlove, Thomas	Vict., Black Bull	Canal street	
Mansfield, Margaret		Normanton terrace	
Mansfield, Thomas	Labourer	Bradshaw street	F
Mansfield, John	Wagoner	Litchurch street	
Mansfield, William	Vict., Canal Tavern	Cockpit hill	B
Mansfield, Thomas	Gentleman	St. Alkm. ch. yd.	F
Mansfield, George	Maltster, St. Michael's lane	Alvaston	
Mansfield & Morton	Maltsters	St. Michael's lane	
Mansfield, John	Butcher	Canal street	B
Mansfield, Joseph	Shoemaker	Parker street	
Mansfield, George	Maltster, King street	York street	F,B
Manuel, Anthony	Cabinet maker and broker	27, Full street	
Marlow, William	Fitter up of engines	Litchurch street	
Marr, William	Mechanic	Parker street	
Marler, Susan	Shopkeeper	St. James's lane	
Mart, Samuel	Patten maker	Talbot street	
Marridge, Thomas	Porter at Station	Canal street	
Marriott, Mrs.		Derwent street	
Marriott, John	Warehouseman	Darley	
Marriott, Christopher	Butcher	6, Bridge gate	B
Marriott, Edward	Joiner	1, Derwent street	B
Marriott & Garratt	Joiners and builders	1, Derwent street	
Marriott, William	J. joiner	Ct. 9, Bridge gate	
Marriott, Thomas	Beer seller	John street	B

Marriott, Thomas	Framework knitter	Ct. 9, Bridge gate	
Martin, Sarah	Needle maker	Bridge gate	
Martin, Edward	Stocking manufacturer	Agard street	
Martin, Charles	J. bricklayer	Bradshaw street	
Martin, Thomas	Cement manufactory	City road	B
Martin, William	Well sinker	6, Dunkirk	
Martin, John	Butcher, Shambles	2, Exeter place	B
Martin, Joseph	Butcher, Old shambles	St. Mary's gate	B
Martin, Joseph	Shoemaker	7, Orchard street	
Martin, Anthony	Turnkey at gaol	Fowler street	
Martin, Charles	Shoemaker	36, Goodwin st.	B
Martin, John	Whitesmith	1, Bridge gate	B
Marsden, William	Grocer and tea dealer	25, Market place	B
Marsden, Samuel		Alfreton	F
Marsden, Joseph	Baker and flour dealer	24, London road	F,B
Marsh, John	J. weaver	Litchurch street	
Marsh, Richard	J. weaver	Ct. 9, Bridge gate	
Marsh, John	Works at Wright's mill	Mundy street	
Marshall, William	Locomotive department	Sacheverel street	
Marshall, William	Sawyer	Litchurch street	
Marshall, Joseph	Farmer	Abbey Barns	Fr
Marshall, Sam.&Jam.	Stonemasons	29, Bath street	
Marshall, John	Labourer	Grove street	
Marshall, James	Beadle at All Saints	Full street	
Marshall, Thomas	Beerseller,& sexton at St. Alks.	St. Alkmun.ch.yd.	Fr
Marshall, George	Gardener	19, Kensington st.	B
Marshall, Samuel	Joiner	St. Alkmun.ch.yd.	Fr
Marshall, Sarah	Shopkeeper	17, St. Helen's street	
Marshman, William	Road surveyor	Traffic street	B
Markes, Mrs. Sarah		Wilmot street	
Marson, John	Tailor	Devonshire street	
Maskery, John	Brazier and tinman	15, Willow row	B
Maskery, James	Shoemaker	54, Willow row	
Mason & Gilbertson	Brewers, Burton-upon-Trent, agent for Derby, Mr.Smithson, at the Town hall cellars	Market place	F
Mason, John	Architect, and surveyor of bridges for southern division of the county, and commissioner in the court of requests, for the borough of Derby	52, London road	B
Mason, William	J. tailor	Sitwell street	
Mason, Thomas	Hostler	Ct. 5, St. Peter's st.	
Mason, John	Colour merchant, and grainer's tool manufacturer	London road	B
Mason, Robert	Japanner	30, Exeter street	B
Mason, Joseph	Varnish and colour manufacturer	5, Derwent street & Burton road	F,B
Mason, Thomas	J. joiner	Nun's street	Fr
Mason, George	Framework knitter	Ct. 9, Brook street	
Mason, John	Traveller	Parker street	B

Mason, Thomas	Fishmonger, poulterer, and dealer in game, and oyster rooms	4, Iron gate	B
Mason, Mrs.	Vict., Old Boat	Morledge	
Massey, Miss	Milliner and dressmaker	St. Mary's gate	
Massey, Joseph Spor	Solicitor	13, Full street	B
Massey, Jonathan & Elijah	Drapers and haberdashers	40, Corn market	F,B
Massey, Elijah	Draper	Corn market	F
Mather, William	Baker	20, Fowler street	
Mather, Ann	Grocer and tea dealer	Brook street	
Mather, Mrs.		Rose hill	
Mather, John	Boarding and day school for young gentlemen	Osmaston street	B
Mather, Thomas	Turnkey at gaol	Fowler street	
Matthews, Jerry	Hostler	Litchurch street	
Matthews, Ann	Shopkeeper	Upper Brook street	
Mawe, Joseph	J. spar turner	Parker street	
Mawe, Thomas	Machinist and whitesmith	9, Wright street	F,B
Mayer, Charles	Shopkeeper	17, Exeter street	B
Mayer, Thomas	Vict., Punch Bowl	Nottingham road	B
Mayer	J. smith	Parker street	
May, Peter	J. hatter	Burton road	
Mc'Clair, George	Saddler & harness maker	11, Queen street	B
Mc'Corsie, William	Baker and flour dealer	20, Bold lane	B
Mc'Donald, Morley	J. weaver	Duke street	
Mc'guire, Charles	Clothier and broker	Morledge	B
Mead, Henry	Fitter up of castings	Eagle street	
Mead, Edward	Fitter up of castings	Cockpit hill	
Mead, William	Butcher	Brook street	B
Mead, Thomas	Fishmonger	Castle street	
Mead, George	Dyer and scourer	St. James's lane	F,B
Mead, George	J. Maltster	Bloom street	
Meakin, Henry	Corn miller, Nun's mill	St. Michael's lane	B
Meakin, James	Shoemaker	17, Goodwin st.	B
Meakin, George	Shoemaker	14, Brook street	B
Meakin, William	Shoemaker	5, River street	
Meakin, William	Framework knitter	Ashbourn road	
Meakin, Thomas	Baker	Nun's street	
Meakin, William	Shoemaker	23, Exeter street	F,B
Meakin, John	Framework knitter	Ashbourn road	
Meakin, James	Gentleman	Britannia street	F
Meakin, Benjamin	Corn miller	St. Michael's lane	
Meakin, Thomas	Shoemaker	Brook street	
Mee, Josiah	Stonemason	Castle street	
Mellor, James	Salt warehouse	King street	F,B
Mellor, John Wm.	Milk seller and grocer	77, Devonshire st.	F
Mellor, Job		Nottingham	F
Mellor, John	Coach proprietor	Derby & Ashbourn	
Mellor, David	Twisthand	Cross lanes	
Mellor, Sarah Ann	Earthenware dealer	8, Victoria street	B
Mellor, John	Dealer in cotton waste	Agard street	B

Mellor, Mrs. Colonel		Vernon street	
Mellor, John		23, King street	B
Merry, John	Vict., Three Nuns	Nun's street	B
Merry, Thomas	Agent to Tunley & Hodgson	1, Castle street	B
Merry, William	Grocer and tea dealer	50, Bridge gate	B
Meynell, Thomas	Shopkeeper	Goodwin street	
Meynell, Miss Mary		Friar gate	
Middleton, Richard	Framework knitter	Normanton road	
Middleton, John Chas.		Melbourn	F
Middleton, Rev. J.	Primitive methodist minister	Sacheverel street	
Middleton, Mrs. & Miss		London road	
Mier, Charles	Book-keeper	Exeter street	
Miers, Robert	Carpenter at Taylor's mill		B
Millikin, William	Draper	Goodwin street	
Millington, Joseph	Gardener	Lady Grove	
Millington, James	Overlooker at the silk mill, Chester road	Bag lane	
Millington, Eliza	Milliner and dressmaker	Amen alley	
Millington, Robert	Shoemaker	Bridge gate	
Millington, Henry	Gardener	St. Helen's street	
Millford, Thomas	Silk weaver	Lodge lane	
Millott, Joseph	J. wheelwright	Short street	
Milnes, John	Gentleman	7, Devonshire street	
Mills, James	Lace manufacturer	2, Friar gate	B
Milner, John	J. weaver	Brook street	
Milner, John	J. joiner	Bloom street	
Milner, Jacob	J. corn miller	10, City road	
Milner, Edward	Joiner	Bloom street	
Milner, Thomas	J. weaver	29, Nun's street	
Milner, William	Millwright	Devonshire street	
Milner, John	Joiner	41, Burton road	B
Milner, George	Editor of the Derby Mercury	Kedleston road	
Milward, William & Son	Rope, twine, and fishing tackle manufacturers	26, Market place	F,B
Milward, Wm., jun.	Rope, twine, and fishing tackle manufacturer	Market place	F,B
Millward, William	Labourer	Devonshire street	
Mitchell, John	Clerk at Messrs. Holmes	Sitwell street	
Mitchell, Thomas	Rope maker	6, New street	B
Mitchell, T. and J.	Rope makers	Fowler street	
Moody, George	Bricklayer	7, Chapel street	B
Moody, Thomas	Cabinet maker	Wilmot street	F
Moody, John	Clerk to the Derby Poor Law Union, and superintendent registrar	54, Friar gate	F,B
Moorcroft, Peter	Book-keeper	Ct. 5, Agard street	
Moorcroft, Thomas	J. joiner	Eagle street	
Moorcroft, William	Woollen draper and tailor	5, Jury street	
Moorcroft, Henry	Chemist and druggist	Rotten row	B
Moorcroft, Benjamin	Hostler	Grove street	
Moore, Henry	Locksmith	Sadler gate	
Moore, F.	Vict., Green Man	St. Peter's street	

Moore, John	Shopkeeper	Goodwin street	B
Moore, Mrs. Ann		George street	
Moore, Joseph	Works at spar works	Parker street	
Moore, John	Framework knitter	Castle street	
Moore, William	Joiner	Traffick street	
Moore, Abraham	J. jeweller	Sitwell street	
Moore, Henry	Auctioneer and appraiser	St. Alkm. ch. yd.	Fr
Moore, Thomas, jun.	J. dyer	15, Eagle street	
Moore, John	Joiner	Normanton road	
Moore, James	Wholesale jeweller and manu-facturer	London road	B
Moore, John	Horse dealer	Devonshire street	
Moore, Joseph	J. joiner	Bloom street	
Moore, Horatio	Plumber	Duffield	F
Moore, Thomas	J. jeweller	Eagle street	
Moore, William	Joiner and shopkeeper	Bag lane	
Moore, Thomas	Coach builder	Curzon street	B
Moore, William	Gardener	Siddals lane	
Moore, John	Silk stocking manufacturer	Ct. 4, Agard street	
Moore, Henry	Artist, ornamenter of marble, and engraver	Green hill	B
Moore, Ambrose	Silk throwster	London	F
Moore, Ambrose & Co.	Silk throwsters and manufac-turers	Devonshire street	
Moore, Edward	Shoemaker	5, River street	B
Moore, William	Shoemaker	Castle street	
Moore, Peter	Vict., Railway Tavern	Canal street	F, Fr
Moore, John	J. coach builder	33, Full street	
Moore, Samuel	Shopkeeper	Bradshaw street	
Moore, John	Gardener and shopkeeper	Siddals lane	F
Moore, William	Shoemaker	William street	Fr
Moore, Henry	Builder	Uttoxeter road	F
Moore, Samuel	Vict., Mason's Arms	9, Albion street	B
Moorley, William	Blacksmith	Albion street	
Moorley, William	Weaver	42, Brook street	B
Moorley, James	Joiner	Osmaston street	B
Moorley, Thomas	Joiner	24, Green lane	Fr
Moorley, Peter		Brook street	F
Morgin, Thomas	Linen draper	Bradshaw street	
Moran, Maria	Dressmaker	Sadler gate	
Morledge, Francis	Works at Wright's mill	Uttoxeter road	Fr
Morledge, William	Baker and flour dealer	Siddals lane	
Morley, Samuel	Lace manufacturer	Castle gate, Nottingham	F
Morley, Samuel	Butcher	Parker street	
Morley, John	Tea dealer and grocer	19, Iron gate, and St. Peter's street	B
Morley, William	Riband weaver	Brook walk	Fr
Morley, Samuel	Vict., Devonshire Arms	10, Queen street	B
Morley, James	Watchman	Wright's yd., Agard st.	
Morley, James	Twisthand	Park street	
Morley, Benjamin	Wheelwright	Devonshire street	
Morley, William	Joiner	Parker street	

Morley, John	Lace manufacturer	Castle gate, Nottingham	F
Morley, William, jun.	Lace manufacturer	London road	F
Morley, William	Lace manufacturer	London road	F,B
Morley, Edward	Gentleman	23, Wilmot street	F,B
Morley, William	Iron and tin plate warehouse	Wardwick	Fr
Morley, John		Manchester	F
Morley, George	Petrifactioner	Ashbourn road	B
Morley, William	Hairdresser	15, Bridge gate	
Morley, Edward	Labourer	Litchurch street	
Morley, Henry	Fettler at Britannia foundry	Duke street	
Morley, Jonathan	J. weaver	Grove street	
Morley, Thomas	China painter	Traffic street	
Morley, Samuel	Vict., Devonshire Arms	Queen street	
Morley, James	J. weaver	Orchard street	Fr
Morton, Henry	Vict., Coach and Horses	Sadler gate	B
Mosedale, William	Millwright and engineer	Nun's street	B
Mosedale, James	Sawyer	Siddals lane	
Mosedale, William	J. millwright	Devonshire street	
Moseley & Nephew	Carvers and gilders, jewellers and silversmiths, spar and marble museum, picture gallery, and British Plate Glass warehouse, wholesale and retail	36, Corn market	B
Moseley, Henry	Carver and gilder, and agent to the Globe Insurance Company	Corn market	B
Moseley, Robert	Gentleman	Park street	B
Moseley, John	Fitting smith	Bradshaw street	
Moseley, Mrs.		Friar gate	
Moseley, Henry	J. weaver	Duke street	
Moseley, Wm. W.	House painter	Friar gate	F,B
Moseley, Ralph B.	Works at silk mill	Albion street	
Moseley, William	Moulder	Erasmus street	
Moseley, William	Labourer	Bag lane	
Mosley, James	Framework knitter	Upper Brook st.	Fr
Mosley, Samuel	Framework knitter	Waterloo street	Fr
Moss, John, esq.	Solicitor to the Derby and Derbyshire Banking Company	St. Peter's st.	F,B
Moss, Henry	Builder	Traffic street	F,B
Moss, Thomas	J. coach builder	Traffic street	B
Moss, John	Tailor	St. Peter's ch. yd.	
Moss, Miss		Babington lane	
Moss, John	Beer seller	Bridge gate	
Morvey, Henry	Net weaver	Devonshire street	
Mottram, James	J. joiner	Burton road	
Moult, William	Framework knitter	Hope street	Fr
Mousley, Benj., sen.	Gentleman	Park street	
Mousley, Benj., jun.	Corn factor	Park street	
Mousley, William Eaton, esq.	Solicitor	Full street	F,Fr

Mousley and Son	Solicitors	Full street	
Mousley, Rev. Wm.	Eaton, jun.	Full street	F
Mousley, John Hardcastle,	Solicitor	Full street	F
Mountford, Thomas	Works at china factory	Erasmus street	F
Mountford, William	Cashier at Messrs. Holmes, coach builders	Osmaston street	
Mountford, Thomas	Upholsterer	Kensington street	
Mountford, Benjamin	Shoemaker	Kensington street	
Mozley, Henry, and Sons	Wholesale booksellers, printers, publishers, and stationers	Friary and Brook street	F,B
Mozley, Henry, esq.	Wholesale bookseller	Friary	F,B
Mozley, John	Wholesale bookseller	90, Friar gate	B
Mozley, Charles	Wholesale bookseller	Friary	B
Mozley and Flack	Solicitors	Victoria street	
Mozley, Henry, jun.	Solicitor, coroner for the hundred of Appletree	Victoria street	B
Mozley, George	Framework knitter	Ashbourn road	
Mozley, Samuel	Labourer	32, Devonshire street	
Mozley, Burrows	Bricklayer	Albion street	
Murfin, George	Shopkeeper	Bag lane	
Murphin, John	Tailor	St. Peter's ch. yd.	
Murphy, George	J. engineer	Bag lane	
Murphy, James Brabazon	Surgeon dentist	Vicarage house, St. Peter's street	B
Musgrove, Joseph	Shoemaker	Kensington street	
Mycock, Peter	J. silk weaver	Grove street	
Nadin, John	Beer seller	Canal side	
Nadin, Samuel	J. joiner	Bloom street	
Nadin, William	Shopkeeper	Traffic street	
Nall, William	Shopkeeper	53, Bridge street	
Nash, John	Framework knitter	Ct., Kensington st.	Fr
Nash, William	Gardener	Kensington	Fr
Natt, Joseph	Carver and gilder	Osmaston street	B
Neal, Nathaniel	Boot & shoe maker	32, Sadler gate	B
Neale, John	Maltster & brickmaker	Albion street	
Neale, John	Shopkeeper	Eagle street	F
Neale, Edward	J. carpenter	Cross lanes	F
Neale, Joseph	Labourer	18, Green lane	
Neale, Thomas	King's Arms Inn, & County Family hotel	St. Mary's gate	B
Needham, Thomas	Pipe manufacturer	Agard street	Fr
Needham, Jasper	Framework knitter	Parker street	
Needham, William	Framework knitter	40, Leonard street	Fr
Needham, Edward	Saddler & harness maker	30, Bridge gate	Fr
Needham, William	Joiner	14, Kensington st.	F
Needham, Hannah	Shopkeeper	High street	
Needham, William	Alms houses	Full street	Fr
Needham, Henry	Pipe manufacturer	Agard street	Fr
Needham, Luke	J. millwright	Willow row	Fr
Needham, Stephen		Belper	Fr
Needham, Thomas		Belper	Fr

Newbold, William	Labourer	Castle street	
Newbold, William	Lock and whitesmith	40, Sadler gate	F,B
Newham, John	Licensed to let post horses for hire; flies, &c. on the shortest notice.	Agard street	B
Newham, William	Shoemaker	23, Walker lane	F,B
Newham, George	Shoemaker	Devonshire street	
Newell	Twisthand	Devonshire street	
Newell, William	Gentleman	Bridge street	B
Newell, William, jun.	Manager in Mr. Peet's mill	Upper Brook street	B
Newman, John	Grocer	Litchurch street	
Newsome, Henry	Schoolmaster	Uttoxeter road	
Newsome, Mary Ann	Milliner	Uttoxeter road	
Newton, Robert, esq.		The Leylands	Fr
Newton, Henry	Sergeant at mace, and plaster merchant	Chellaston	
Newton, William	Butcher	York street	
Newton, Richard	Farmer	Burton road	B
Newton, William Leaper, esq.	Banker, justice of peace, alderman, and chairman of North Midland Railway	23, Iron gate, and Leylands	F,Fr
Newton, George	Works at china factory	26, Bath street	
Nevill, George	J. bricklayer	Litchurch street	
Nicholson, Samuel	Shopkeeper	Willow row	
Nicklinson, Henry	Sadler and harness maker	8, Rotten row	F,B
Nicklinson, John	Higgler	Sacheverel street	
Nightingale, Thomas	Beer seller	Sacheverel street	
Noakes, Robert F.	Traveller	Wilmot street	
Noble, Thomas	Labourer	Bloom street	
Noble, John	Twisthand	Markeaton lane	
Noble, Godfrey	Shopkeeper	19, Eagle street	B
Norris, Henry	Vict., Duke of Wellington	43, Brook street	B
North, John Hall	Vict., Half Moon	Littleover	F
Northwood, George	J. cabinet maker	Talbot street	
Norton, William	Tailor	Green lane	B
Norton, John	Tailor	Osmaston street	B
Norton, David	Shopkeeper and beer seller	Morledge	
Norton, Thomas	Tailor	5, Tenant street	B
Norton, Josiah	Professor of music and piano forte tuner, and organist at St. John's church	2, Darwin terrace	B
Norman, Charles	J. weaver	Sacheverel street	
Nutt, W. J.	Gentleman	Bath street	
Nuttall, William	J. stonemason	Traffic street	
Nuttall, Samuel	Framework knitter	Darley lane	B
Oakden, Sarah	Milliner and dressmaker	Nun's street	
Oakden, Charles	J. tailor	Liversage street	
Oakes, James, esq.	Magistrate	Riddings	F
Oakes, Walter	Turnkey at gaol	Fowler street	
Oakley, James	Shopkeeper	Siddals lane	F
Oakley, Absalom	Labourer	Eagle street	

Oakley, Thomas	Timber merchant, and circular saw mills	Siddals lane & Eagle street	B
Odell, Philip	China painter	Erasmus street	
Odery, James	Tailor	5, St. Mary's gate	B
Offle, William	Works at shot tower	Bag lane	
Ogden, Francis	Butler	Ashbourn road	F
Oldham, Abraham	Farmer and joiner	Dog kennel lane	B
Oldhouse, Richard	J. painter	Duke street	
Ollester, Isaac	Works at shot tower	Erasmus street	
Oliver, Elizabeth	Ladies' boarding school	St. Helen's street	
Olliver, Elias	Maltster	Uttoxeter road	B
Olliver, Samuel	Gentleman	Wilmot street	
Olliver, James	Rope spinner	Eagle street	
Olliver, Thos., jun.	Tanner	39, Full street	B
Olliver, Thos., sen.	Tanner	Full street	B
Ordish, Noah	Gentleman	Wilmot street	F,B
Ordish, Joseph	Silk hand	Mundy street	Fr
Ordish, Thomas	Joiner and carpenter	Nun's street	
Orenshaw, George	Baker and confectioner	Sadler gate	
Orme, James	Joiner	Siddals lane	B
Orme, Samuel	Vict., Dusty Miller	Cockpit hill	B
Orme, William	Builder	Siddals lane	F,B
Orme, Frederick	Joiner and builder	Bridge street	Fr
Orme, Benjamin	Joiner and builder	Bridge street	Fr
Orme, Thomas	Joiner	Kensington street	F,B
Orton and Arnold	Cheesefactors	St. Alkm. ch. yd.	
Orton, James	Cheesefactor	Woodford,Staffords.	F
Osbiston, Samuel	Farmer	Wilsthorpe	F
Osborne, Joseph	Gentleman	Spondon	Fr
Osborne, Joseph	Grocer and baker	St. Peter's street	B
Osborne, Jeremiah	Framework knitter	19, Exeter street	B
Osborne, Sarah	Ladies' day & boarding school	St. Mary's gate	
Osborne, Richard	Shopkeeper	Brook street	
Osborne, William	Shoemaker	Brook street	
Otterwell, Thomas	Nail manufacturer	Nottingham road	B
Owen, Miss		Ashbourn road	
Owen, William	Tailor	Iron gate	F
Owen, John		Milford	F
Owen, James	Baker and flour dealer	50, St. Peter's st.	F,B
Owen, Thomas	Framework knitter	Bloom street	
Owen, Samuel	Tailor	St. Alkm. ch. yd.	B
Page, Edward	Lapidary	Drewry lane	
Page, Charles	Beer seller	Bourne street	Fr
Page, Thomas	Brass and iron founder	Corn market & Morledge	B
Page, Charles	Jeweller	Traffic street	Fr
Page, Henry	Baker and flour dealer	2, Burton road	B
Page, Edward	Patten and patten ring maker	38, Walker lane	B
Page, John	Jeweller	Wilmot street	F,B
Page, Henry	Patten ring maker	Brook street	
Page, Benjamin	Patten ring maker	Eagle street	F,B
Page, William	Jeweller	Sacheverel street	F,B

Page, David	Patten manufacturer	Willow row	
Paget, Thomas, esq.		Humberston gate, Leicester	F
Paget, Thomas Tertius, esq.		Humberston gate, Leicester	F
Paget, John, esq.		London	F
Palmer, John	Framework knitter	8, Normanton road	B
Palmer, John & Son	Nursery and seedsmen	28, Iron gate	
Palmer, John	Nurseryman	Iron gate	F,B
Parker, John	Shopkeeper	Queen street	
Parker, Richard	Baker and flour dealer	Devonshire street	B
Parker, George	Labourer	Albion street	
Parker, John	Hairdresser, perfumer, dealer in toys and cutlery	Queen street	
Parker, John	J. silk throwster	Leonard street	
Parker, John	Brazier	Ct. 1, Willow row	
Parker, Mrs.		Sacheverel street	
Parker, John & Son	Braziers and tin plate workers	18, Sadler gate	B
Parker, Charles	Compositor	21, Bath street	Fr
Parker, William	J. coachmaker	Grove street	
Parker, John	Beerseller	Bag lane	
Parkes, William	J. copper plate printer	Parker street	
Parkes, Marmaduke	Whitesmith and bell hanger	Friar gate	Fr
Parkes, George	Coal merchant	10, Nottingham road	
Parkes, William	Framework knitter	Agard street	Fr
Parkes, John	Whitesmith	15, Brook street	
Parkins, Thos. & Son	Tailors and woollen drapers	6, Sadler gate	B
Parkins, James	Tailor and woollen draper	Cheapside	B
Parkinson, William	Framework knitter	12, Normanton road	
Parkinson, Thomas	J. watchmaker	Green street	
Parr, Joseph	Pindar	5, St. Alk. ch. yd.	F,Fr
Parr, Benjamin	Shoemaker	Bag lane	Fr
Parrott, William	Works at factory	Castle street	
Parrott, Francis		Deptford	F
Parry, Grace	Dealer in flour	Cheapside	
Parsons, Joseph	J. weaver	Agard street	
Parsons, Joseph		Long Eaton	F
Pattyson, Thomas	Shopkeeper and beer seller	John's street	B
Payne, James	Vict., Wagon and Horses	Ashbourn road	B
Payne, John	Turnkey at gaol	Uttoxeter road	
Payne, Joseph	Turnkey at gaol	Uttoxeter road	
Peach, John	Gentleman	Kedleston road	
Peach, Robert	Solicitor	Quorndon	
Peach, John	Framework knitter	Leonard street	Fr
Peach, Henry	Foreman to Mr. Severne, jeweller	39, Osmaston st.	F,B
Peach, John	Labourer	Litchurch street	
Peach, Joseph	Fishing tackle manufacturer	St. Peter's street	B
Peach, Joseph	Framework knitter	Devonshire street	
Peach, William	Iron founder	City road	F,B
Peach, Falconer, & Co.	Iron founders, Union foundry	City road	F
Peach, Thomas	Framework knitter	Leonard street	
Peach, Thomas	Physician and magistrate	Langley Hall	F
Peake, Samuel	Baker and flour dealer	27, Burton road	

Peake and West	Straw hat makers	Green lane	
Peal, William	Framework knitter	Mansfield road	Fr
Pearce, Joseph		Wingerworth	F
Pearce, Thomas	Cooper	Bag lane	
Pearson, William	Baker and flour dealer	21, Bridge street	B
Pearson, Samuel	Weaver	Litchurch street	
Pearson, James	Shoemaker	High street	
Pearson, Thomas	Weaver	Litchurch street	
Pearson	Weaver	Spring gardens	
Pearson, John	Vict., White Lion	Friar gate	F,B
Peat, Joseph	Butcher	Spondon	F
Peat, Richard	Draper and shoemaker	Park street	F,B
Pedley, John	Railway coach, house, and sign painter	Tenant street	
Pedley, Mrs.	Large's clergyman's widows alms houses, Friar gate		
Pedley, William	Moulder	Willow row	F
Peet, Isaac	Mechanic	Talbot street	B
Peet, Thomas	Currier	6, Bath street	
Peet, Chas. Septimus	Hosier and manufacturer, warehouse Bridge street	Cumberland terrace, Lloyd sq.,London	F,B
Peet, James & Charles Septimus	Manufacturers of hosiery, galloons, and doubles	Bridge street	B
Peet, James	Silk manufacturer	Friar gate	F,B
Pegg, Charles	Coal dealer	Nun's street	
Pegg, James	Dealer in rags, bones, &c.	Walker lane	B
Pegg, Samuel	Shopkeeper	22, City road	B
Pegg, John	Labourer	Canal street	
Pegg, George	Higgler	Grove street	
Pegg, James	Works at railway	Bloom street	
Pegg, Elizabeth	Butcher	Bridge gate	
Pegg, John	Beer seller	William street	F,B
Pegg, Jacob	Tailor	Back Sitwell street	F
Pegg, Thomas	Gentleman	2, Grove terrace	F,B
Pegg, Mrs.	Lodging house	Traffic street	
Pegg, Robert & Co.	Manufacturing chemists, colour, Roman cement, and paint and plaster manufacturers	Uttoxeter road	
Pegg, Robert	Colour manufacturer, offices Goodwin street and Uttoxeter road	Vernon street	B
Pegg, Charles	Engineer	Park street	F,B
Pegg, John	J. tanner	Nun's street	B
Pegg, William	Shopkeeper	3, Nottingham road	B
Pegg, William	Hairdresser	Friar gate	B
Pegg, William	Gentleman, 75, River street,	Hulme, Manchester	F
Peirce, John	Framework knitter	Uttoxeter road	Fr
Pemberton, George	Brazier and tin plate worker	St. Peter's street	B
Pemberton, William	J. bricklayer	20, Nun's street	
Pemberton, Sarah	Beerseller, Bank Tavern	Friar gate	
Pemberton, Richard	J. bricklayer	59, Willow row	
Pemberton, John	J. tin plate worker	Sitwell street	B

Pemberton, George	J. bricklayer	Sitwell street	B
Pendleton, William	Farmer	Burnaston	F
Penton, James	Tailor	20, St. Helen's street	
Pepper, John	Book-keeper at railway	Wilmot street	B
Pepper, Francis	Horse breaker, trainer, and clipper	York street	B
Peters, Edward	J. jeweller	4, Short street	
Peters, John	J. smith	Eagle street	
Percival, William	Bricklayer	Bradshaw street	
Percival, John	Shoemaker and shopkeeper	Sacheverel street	
Perkins, William	Labourer	Bag lane	
Perkins, Henry	Hairdresser and perfumer, and dealer in toys	Corn market	B
Pettit, John	Engineer at railway	Canal street	B
Philips, William	Gardener	Parker street	
Phillips, William	Agent	Willington	F
Pick, Abraham	Soap boiler and chandler, wholesale and retail grocer and tea dealer	20, Queen street	B
Pickering, Jos. Henry	Solicitor	Queen street	
Pickering, William	Joiner and cabinet maker, and carver after the antique	King street	
Pickford, William	Gentleman	Park street	F
Pickford and Co.	General carriers to all parts of the kingdom by canal and railway	Siddals lane and Park street	B
Pierce, James	15, Fore street, Cripplegate, London		F
Piggin, Thomas	Vict., Bishop Blaze	Morledge	B
Pigott, Robert	J. printer	Sitwell street	B
Pigott, Elizabeth	Shopkeeper	Goodwin street	
Pike, Isaac	Plasterer	16, Parker street	F,B
Pike, Washington	Cornfactor and mealman	Cheapside	B
Pike, John Gregory	Minister of General Baptist chapel, Brook street	Parker street	B
Pike, Walter and William	Booksellers, stationers, and printers	39, Corn market	
Pike, Walter	Publisher of the Derby Reporter, on Thursdays	Normanton	F,Fr
Pike, William	Bookseller, stationer, & printer	Normanton road	F,Fr
Pike, Isaac	Plasterer	Cheapside	F
Pimm, Mrs.		Friar gate	
Pimm, Timothy	Gentleman	Ford street	F,B
Pipes, Thomas	Labourer	Eagle street	
Pipes, Samuel	Tailor	Normanton road	
Pipes, Thomas	Boot, shoe, and patten maker	St. Peter's street	B
Pitman, Rich. Brown	Painter & vict., Hen&Chickens	Walker lane	F
Pitt, William	Nail manufacturer	Bag lane	
Plackett, William		Duffield	Fr
Plant, Joseph	Moulder	City road	
Plant, John	Overlooker at Bridgett's mill	Ct., Bridge street	
Platts, Ann	Hosier and haberdasher	16, Iron gate	
Platts, William	Vict., Duke of Clarence	Mansfield road	B

Platts, John	Shopkeeper	Siddals lane	
Platts, William	Carpenter and joiner	Ct. 3, Queen street	
Pool, Thomas	Shoemaker	Albion place	
Pool, William	Carpenter and builder	Friar gate	F,B
Pool, John	Bricklayer	Devonshire street	
Pool, Benjamin	Brickmaker	15, Goodwin street	B
Poole, William	Clock and watch maker	76, Devonshire street	
Popple, John	Bookbinder	Ashbourn road	B
Porter, Caleb	Traveller	Brook street	
Porter, John	Ale and porter brewer	Ashbourn road	F,B
Porter, Henry	Bookseller	Park street	
Porter, Joseph	Labourer	Burton road	
Porter, Thomas	China painter	Brook street	Fr
Porter, Thomas	Bricklayer and bird preserver	Brook street	
Porter, James	J. joiner	6, Talbot street	
Porter, Thomas	Works at shot tower	Bag lane	
Porter, William	Officer of excise	Darwin terrace	
Porter, Robert	Hairdresser	26, Brook street	
Portmore, Thomas	Framework knitter	Fowler street	Fr
Potter, David	Wood turner	Curzon street	B
Potter, David	Wood turner	Talbot yard	F
Potter, William	Labourer	Upper Brook street	B
Potter, Joseph	Hat manufacturer	12, Bold lane	B
Potter, John	Labourer	Brook street	
Potter, Mary	Dress and straw hat maker	12, Bold lane	
Potter, Thomas	J. weaver	Brook street	B
Potter, Joseph	J. tailor	Nun's street	
Potter, James	Butcher	Ashbourn road	B
Potter, Charles	Butcher	Friar gate	B
Potter, George	J. bricklayer	South street	
Potter, William	Milk seller	14, Talbot street	
Potter, Thomas	Turnkey at gaol	York street	
Potter, James	Hatter	Burton road	
Potter, Samuel	Carpenter and builder	Devonshire street	
Potts, Thomas	Gentleman	15, Markea. lane	F,Fr
Potts, Thomas	J. joiner	Traffic street	
Potts, Robert	Milk seller	New street	
Potts, John	Wagoner	Ct. 6, Bag lane	
Potts, Richard	Shopkeeper	Friar gate	
Potts, Patrick		Nottingham	F
Pountain, John	Book-keeper	Park street	B
Pountain, Thomas	Farmer	Cowsley	B
Pountain, Benjamin	Wine and spirit merchant	Rotten row	B
Pountain, Thomas	Lace manufacturer	6, Devonshire street	B
Pountain, Thomas	Wine and spirit merchant	Market place	B
Pountain, J. and T.	Farmers	Nottingham road	B
Powell, William	Clerk at Mr. Wright's, cheese-factor	Summer hill	
Powell, William	J. brewer	Grove street	
Powell	Butler and valet to Admiral Curzon	Ashbourn road	
Powell, William	Traveller	Park street	B

Poyser, Mrs. Samuel		Kedleston road	
Poyser, Edwin	Tailor	29, St. Helen's street	B
Poyser	J. shoemaker	Traffic street	
Poyser, John	J. shoemaker	4, Agard street	
Poyser, John	Shoemaker	8, Devonshire street	
Poyser, George	Tailor	Market place	
Poyser, Henry	Shoemaker	Ct. 9, Brook street	Fr
Poyser, William	Last, boot tree, and patten maker	Ct., Sadler gate	B
Poyser, Michael	Joiner and cabinet maker	42, Osmaston street	B
Pratt, Charles	Treasurer, chamberlain, and inspector of corn returns	13, Osmaston street, office Mkt. place	B
Pratt, Thomas	Schoolmaster	7, Friar gate	B
Pratt, John	Shopkeeper	Siddals lane	B
Pratt, George	Stonemason	4, Mansfield road	
Pratt, Thomas	Sexton at St. Peter's church	31, Eagle street	
Presbury, William	Farmer	Little Chester	F
Prescud, John	Master of National school	Traffic street	
Prescud, Mary	Mistress of Infants' school	Siddals lane	
Preston, Thomas	J. tin plate worker	Bloom street	Fr
Price, James	Gentleman	Littleover	F
Price, John	Architect and surveyor, office Victoria street	Littleover	F,B
Price, James	House and sign painter	30, St. Mary's gate	B
Price, George, sen.	Eating house, licensed to let post horses	Sadler gate	F,B
Priest, John	Blacksmith	Bag lane	B
Priest, William	Blacksmith	Bag lane	
Prince, Mrs. Godfrey		Cheapside	
Prince, William	Pawnbroker & general salesman	Queen street	B
Prince, John	Vict., Old Telegraph, butcher & eating house, contractor to convey mail bags to Kegworth	2, Morledge	B
Prince & Bolsover	Pawnbrokers & general salesmen	36, Queen street	
Prince, John	Baker, flour dealer, and seedsman	St. Alkmund's church yard	
Pryer, Stephen	Solicitor's clerk	7, St. Mary's gate	B
Purdy, Joseph	Sawyer	81, Devonshire st.	B
Purdy, Thomas	Gardener	Bag lane	
Purfield, William	J. weaver	Litchurch street	
Purkin, Henry	Lace hand	Sacheverel street	
Purslove, John	Frying pan and dust pan manufacturer	Bloom street	
Quin, James	Tailor and draper	13, St. James's lane	
Raby, James	Moulder	Erasmus street	
Radford, Francis	Upholsterer & cabinet maker	Brook street	
Radford, S.	Milliner and straw hat maker	Brook street	
Radford, John	Butcher	Sitwell street	
Radford, Henry	Butcher, shop Market head	Friar gate	F,B

Radford, John	Butcher	Friar gate	B
Radford, Francis	Butcher	Corn market	
Radford, William	Vict., Bell and Castle	Burton road	B
Radford, William	Unsworth & Co's. factory	Siddals lane	
Radford, Samuel Richardson, esq.			F
Radford, John	Baker and flour dealer	Corn market	F,B
Radford, William	Butcher	Burton road	F,B
Radford, Thomas	Sawyer	Castle street	
Radford, John	Huckster	Bag lane	
Radford, Alexander, esq.		New Uttoxeter rd	F,B
Radford, Joseph	Butcher	Liversage street	
Ramage, William	Locomotive department	Railway station	
Ramsall, Edwin	Butcher & vict., Durham Ox	St. Peter's street	F,B
Randall, Henry	Hair cutter	Albion street	
Randall, George	Hairdresser, perfumer, and dealer in jewellery & toys	12, Rotten row	F,B
Randles, Thomas	Gentleman	Osmaston road	
Ratcliffe, John	Traveller	Osmaston street	
Ratcliffe, Thomas	Labourer	Cuckold's alley	
Ratcliffe, Mrs.		Liversage street	
Ratcliffe, Joseph	Shoemaker	8, Morledge	Fr
Ratcliffe, William	J. joiner	Hill street	
Ratcliffe, Thomas	Labourer	Parker street	F
Ratcliffe, Elizabeth	Beer seller	Wright street	
Ratcliffe, John	Wine and spirit merchant	11, Corn market	B
Ratcliffe, William and John	Furnishing ironmongers and colourmen	Corn market	B
Rawlins, John	Gentleman	7, Parker street	B
Ray, William	Clothier	St. James's lane	
Ray, William	J. joiner	Liversage street	
Raynor, John	J. stonemason	Leonard street	
Reader, James	Basket maker	Ct., Friar gate	
Redfearn, John	Stonemason	Grove street	
Redfearn, John	Canal surveyor	Siddals lane	B
Redfearn, Joseph	Hostler	Liversage street	
Redfearn, John	J. tailor	Fingal street	
Redfearn, John	Labourer	Spring gardens	
Redfearn, Barnabas	Silk weaver	Leonard street	
Redfearn, Isaac	Dealer in rags, bones, &c.	Walker lane	
Redfearn, William	Framework knitter	Grove terrace	
Redfearn, Samuel	Framework knitter	Ct. 1, Morledge	
Redfearn, Philip	Butcher	Grove street	
Redfearn, Robert	Silk weaver	Burton road	
Redfearn, Joseph	Brickmaker	Mundy street	F
Redfearn, William	Butcher	Goodwin street	Fr
Redfearn, John	Stonemason	3, Green street	B
Redfern, Benjamin	Tailor	Osmaston street	
Redfern, Philip	Tailor	St. James's lane	B
Redfern, John	Brickmaker and beer seller	Nun's street	F,B
Redgate, Robert	Weighing machine, and beadle at St. John's church	Bridge street	

Redgate, Richard	Beadle and sexton at St. Werburgh's church	Short street	B
Redwood, Thomas	Framework knitter	Agard street	
Reedman, William	Foreman at Schweppe and Co's. soda water manufactory	Agard street	B
Reeves, John	Maltster and vict., Angel Inn	Corn market	F,B
Revill, Thomas	Stonemason	Brook street	
Revill, Daniel	J. silk throwster	Canal street	
Rewcastle, Nathaniel	Hairdresser	44, Willow row	B
Rewcastle, John	Hairdresser	Green lane	B
Rewcastle, David	Hairdresser, umbrella and parasol maker	3, Queen street	B
Rice, Henry Howard		Derby	Fr
Rice, Thomas	J. wheelwright	Albion place	
Rice, Wm. Henry	Plasterer	Devonshire street	
Rice, Richard	Agent to Pickford and Co.	Siddals lane	B
Rice, Benjamin, jun.	Plumber and glazier	16, Friar gate	F,B
Rice, Benjamin, sen.	Coal merchant	1, Cavendish st.	F,B
Rice, William	Plumber and glazier	Curzon street	Fr
Richardson, Samuel	Tailor	Osmaston road	
Richardson, Thomas	J. brickmaker	Ct. 1, Willow row	
Richardson, Wm. & J.	Curriers and leather factors	St. Peter's street	F,B
Richardson, John	Currier and leather factor	Sitwell street	F,B
Richardson, James	Tailor	33, Osmaston street	B
Richardson, John	Brazier and tin plate worker	39, Bridge gate	B
Richardson, William		Breadsall	F
Richardson, George	Framework knitter	Union buildings	
Richardson, Charles	Vict., Dog and Partridge	13, Tenant street	B
Richardson, Peter	Shoemaker	Ct. 1, King street	
Richardson, Thomas	Wholesale printer & bookseller	Ashbourn road	F,B
Richardson, Joseph H.	Wholesale printer & bookseller	Ashbourn road	F
Richardson, John	Framework knitter	Brook walk	
Richardson, John	Hairdresser	King street	B
Rickards, Thomas	Joiner and modeller	York street	
Rickards, Richard	J. stonemason	9, Chester place	
Rickard, George	Agent to Derby Canal comp., and clerk at Savings bank	Friar gate	F
Rickman, Geo. Henry	Station master	Railway terrace	
Ride, Thomas	Nail manufacturer	30, Green lane	B
Ride, James	Higgler	Siddals lane	
Ride, Samuel	Vict., Goat's Head	32, Willow row	B
Riding, Peter	Vict., Freemason's Arms	Albion street	F,B
Riding, Joseph	Beer seller and shopkeeper	Eagle street	
Riding, John	Bricklayer	Back Sitwell street	
Riley, William	Framework knitter	Markeaton lane	
Riley, John	Gardener and seedsman	39, Parker street	B
Riley, Samuel	Bricklayer	5, Charles street	B
Riley, Jacob	J. Cabinet maker	Talbot street	
Rimington, George	Bread and biscuit baker	Park street and Carrington street	B
Rimington, John	Governor of Derby Infirmary	London road	F
Rimington, Mrs.	Matron of Derby Infirmary	London road	

Robertson, Eliza	Dealer in water colours	St. Alkm. ch. yd.	
Robertson, George	Labourer	Litchurch street	
Roberts, Benjamin	Labourer	Cockpit hill	Fr
Roberts, James	Framework knitter	St. Peter's street	Fr
Roberts, Thomas	Bookseller, bookbinder, stationer, & stereotyper, general news agent, and agent for all periodical publications—Morning papers delivered same morning as published in London.	St. James's lane	B
Roberts, William	Bookbinder	35, Willow row	B
Roberts, William	Alms houses	Full street	Fr
Roberts, John	Gentleman	Uttoxeter road	
Roberts, Walter	Plumber and glazier	Bold lane	F,B
Roberts, Thomas	Labourer	8, Cannon street	Fr
Roberts, Wolstan	Clock and watch manufacturer, gold and silversmith, and working jeweller	56, Sadler gate, and Bold lane	B
Roberts, William	Chimney sweeper	14, Willow row	B
Roberts, John	Framework knitter	Cannon street	Fr
Roberts, Sam. John	Hatter and furrier	Market place	Fr
Roberts, Walter	J. plumber	Full street	F
Roberts, William	Maltster	Short street	
Robinson, John	Labourer	Grove street	
Robinson, William	Blacksmith, shop Brook st.	Kensington	
Robinson, George	J. painter	Brook walk	Fr
Robinson, Thomas	Moulder	12, Darwin row	
Robinson, George	J. coach builder	South street	
Robinson, Luke	Labourer	Bridge street	
Robinson, Robert	Silk mercer, linen and woollen draper	St. Peter's bridge	B
Robinson, John	Silk manufacturer	Sacheverel street	B
Robinson, Robert	J. joiner	Erasmus street	
Robinson, J. & Thos.	Silk manufacturers	Sacheverel street	B
Robinson, James	Compositor	Sitwell street	B
Robinson, John	Beer seller	15, Bold lane	B
Robinson, James	Brass, iron, and wood turner, machineist, and patent axle manufacturer	6, Wright street	B
Robinson, Thomas	Iron and nail merchant	Bridge street	F,B
Robinson, Samuel	House and sign painter	12, Brook walk	B
Robinson, Joseph	Bookbinder	Parker street	
Robinson, George	Shopkeeper	Albion street	
Robinson, John Smythe		King William street, London	F
Robinson, Edward	Joiner	44, Nun's street	F,B
Robinson, William	Tailor	44, Nun's street	B
Robinson, Francis	Draper	Exeter street	
Robotham, William	Solicitor	College place	B
Robotham, George	Baker and confectioner	Corn market	B
Robottom, George	Joiner	Upper Brook street	F
Rodgers, David	Silk weaver	24, Bridge street	

Rodgers, John	China painter	Bloom street	
Rodgers, William	Broker	14, Willow row	B
Rodgers, Thomas	Shoeing smith, farrier, and vict., Old Three Crowns	24, Bridge gate	B
Roe, William	Book-keeper	Wilmot street	B
Roe, Richard		Quarndon	F
Roe, Henry	China painter	27, Erasmus street	
Roe, William	Labourer	Eagle street	B
Roe	J. wheelwright	Large's street	
Roe, Mary	Milliner and dressmaker	London road	
Roe, John	Horse dealer and licensed to let post horses	Curzon street	
Roe, William	Chair turner	Nottingham road	B
Roe, James	J. weaver	Normanton road	
Roe, William	Shoemaker	7, Grove terrace	B
Roe and Oakley	English and foreign timber merchants, dealers in Newcastle tiles, floor bricks, &c.	Cockpit hill and Siddals lane	
Roe, William	Land surveyor	Osmaston street	
Roe, Thomas	Timber merchant	25, Eagle street	B
Roe, William	Postboy	Green lane	
Roebuck, Thomas	Tallow chandler	Grove street	
Roebuck, Thomas	Animal painter, Tiger Inn	Corn market	
Roffey, Edward	Engine driver for the North Midland Railway company	Canal street	
Rollinson, Edward	Looker over at Taylor's mill	Castle street	
Roome, John	J. tailor	Ct., Bridge street	
Roome, William	Bricklayer	Devonshire street	
Roome, Abraham	Framework knitter	Talbot street	
Roper, John	J. rope maker	New street	
Roper, James Thos.	Hostler	Orchard street	B
Rose, James	J. clock and watchmaker	Albion place	
Rose, Joseph	Gardener	5, Cannon street	B
Rose, Thomas	Bookbinder	Large's street	
Rosigh, M. de & Co.	French and English boot and shoe manufacturers	26, Iron gate	
Ross, George	Gentleman	Burton road	B
Rotherham, John	J. painter	Ct. 6, Bold lane	
Rouse, William	Framework knitter	Belper	Fr
Rouse, John	Framework knitter	Friar gate	Fr
Rouse, William	Labourer	Darley lane	Fr
Rouse, John	Alms houses	Full street	Fr
Rouse, Edward	J. engineer	St. Mary's bridge	Fr
Rouse, Jesse	Framework knitter	Ct., St. Mary's gate	Fr
Rouse, Edward	China painter	Erasmus street	Fr
Rouse, Thomas	Policeman	Darley lane	Fr
Rowbottom, Joseph		Derby	Fr
Rowbottom, William	Bookseller, printer, bookbinder, stationer, and paper hanging warehouse, Derbyshire Courier office, agent for London daily papers	1, St. Mary's gate	F,B

Rowbottom, George	Shoemaker	Brook street	F
Rowbottom, Samuel	Schoolmaster	Breadsall	F
Rowbottom, Sam. jun.	Bookseller	St. Mary's gate	F
Rowbottom, Richard	Shopkeeper	Willow row	
Rowbottom, Richard	Book-keeper	Sitwell street	
Rowell, Frederick	Second master of the Free Grammar School	St. Peter's ch. yd.	
Rowe, Thomas	J. weaver	Devonshire street	
Rowe, Charles	Wagoner	7, Brook walk	
Rowland, Thomas	Framework knitter	19, Bloom street	
Rowland, Richard	J. coach builder	Hill street	
Rowley, Sarah	Vict., Stag and Pheasant	Brook street	
Rowley, William	Vict., Sun Inn	103, Friar gate	B
Rowley, John	Tailor	Hope street	
Rowlston, Francis		Cambden Town, London	F
Roworth, John	Beer seller, Rose & Thistle	Chapel street	B
Rudkin, John Charles	Surgeon	26, Friar gate	B
Rudkin and Fox	Surgeons	Ford street	
Rushton, John	Beer seller and shoemaker	Lodge lane	B
Rushton, John	J. jeweller	25, Eagle street	B
Russell, John	Vict., Barley Mow	St. Peter's street	B
Russell, Robert	Barley Mow	St. Peter's street	
Russell, Joseph	Farmer	St. Peter's street	
Rutherford, Mrs.		Wilmot street	
Rutland, Thomas	China painter	14, Erasmus street	Fr
Ryley, Henry	Overlooker at Baker's mill	Agard street	B
Sadler, Charles	Hairdresser and perfumer	Iron gate	
Sadler, Wm. Ford	Nursery man	London road	F,B
Saint, John	Gentleman	26, King street	F,Fr
Saint, Thomas	J. jeweller	32, Leonard street	
Sale, Charles	Ale & porter dealer, Iron gate	1, Parker street	B
Sale, Joseph	Solicitor, and coroner for the Hundred of Repton and Gresley	Osmaston road	B
Sale, William	Hatter, draper, and hosier	19, Corn market	B
Salisbury, Richard	Butcher	King street	B
Salisbury, Henry	Tobacco pipe manufacturer	17, Willow row	F,B
Salt, Lucy	Dress and straw hat maker	73, Bridge street	
Salt, Sarah	Baker and flour dealer	23, Burton road	
Salt, John	Servant to Edw. Strutt, esq.	69, Bridge gate	B
Salt, James		Kedleston	F
Sandars, Francis	Gentleman	81, Friar gate	F,B
Sandars, Charles	Gentleman	Friar gate	F,B
Sandars, John	Grocer and tea dealer, hop and seed merchant, soap and candle manufacturer, and agent to the Pelican and Phœnix Fire and Life Insurance offices, magistrate for the borough, and alderman	13, Market place	F,Fr

Sandars & Haywood	General ironmongers, iron, steel, and tin plate merchants, tin plate workers, bell hangers and copper smiths, iron and brass founders	12, Market place	F,B
Sandars and Clarke	Wine and spirit merchants	Market place	F,B
Sandars, Alexander	Locomotive department	Leonard street	
Sandars, Joseph	Boot and shoe warehouse	52, Sadler gate	F,B
Sandars, Samuel	J. silk weaver	South street	
Sandars, Joseph	Shoemaker	Ct. 5, Willow row	
Sandars, William	Tailor	Leonard street	
Sandars, William	J. silk weaver	Short street	
Sandars, Joseph, esq.		Liverpool	F
Sandars, Joseph, jun.	Gentleman	Eccleshall, Staffordshire	F
Sanderson, Samuel	Porter	Thorn tree lane	
Sands, Edward	Traveller	Parker street	
Sargeant, Charles	Book-keeper at Station	Eagle street	
Saxton, William	Labourer	Litchurch street	
Schweppe, J. & Co.	Soda water manufacturer	Friar gate	
Scott, William	Bookbinder	3, Charles street	B
Scour, John	Framework knitter	Brook street	
Seal, James	Earthenware dealer	Albion place	
Searl, William	Gentleman	11, Wardwick	F,B
Sedgwick, William	Tailor	27, Ford street	
Sephton, William	Boat builder and beer seller, Boat Tavern	Nottingham road	B
Sessions, Samuel	Plasterer	St. Peter's church yd.	
Severne, Francis	Solicitor	32, Osmaston st.	F,B
Severne, Hen. de Milt	Wholesale jeweller	Osmaston street	B
Shardlow, Michael	Gentleman	Shardlow	F
Sharlock, Joseph	J. wood turner	Peach's row	
Sharp, Benjamin		Mickleover	F
Sharp, Benjamin	Framework knitter	Fowler street	B
Sharp, Mary	Milliner	34, Friar gate	
Sharpe, Gabriel	Silk framework knitter	Osmaston street	
Sharpe, Maria	Schoolmistress	Albion street	
Sharpe, Richard	Nail maker	12, Darley lane	
Sharpe, George	J. blacksmith	Peach's row	
Sharpe, John	Framework knitter	Bag lane	
Sharrard, John	Lamp man at Station	Canal street	
Sharratt, Thomas	Framework knitter	Cannon street	
Shaw, Thomas	Whitesmith and machineist	Wright street	
Shaw, Charles	Whitesmith and machineist	Ct. 3, Willow row	B
Shaw, William	Gentleman	Vernon street	F,Fr
Shaw, Thomas	J. joiner	Erasmus street	
Shaw, James	Plasterer	Green street	
Shaw, William	Tailor, pawnbroker, and general dealer	3, Cockpit hill	B
Shaw, John	J. painter	Ct. 3, Bridge street	B
Shaw, William	Cornfactor	52, Friar gate	F,B
Shaw, Thomas	Labourer	Burton road	

Shaw, John Vickers	Gardener and seedsman	Friar gate	
Shaw, John	Gardener	Cockpit hill	
Shaw, Mary	Shopkeeper	3, Ford street	
Shaw, Samuel	Butcher	Rook hills	F
Shaw, Christopher	Butcher	Back Sitwell street	
Shaw, Joshua	Beadle at St. Peter's church	Duke street	
Shaw, John	Chemist and druggist	8, Corn market	B
Shaw, John	Blacksmith and shopkeeper	Canal street	
Shaw, Francis	Cornfactor and corn miller, mill Duke street	Cherry street	F,Fr
Shaw, Griffith	Gardener	Friar gate	
Sheen, James	Porter at Railway Station	John street	B
Sheldon, Charles	J. joiner and cabinet maker	35, Bath street	
Shelley, Richard	Fitter-up of engines	River street	F
Shenton, William	Slater	Liversage street	
Shenton, Edward & Son	Slaters and slate merchants, tomb & headstone engravers	8, George street	B
Sheppard, James T.	Draper	4, Cherry street	B
Sheppard, James T. and Co.	Linen and woollen drapers, silk mercers, hosiers, & haberdashers, family mournings, funerals undertaken, &c.	Market head	B
Sheppard, Thomas	Accountant, and reporter	John street	
Sheppard, Sarah	Straw bonnet warehouse		
Shepherd, Thomas	Beer seller & shoemaker	Sitwell street	B
Shepherd, John	Currier and leather factor	Bag lane	F,B
Shepherd, Samuel	J. whitesmith	Brook street	
Shepherd, Slater	Butcher	Brook street	
Shepherd, Joseph	Labourer	Cross lanes	Fr
Shepherd, John	J. joiner	Eagle street	B
Shepherdson, John	Fluor spar manufacturer	4, Queen street	Fr
Sherwin, William	Chemist and druggist	18, Queen street	B
Sherwin, John	Schoolmaster	Litchurch street	
Sherwin, Samuel	Bailiff to W. E. Mousley, esq.	Ford street	F,B
Sherwin, John	Maltster	Normanton road	
Sherwin, Samuel	Farmer	Kedleston road	B
Sherwin, Thomas	J. colourman	Ct. 3, St. Mary's gate	
Sherwin, William	Grocer and flour dealer	Bridge street	
Sherwin, William	Keeps patent mangle	John street	F
Shields, John	Twisthand	Brook street	
Shiers, Mary Josephine	Vocalist and professor of music	London road	
Shilcock & Hipworth	Linen and woollen drapers	5, Iron gate	B
Shipley, Thomas	Clerk at Mason's colour works	Willow row	
Shipley, Cadwallader	Shoemaker	20, Willow row	B
Shipley, William	Shoemaker	William street	
Shipley, James	Watchmaker	Ct. 2, Bold lane	F,B
Shipley, John	Moulder	11, Erasmus street	
Shipley, James	Farmer	Ashbourn road	B
Shipley, William	Gentleman	Sitwell street	F,B
Shore, Joseph	Painter	Albion place	B

Shore, John	Bailiff	St. Peter's street	
Short, Thos. Wilkins	Shoemaker	Traffic street	
Short, Rev. T.	Minister Wesleyan chapel	King street	
Sidebottom, Joseph	Plumber and glazier	Derwent street	F,B
Sidley, Thomas	J. weaver	Markeaton lane	
Sikes, Rev. Joseph		Newark-on-Trent	F
Sills, John	Model maker	7, Charles street	B
Simmons, John	Book-keeper at Railway	John street	
Simms, Mary	Bonnet box maker	Ct. 1, St. Mary's gate	
Simms, James	Builder	Hope street	B
Simms, William	Stonemason	Osmaston street	F
Simpson and Frear	Solicitors	St. Mary's gate	
Simpson, Joshua	Painter and stainer	Cockpit hill	Fr
Simpson, Edward	Vict., Lord Byron	Sadler gate bridge	Fr
Simpson, Rev. Robt.		Newark	F
Simpson, James	J. painter	Cockpit hill	
Simpson, Henry	Hairdresser and perfumer	Osmaston road	
Simpson, William	Plasterer	Spondon	Fr
Simpson, Munday	China painter	1, Erasmus street	Fr
Simpson, Joseph	Plasterer	Cockpit hill	F,Fr
Simpson, John	Baker and flour dealer	29, Walker lane	B
Simpson, Thomas	J. weaver	Litchurch street	
Simpson, Thomas	Plasterer	Devonshire st.	F,Fr
Simpson, Miss	Schoolmistress of Female British school	Chapel street	
Simpson, John	Vict. and painter	Devonshire street	F,B
Simpson, Samuel	Vict., Plasterer's Arms Inn	Siddals lane	Fr
Simpson, Benjamin	Plasterer and painter	Albion street	Fr
Simpson, Frederick	Surveyor and civil engineer, office Queen street	Spondon	F
Simpson, Charles	Cheesefactor	Iron gate	F,B
Simpson, James B. esq.	Solicitor, clerk to the commissioners of taxes, and commissioner for taking acknowledgments of deeds by married women	35, St. Mary's gate	F,B
Simpson, George	Vict., Devonshire Arms	11, Devonshire st.	F,Fr
Simpson, William	J. currier	Bag lane	Fr
Simpson, Thomas	Painter	Rivett street	Fr
Simpson, Edward		Alvaston	F
Simpson, Edw. Lloyd	Manufacturer	Spondon	F
Simpson, William	Butcher	Derby	Fr
Simpson, Charles	Painter	Siddals lane	Fr
Simpson, Joseph	Plasterer	Hill street	Fr
Simpson, William, esq., M.D.		Hilton cottage	Fr
Simpson, Henry	Painter	Siddals lane	Fr
Simpson, Thomas	Plasterer	Walker lane	Fr
Simpson, Robert	Plasterer	Bag lane	Fr
Simpson, Joseph	Shoemaker	St. Peter's street	Fr
Simpson, Isaac, sen.	Painter	Cockpit hill	Fr
Simpson, Turner & Co.	Silk throwsters	Canal street	B
Simpson, William	Painter	Castle street	

Simpson, Adam	Foreman to Mr. Sandars, chandler	Bridge street	B
Simpson, William	Baker	Bloom street	Fr
Simpson, Edward	Goldsmith and jeweller	Osmaston street	F
Simpson, Isaac, jun.	Painter	Cockpit hill	Fr
Simpson, John	Gardener	Castle street	
Simpson, John	Plasterer	Burton road	Fr
Simpson, William	Vict., Holly Bush	84, Bridge street	F,B
Simpson, Samuel	Painter	Hope street	Fr
Simpson, John	Gentleman	Osmaston road	
Simpson, Francis	Plasterer	Eagle street	Fr
Simpson, William	Beer seller	Albion street	
Simpson, James	Butcher	Devonshire street	Fr
Simpson, Thomas	Butcher	Nun's street	Fr
Simpson, Henry	J. corn miller	Devonshire street	Fr
Sims, William	Butcher	Burton road	B
Sims, John	Lace manufacturer	Sitwell street	F,B
Sims, John	Governor of county gaol	South street	
Sing, Rev. Thomas	Catholic priest	Bridge gate	F,B
Sison, Michael	Vict., Shakspeare	17, Bold lane	B
Sisson, Mary	Straw bonnet maker	Parker street	
Skevington, John	Shopkeeper	9, Green lane	B
Slack, Frederick	Hosiery warehouse	St. Helen's street	
Slack, Samuel	Cow keeper	Kedleston road	
Slack, William		Quorndon	F
Slack, William	Tailor	Old Uttoxeter road	B
Slater, Joshua	Higgler	8, Charles street	F,B
Slater, William	Coal dealer	Devonshire street	
Slater, Robt. Gilman	Joiner,builder & cabinetmaker	Vernon street	F,B
Slater, Augustus		Houndsgate, Nottingham	F
Slater, John	Labourer	Eagle street	
Slater, Thomas	Grocer	Upper Brook street	B
Slater, James	Lodging house	19, Walker lane	
Slater, Jacob	Gardener and milk seller	Uttoxeter road	B
Slater, Edward	Shopkeeper	Erasmus street	Fr
Slater, George	Baker and flour dealer	Canal street	
Slater, Elizabeth	Milliner and dressmaker	Brook street	
Slater, Matthew	Gentleman	Cross lanes	B
Slater, Samuel	J. wheelwright	Eagle street	
Slater, William	Builder	Fowler street	F
Slater, John	Butler	Brook street	Fr
Slater, John	Butcher	25, Brook street	B
Slater, John		Siddals lane	F
Slater, William	Plumber and glazier	Bag lane	Fr
Slinn, Thomas	Bricklayer	Friar gate	Fr
Slinn, James	Bricklayer	Cross lanes	Fr
Smallwood, William	Framework knitter	Brook street	
Smallwood, William	Timber merchant, Exeter st.	Kedleston road	F,B
Smedley, Mary	Vict., Wheel Inn	Friar gate	
Smedley, John	Jeweller	Corn market	
Smedley, John	Vict., White Bear Inn	Derwent row	F,B
Smedley, George	Shoemaker	Kensington	

Smedley, James	Plumber and glazier	Friar gate	
Smedley, William	J. coach builder	Eagle street	F
Smedley, Samuel	Vict., Castle Fields Inn	Siddals lane and Traffic street	F,B
Smedley, William	J. tanner	Bradshaw street	
Smeeton, Robert	Fitter	North street	
Smithard, Samuel	Watch manufacturer and jeweller, shop Corn market	Sacheverel street	B
Smithard, Joseph	Tailor	2, Tenant street	B
Smithard, John	Hairdresser	11, Morledge	B
Smithard, Simeon	J. chairmaker	Liversage street	
Smith, Thomas	Works at saw mills	City road	Fr
Smith, William	Labourer	Castle street	
Smith, Thomas	Butcher	Litchurch street	
Smith, Thomas	Brushmaker	William street	
Smith, James	Tailor	2, Bridge gate	B
Smith, Thomas	Shopkeeper	Burton road	B
Smith, John	J. painter	Siddals lane	Fr
Smith, Thomas	Nail maker	Devonshire street	
Smith, Elisha	Bleacher	Little Eaton	F
Smith, Thomas	J. engineer	Ford street	
Smith, Charles	Grocer and tea dealer	Talbot street	F,Fr
Smith, James	Tailor	Siddals lane	
Smith, John	Joiner	Old Uttoxeter road	B
Smith, John	Bleacher	Little Eaton	F
Smith, William and Son	Appraisers, surveyors, loan and land agents, coach timber benders, dealers in patent axletrees, springs, &c., and agents to the Derby and Nottingham Life and Fire Assurance company	23, St. Alkmund's ch. yard	F,B
Smith, John	Framework knitter	Dunkirk	B
Smith, John	Beerseller, Red Cow	Bath street	F
Smith, George Slater	Baker and confectioner	Friar gate	B
Smith, John	Bookseller	Liversage street	
Smith, Samuel	Whitesmith, brazier, and tin plate worker, manufacturer of the portable hot air and steam medicated vapour baths, &c.	16, Corn market	F,B
Smith, Samuel, jun.	Whitesmith and brazier	Corn market	
Smith, Joseph	Fetler at foundry	8, Duke street	B
Smith, John	Shopkeeper	12, Goodwin street	
Smith, John	Joiner	Bridge gate	
Smith, William	Hairdresser	Eagle street	
Smith, Charles	Vict., Windmill	25, Willow row	F,B
Smith, Joseph	Foundryman	Duke street	
Smith, Christopher	House painter	26, River street	B
Smith, Charles	Baker and confectioner	Friar gate	F
Smith, Charles	Baker	Bridge gate	
Smith, John	Baker and flour dealer	Brook street	

Smith, Geo. Warwick	Gentleman	Elms, Duffield road	B
Smith, Thomas	Engineer	Canal street	
Smith, George	Wood turner and chair manufacturer	London road	F,B
Smith, John	Labourer	Cuckold's alley	
Smith, Joseph	Tobacco manufacturer	St. Peter's street	B
Smith, Ralph	Vict., Shakspeare	16, Sadler gate	B
Smith, William	Butler	Ashbourn road	
Smith, Thomas	Milk seller	Canal street	
Smith, William	Plumber and glazier	3, George street	B
Smith, Edward	Builder and carpenter	32, Queen street	F,B
Smith, James	Bookseller and bookbinder	Liversage street	
Smith, Joseph	Vict., Swan with two Necks	St. James's lane	F,B
Smith, George	Turner	Old George yard	
Smith, Joseph	Framework knitter	Litchurch street	
Smith, Thomas	Engineer	Agard street	
Smith, Samuel & Co.	Bankers, draw on Smith, Payne, and Smith, London	Rotten row	
Smith, Thomas	Tape weaver	Large's street	
Smith, Thomas	Brazier and tin plate worker	61, St. Peter's st.	F,B
Smith, Joseph	J. bricklayer	Ct. 7, Bold lane	
Smith, Henry	Breeches maker and glover	St. Mich. ch. yd.	F,B
Smith, George	Printer, office Summer hill	Drury lane	B
Smith, John	Framework knitter	Litchurch street	
Smith, George	Brush manufacturer	15, Sadler gate	B
Smith, John	Vict., Seven Stars, and Bowling Green Inn	Nottingham road	B
Smith, Elizabeth	Shopkeeper	Osmaston street	
Smith, William, jun.	Cooper	Tenant street	Fr
Smith, John	Cooper	Tenant street	Fr
Smith, Edward	Cooper	Tenant street	Fr
Smith, William	Works at tape factory	George street	Fr
Smith, Thomas	Bookseller	Cheapside	Fr
Smith, William, sen.	Cooper	11, Tenant street	Fr
Smith, Thomas	J. joiner	River street	
Smith, Thomas	Butcher	9, Morledge	B
Smith, Lewis	Twisthand	Devonshire street	
Smith, James	J. coach builder	Devonshire street	
Smith, David	Cooper	36, Morledge	Fr
Smith, Abraham	Sawyer	Devonshire street	
Smith, Miss Elizabeth		Ashbourn road	F
Smith, Charlotte	Shopkeeper	Agard street	
Smith, John	Gentleman	Wirksworth	F
Smith, John	Fitter-up	Eagle street	
Smith, Joseph	J. weaver	Burton road	
Smith, Samuel	Brazier and tin plate worker	20, London road	B
Smith, Wm. Bishop	Clock maker	Brook walk	Fr
Smith, Samuel	Shopkeeper	Grove street	Fr
Smith, John	Joiner	23, Darley lane	F,B
Smith, William	Milk seller	Darley lane	F,B
Smith, Wm. Seth	Coach shaft bender	King street	B
Smith, Lewis	Basket maker	35, Morledge	B

Smith, John	Shoemaker	Kensington	
Smith, Samuel	Distiller of herbs	Ct. 9, Bridge gate	
Smith, Timothy	Porter at Station	9, Bag lane	
Smith, Joseph	Broker	Willow row	Fr
Smith, John	Joiner	Kensington street	F
Smith, Thomas	Engineer	13, Erasmus street	
Smith, John	Sugar boiler	High street	
Smith, Christopher	Painter	River street	
Smith, William	Tailor	Erasmus street	
Smith, Charles	Framework knitter	Upper Brook street	B
Smith, Robert	Book-keeper	Osmaston road	
Smith, Thos. Daniel St. George	Solicitor	42, Full street	B
Smith, Thomas	Beer seller	King street	
Smith, Joseph	Vict., Royal Telegraph Inn	London road	B
Smith, James	Cooper	41, Full street	F,B
Smith, John	Weaver	10, Charles street	B
Smith, Henry	Coach builder and vict., Old Plough	42, London road	B
Smith and Co.	Grocers and provision stores	London road	
Smith, Mrs.	Midwife	Siddals lane	
Smith, Thomas		Darley	F
Smith, John	Overlooker at Madeley's mill	George street	F
Smith, Gervase	Gentleman	Friar gate	F
Smith, Abel, esq.		London	F
Smith, George Robert, esq.		London	F
Smith, John Henry, esq.		Kingston-on-Hull	F
Smith, Joseph	Engineer	Canal street	
Smithson, Christopher	Ale, porter, and wine vaults, town hall cellars	Sacheverel street	B
Sneasby, William	Dean's row, Nottingham		F
Snow, Walter	Vict., Plumber's Arms	Bag lane	B
Soar, John	Blacking manufacturer	Walker lane	Fr
Soar, Thomas	Blacking manufacturer	Bridge street	F
Soar, William	Hostler	Goodwin street	Fr
Soar, John	Butcher	Mickleover	F
Somerside, George	J. engineer	Litchurch street	
Soresby, James & W.	Wharfingers and carriers by land and water to all parts of England	Siddals lane	B
Sowter, John	Gentleman	London road	F,B
Sowter, George	Gentleman	3, Kedleston road	F,B
Sowter, William	Corn miller and maltster	9, Darwin terrace	F,B
Sowter, George	Labourer	South street	
Sowter, William	Baker and flour dealer	Friar gate	
Sowter, Fredk. Geo.	Beer seller	Quorndon	F
Sowter, Joseph	Baker	Brook street	
Sowter, William	Carpenter and builder	Castle street	F,B
Sowter, Thomas	Baker and flour dealer	45, Willow row	B
Sowter, Charles	Maltster, baker, and dealer in flour	35, Friar gate	F
Sowter, William	Labourer	Thorn tree lane	

Sparks, James	Boot and shoemaker, shop St. Peter's street	South street	B
Sparks, George	Coal dealer	Nottingham road	
Sparks, William	Petrifaction warehouse	20, King street	F
Spencer, Henry	Woollen draper and tailor	Friar gate	B
Spencer, William	Schoolmaster, and agent to the National Assurance Company	4, Green lane	F,B
Spencer, Wm. George	Private teacher	8, Wilmot street	F,B
Spencer, Henry	J. silk weaver	Bradshaw street	
Spencer, Thomas	Hinton charter house, Somersetshire		F
Spencer, J. Anthony	Compositor	49, Bridge gate	B
Spencer, Harriet	Milliner, and straw bonnet manufacturer	49, Bridge gate	
Spencer, Charles	Baker and flour dealer	Old Uttoxeter road	B
Spencer, Jacob	Tailor	Litchurch street	
Spencer, John	Licensed to let post horses for hire	St. Peter's street	B
Spencer, Hannah	Vict., New Inn, coach, commercial, and posting house	14, King street	
Spencer, John	Private teacher	Wilmot street	
Spendlove, John	Beer seller	39, Eagle street	B
Spendlove, George	J. wheelwright	Traffic street	F,B
Sperry, Edward	Linen and woollen draper	45, Queen street	B
Sperry, Mrs.		Osmaston road	
Sperry, Wm. Heawood	Book-keeper	Osmaston road	F,B
Sperry, Frances	Haberdasher	4, Rotten row	
Spinks, Thomas	Spar manufacturer	Queen street	
Spooner, Thomas	Moulder	2, Chester place	
Spooner, William	Moulder	11, City road	Fr
Spooner, Richard	J. engineer	Bradshaw street	
Spooner, Jacob		Breadsall	Fr
Sprintall, Richard	Moulder	Chester place	
Sprintall, Joseph	J. smith	23, Chester place	
Sprintall, George	Moulder	6, City road	
Sprintall, Samuel	Moulder	11, City road	
Sproat, Robert	Shopkeeper	Goodwin street	B
Squires, James	Silk hosiery manufacturer	14, Bridge street	B
Stacey, Joseph	Gentleman's servant	Spring gardens	F,B
Stables, Mrs. Eliz.		Wilmot street	
Stafford, Joseph	Grocer and tea dealer	London street	B
Stainsby, David	Cooper	Uttoxeter road	Fr
Stainsby, Charles	Cooper	Bridge gate	Fr
Staley, Francis	Labourer	Borrough's walk	Fr
Stanesby, James	Hat manufacturer	2, Queen street	B
Stanesby, Richard	Cooper	25, Full street	B
Stanesby, Mrs.		28, Leonard street	
Stanesby, Thomas	Cooper	St. Peter's street	B
Stanford, John Osb.	Book-keeper	Sitwell street	B
Staniforth, James	Mounter	Ct. 3, Full street	B
Stanley, Thomas	Gardener and seedsman	24, Friar gate	B
Starr, William	J. stonemason	Bradshaw street	

Statham, John	Beer seller	John street	
Statham, William	Veterinary surgeon	6, Derwent street	F,B
Statham, Thomas	Engineer	John street	B
Stear, John	J. coach builder	Hill street	
Steel, Mary	Draper and haberdasher	Burton road	
Steel, Thomas, sen.	Butcher	56, Willow row	B
Steel, Thomas, jun.	Butcher	Sadler gate	B
Steel, Catherine	Shopkeeper	30, Leonard street	
Steel, Horatio	China painter	Siddals lane	
Steer, Samuel	Baker and shopkeeper	4, Exeter street	F,B
Steer, John	Umbrella & parasol manufacturer, optician and toyman	4, Market head	Fr
Steer, Aaron	Vict., Odd Fellows' Arms	King street	B
Stenson, Joseph	Plasterer	Devonshire st.	F,Fr
Stenson, Thomas	Farmer	Litchurch	Fr
Stenson, William John	Bookseller, stationer, & music warehouse, and organist at St. Peter's church	1, Corn market	F,Fr
Stephenson, John	Railway contractor, and coal and lime merchant, principal office Railway Station	Ashbourn road	F
Sterland, Martha	Lodging house	York street	
Stevens, Henry J.	Architect and surveyor, anti-dry-rot tanks, Kyan's patent, Nottingham road	16, Full street	B
Stevens, John	Sadler	Bridge gate	
Stevens, George	Book-keeper at gas works	1, Liversage street	
Stevens, John		Chellaston	F
Stevens, Benjamin		Hope street	F
Stevens, John		Derby	F
Stevens, James	Jeweller and silversmith	55, Sadler gate	B
Stevens, Benjamin	Engineer	Hope street	F
Stevenson, Edward	Labourer	Bag lane	
Stevenson, William	Gentleman	Litchurch terrace	Fr
Stevenson, George	Framework knitter	43, Bridge street	
Stevenson, Henry	Bricklayer	Sitwell street	
Stevenson, Thomas	Shoemaker	Bold lane	
Stevenson, William	Framework knitter	Parker street	
Stevenson, Thomas	Manufacturer	Queen street	F,B
Stevenson, George	Draper, shop Irongate	Ashbourn road	B
Stevenson, Amos	Gentleman	Normanton road	
Stevenson, William	Chemist and druggist	7, Corn market	F,B
Stevenson, William	Shopkeeper	Willow row	
Stevenson, Rev. John,	10, Chester terrace, Borough road, Southwark		F
Stevenson, Leonard	Foreman of fitters-up, North Midland Railway	15, North street	
Stoddard, John	J. engineer	25, Waterloo street	
Stone, Edward	Vict., Three Tuns	Sadler gate	
Stone, Samuel	Gentleman	20, Notting. road	F,B
Stone, John	Blacksmith	Park street	
Stone, Robert	Gentleman	Castle place	F
Stone, Thomas	Framework knitter	Castle street	

Stone, Richard	Agent and land surveyor, auditor to the Belper and Chesterfield Union, assessor of taxes, and secretary to the Mechanics' Institution	1, Curzon street	B
Stone, Richard & Mary	Grocers & provision warehouse	Wardwick	
Stone, John	Provision warehouse	Willow row	B
Storer, James	Grocer, tea dealer, and chandler, wholesale and retail	5, Corn market	F,B
Storer, Thomas & Son	Tailors, woollen drapers, and hatters, and agent to the Norwich Union Fire office	4, Corn market	
Storer, Richard	Draper, tailor, and hatter	Corn market	B
Storer, James	Bookseller, printer, stationer, patent medicine warehouse, music repository, & agent for Derbyshire Chronicle	3, St. Peter's street	B
Storer, John	Gentleman farmer	Weston-upon-Trent	F
Storer, William	Velvet weaver and draper	South street	
Storer, Thomas	Draper	Corn market	F,B
Storer, John		Lichfield	F
Storer, Samuel	Hosier	Traffic street	
Storer, William	Framework knitter	Osmaston street	
Storer, Thomas	Beer seller	Traffic street	B
Storer, George	Cooper	Grove street	
Storer, Thomas	Baker	86, Bridge street	
Storr, John	Framework knitter	18, Kensington street	
Stothard, Robert	Bricklayer	Sacheverel street	F
Street & Thompson	Boat builders and carpenters	Exeter street	
Street, John	Merchant	18, Exeter street	F,B
Street, William	Boat builder and carpenter	Exeter street	F,B
Street, Alexander	Boat builder and carpenter	28, City road	F,B
Street, Samuel	J. boatwright	Exeter street	F
Street, Samuel		Borrowash	Fr
Street, Edward		Ashby-de-la-Zouch	F
Street, Anthony	Framework knitter	35, Leonard street	
Stretton, Henry	Grocer and tea dealer	Friar gate	
Stretton, William	J. riband weaver	Bath street	
Strong, William	Gentleman	14, Parker street	B
Strong, Thomas	Tobacco pipe manufacturer	Ct. 7, Willow row	Fr
Strong, William	Tobacco pipe manufacturer	Eagle street	
Strong, Sampson	Tobacco pipe manufacturer	Willow row	Fr
Stroud, Robert	Bricklayer	St. Peter's street	Fr
Stroud, Samuel	Lodging house	Walker lane	Fr
Stroud, John	Framework knitter	Brook walk	Fr
Strutt, Joseph, esq.	Alderman and magistrate	St. Peter's street	F,Fr
Strutt, Edward, esq.,	M.P., alderman & magistrate	St. Helen's house	F,Fr
Strutt, John, esq.	Warehouse	Corn market	B
Strutt, Jedediah, esq.	Warehouse	Corn market	B
Strutt, Anthony Radford, esq.	Warehouse	Corn market	B

Stubberfield, T. H.	Schoolmaster of Wesleyan Methodist boys' school	Chapel street	
Stubbings, John	Framework knitter	Union buildings	
Stubbs, Large	Milk seller	Albion place	
Stubbs, Thomas	J. maltster	Old Uttoxeter road	
Stubbs, Daniel		Handsacre, Staffordshire	F
Styles, Wm. Henry	Gentleman	Eagle street	F
Suddall, William	Tailor and draper	24, Sadler gate	F,B
Summer, William	Shoemaker	Green lane	
Summerfield, Thos.	Vict., Duke of Devonshire	39, Goodwin street	B
Sutherland, James	Carver and gilder, manufacturer of barometers, thermometers, and dealer in plate glass	20, Friar gate	B
Sutherland, Daniel	J. carver and gilder	61, Willow row	
Sutliffe, John	Gardener	Green lane	B
Sutton, James & Co.	Carriers by canal, sea, and railway, to all parts of the kingdom, and wharfingers	Old wharf, Cockpit hill	B
Swain John	Joiner	Traffic street	F,B
Swain, William	Framework knitter	Grove street	F,B
Swainston	Gentleman	Kensington street	
Swanwick, John	Grocer and tea dealer	10, Friar gate	B
Swanwick, John Thos.	Land surveyor, registrar of births, deaths, and marriages, for St. Alkmund's district, and agent for the Sun Fire and Life office	25, St. Mary's gate	F,B
Swift, Thomas	Tea, coffee, grocery, and provision warehouse	29, Sadler gate	F,B
Swindell, Charlotte	Shopkeeper	Normanton road	
Swindell, Edward	Bailiff	Ashbourn road	Fr
Swindell, Samuel	Licensed to let post horses and flies	Goodwin street	F,B
Swindell, James	Shoemaker	34, Morledge	
Swindell, William	Framework knitter	Upper Brook st.	Fr
Swindell, Joseph	Shoemaker	11, Darwin row	
Swinnerton, Stephen	Stone and marble mason, and quarryman, Derby, Little Eaton, Breadsall, and Stanton by Dale, grindstone and scythe stone manufacturer	St. Mary's bridge—wharf, Mansfield road	F,B
Symons, Thomas	Cashier and clerk in Messrs. Crompton and Newton's Bank, and maltster—malthouse, St. James's lane—agent to Clerical, Medical, & General Life Assurance Company	North parade	F,B
Symons, Samuel	Whitesmith	Walker lane	F
Taft, Henry	Higgler	17, Lodge lane	

Taft, Elizabeth	Needle maker	Bridge gate	
Tagg, John	Gentleman	Melbourn	F
Tagg, Joseph	Gentleman	Melbourn	F
Tantum, Edward	Beer seller	7, Burton road	B
Tarr, William	Vict., Noah's Ark, and dealer in cattle	15, Morledge	F,B
Tate, John, sen.	Bricklayer	Large's street	B
Tate, John, jun.	Bricklayer	Parker street	
Tatem, James	Hosier and haberdasher	Queen street	F,B
Tathem, Thomas	Quarryman	Canal street	
Tattershaw, Thomas	J. painter	William street	
Tattershaw, William	J. painter	William street	
Tattershaw, William	Shopkeeper and painter	21, Parker street	B
Tattershaw, Richard	Fly driver	St. James's lane	F
Tatum, Henry		Barrowden, Rutland	F
Taylor, James	Coal dealer	Nottingham road	
Taylor, Thomas		Back Sacheverel street	F
Taylor, Thomas	Book-keeper	Sitwell street	B
Taylor, John	Silk riband weaver	Eagle street	
Taylor, George	Joiner & carpenter, Wilmot st.	Sacheverel st.	F,B
Taylor, George	China painter	Siddals lane	B
Taylor, William	Shoemaker	Normanton road	
Taylor, Ambrose	Cheese factor, and agent to W. Worthington and Sons, wine and spirit merchants, Burton-upon-Trent	Wilmot street	B
Taylor, Benjamin	Potter	Siddals lane	
Taylor, Henry	Vict., Angel	3, Burton road	B
Taylor, John	Vict, Old White Horse	85, Friar gate	B
Taylor, Tryphena	Vict., Tiger and Commercial inn, posting house, & railway office	Corn market	
Taylor, Eliza	Beer seller, Queen Adelaide	Canal street	
Taylor, Samuel	J. wheelwright	South street	
Taylor, Joseph	Framework knitter	4, St. Alkm. ch. yd.	
Taylor, Joseph	Weaver	Nun's street	
Taylor, Abraham	Bricklayer	Hope street	F
Taylor, George		25, Dean street, Southwark	F
Taylor, Joseph	Rag merchant	Cannon street	
Taylor, William	Framework knitter	Morledge	B
Taylor, William	Framework knitter	Cannon street	
Taylor, William	J. weaver	Brook street	
Taylor, Benjamin	Police constable	No. 14, Brook street	
Taylor, John	Wheelwright, joiner, and machinist	Bridge foot, Mansfield road	B
Taylor, Joseph	Shoemaker	Green street	
Taylor, Samuel	Gentleman	29, Parker street	
Taylor, James	Silk weaver	Leonard street	
Taylor, John	Framework knitter	Ct. 1, Bridge street	
Taylor, William	Locomotive department	Devonshire street	
Taylor, William	Gentleman	Osmaston street	B
Taylor, Edward	Labourer	South street	

G

Taylor, Thomas	Butcher	Bag lane	
Taylor, Thomas	J. weaver	Brook street	
Taylor, William, sen.	Silk manufacturer, original Derwent silk mill	Bridge gate	F,B
Taylor, William, jun.	Silk manufacturer	Bridge gate	F,B
Taylor, Adolphus	Surgeon	Friar gate	
Taylor, John	Milk seller	Nottingham road	B
Teat, William	Gardener and seedsman	Bridge street	B
Tebbatt, Edward	Hawker	Eagle street	
Temperley, John	Framework knitter	Brook walk	
Tetley, George	Framework knitter	63, Bridge street	B
Tetley, James	Framework knitter	Brook street	
Tetley, John	Tailor	Traffic street	B
Tetley, Samuel	J. weaver	Devonshire street	
Tetley, John	Framework knitter	Ct. 2, Bridge street	
Tetley, William		Mansfield	F
Tempest, John	Baker and flour dealer	3, Talbot street	B
Thacker, Arthur	Manager at Unsworth's mill	Siddals lane	
Thacker, Thomas	Gentleman, author on coursing and breeding	Leonard street	
Thacker, Alpheus	Gentleman	Park street	B
Thacker, George	Joiner	Hill street	
Theabould, William	Book-keeper	Sacheverel street	
Thelen,Fran.Wilhelm	Tailor and woollen draper	14, Iron gate	B
Thoma, Joseph	Clock maker	46, Sadler gate	B
Thomason, John	Draper	Bradshaw street	
Thomason, James	Overseer of china factory	5, Nottingham rd.	F,B
Thompson,Mary Ann	Ladies' boarding school	London road	
Thompson, John	J. coach builder	Litchurch street	
Thompson, William	Shoemaker	37, Green lane	B
Thompson, George	Builder and stone mason	Devonshire street	F,B
Thompson, Edwin	Builder and carpenter	London road	B
Thompson, John	J. joiner	Parker street	
Thompson, Thomas	Gentleman	York street	F
Thompson, Henry	Plumber and painter	Parker street	F,B
Thompson, John Abraham	Superintendent of police	Market place	
Thompson, Thomas	Labourer	Ct. 8, Brook walk	
Thompson, William	Ornamental spar manufacturer	Markeaton lane	
Thompson, George	Shoemaker	19, St. Helen's st.	B
Thompson, John	Turnkey at gaol	South street	
Thompson, Stephen	Beer seller	Canal street	B
Thompson, John	Hat manufacturer	13, Willow row	B
Thompson, Joseph	Porter	North street	
Thorley, Thomas	Blacksmith	St. Michael's lane	B
Thorley, William	Whitesmith	Canal street	
Thorley, John	Trunk maker	3, Walker lane	B
Thorley, William	Shoeing smith	Queen street	
Thornhill, Robert	Labourer	Grove street	
Thorpe, John	J. joiner	Osmaston road	
Thorpe, John & Co.	Cornfactor	Morledge	
Thorpe, Mary	Milliner and dressmaker	Osmaston road	

Thorpe, James	Weighing machine	Cockpit hill	
Thorpe, Francis	Corn factor, Derby & Notting.	3, London road	B
Thorpe, George	Joiner	Devonshire street	
Thorpe, Joseph	Joiner	Thorn tree lane	
Thruscott, Nicholas	Gentleman	Sacheverel street	F
Thumpstone, Charles	Tailor	St. Peter's street	B
Timmons, Thomas	J. weaver	Brook street	
Timperley, Elizabeth	Shopkeeper	London road	
Tinsley, Edwin	Butcher, and dealer in bacon, flour, &c.	77, Devonshire street	
Tipper, Joseph	Lodging house	27, Walker lane	Fr
Tipper, Hugh	J. joiner	Bloom street	
Tipper, Benjamin	6, Grosvenor place, Camberwell, Surrey		F
Titterton, John	Gardener	Fowler street	
Tivey, Edward	Commissioned to put out lace, & Temperance coffee house	Traffic street	B
Todd, Job	Moulder	22, City road	
Tomlinson, Robert	Framework knitter	Ct. No. 2, Irongate	Fr
Tomlinson, Samuel	Tailor	Orchard street	
Tomlinson, Isaac	Labourer	Bag lane	
Tomlinson, Thomas	J. bricklayer	Burton road	
Tomlinson, George	Joiner & cabinet maker	Sacheverel street	F
Tomlinson, Mrs.		Ashbourn road	
Tomlinson, Edward	Plumber and glazier	Old George yard	B
Tomlinson, Joseph	Overlooker at Wright's mill	16, Ford street	B
Tomlinson, Thomas	Vict., Old Oak	13, Agard street	F, B
Tomlinson, Joseph	Butcher	William street	Fr
Tomlinson, James	Police constable	Exeter place	
Tomlinson, John	Turnkey at gaol	Brook walk	
Tooby, Thos. sen.	Lodging house	50, Brook street	B
Tooby, Thos. jun.	Hair dresser	Bridge street	
Tooby, Samuel	Framework knitter	Morledge	F
Tooth, Charles	Shoemaker	26, Full street	
Topham & Fawcett	Silk throwsters	Green lane	
Topham, Charles	Silk throwster	Burton road	B
Topham, Thomas	Butcher	31, St. Mary's gate	B
Topham, Snowden	Shopkeeper and millwright	16, Goodwin st.	B
Toplis, Eliza	Milliner	Bridge gate	
Toplis, James	Engineer	Parker street	
Toplis, James	Labourer	Brook street	
Toplis, Robert	Compositor	16, Derwent row	B
Toplis, John	J. colourman	Bag lane	
Toplis, Thomas	Works at factory	Bag lane	
Toplis, Robert	China painter	Erasmus street	Fr
Torr, James, jun.	Wire worker	30, Morledge	B
Torr, James & Sons	Wire workers	Bold lane	
Torr, James	Wire worker	Bold lane	F
Torr, William	Wire worker	Bold lane	
Torr, Lydia	Stay maker	Bold lane	
Tortishell, John	Jeweller	Devonshire street	
Towle, Thomas	Tailor	Willow row	F, B

Town and county library and news room, Amen Alley, E. Bailey, Librarian

Tracey, Michael	Shoemaker	57, Bridge street	B
Tracey, Thomas	J. weaver	Duke street	
Trafford, Thomas	Gentleman	Wilmot street	B
Trafford, James	Silk weaver	Devonshire street	
Trafford, Miss		Vernon street	
Tranter, Francis	Hoop maker	28, Exeter place	B
Trewin, Rev. P.	Minister, Methodist New Con.	London road	
Trelfa, John	Fettler at foundry	Burton road	
Trickett, Samuel	Cutler	Bloom street	
Trueman, John	Twist hand	Eagle street	
Trueman, Henry	Gentleman	Osmaston parsonage	F
Trueman, William	Harthill,	Eccles, Lancashire	F
Trusswell, John	Cheese & bacon warehouse	33, Corn market	B
Tucker, William	Turnkey at gaol	Fowler street	
Tummond, Thomas Charles	Saddler & hosiery box manu-facturer	Lodge lane	
Tunaley, Edward	J. cabinet maker	Full street	Fr
Tunaley, William	Silk dyer	Upper Brook st.	Fr
Tunaley, Thos. sen.	Silk dyer	4, Tenant street	F,Fr
Tunaley, Thos. jun.	Silk dyer	7, Derwent st.	F,B
Tunaley, Samuel	Silk dyer	17, Derwent row	Fr
Tunaley, Henry	Silk dyer	Tenant street	F,Fr
Tunaley, John	Silk dyer	Tenant street	Fr
Tunaley, Thos. Snape	Dancing master	Full street	B
Tunley & Hodgson	Carriers, by water, to London, Tuesday, Thursday, and Saturday; Liverpool, Manchester, Nottingham, and all the intermediate towns, by wagon and railway	Siddals lane	
Tunnecliff, Elizabeth	Straw hat manufacturer	Wright street	
Tunnicliffe, William	Labourer	Ct. 2, Bridge street	
Tunnicliffe, Joseph	J. carver & gilder	Green lane	
Tunnicliffe, Thomas	Framework knitter	Wright street	
Tunnicliffe, John	Butcher	St. Peter's street	
Tunnicliffe, John	Vict., Horse & Jockey	Sadler gate	F,B
Turner, James		Babington lane	F,B
Tunstall, James	Tape weaver	Kensington	
Turner, John	J. carpenter	Nun's street	Fr
Turner, Edward	Silk manufacturer	Canal street	Fr
Turner, James	Alms houses	Full street	Fr
Turner, James	Porter at Station	Canal street	Fr
Turner, James	China painter	Erasmus street	Fr
Turner, Rhoda	Dressmaker and hosier	Green lane	
Turner, William	Gentleman	Green lane	F,B
Turner, Henry	Tailor	5, Brook street	B
Turner, James	J. silk hand	Canal street	Fr
Turner, Thomas	Vict., Hare and Hounds	24, Erasmus street	B
Turner, Thomas	J. baker	South street	
Turner, Samuel	Shopkeeper and corn dealer	Burton road	
Turner, William	Baker and flour dealer	Eagle street	F,B

Turner, James	Tailor	Canal street	
Turner, John	Works at Pegg's colour mill	Searl street	
Turner, George	Waiter	Sitwell street	B
Turton, Ferdinand	Works at silk mill	Albion street	
Turton, George	Manager at silk mill	Beeston, Notts.	F
Twigg, William	Labourer	North street	
Twigg, William	Tailor	Wilmot street	
Twigg, John		Spath, near Uttoxeter	F
Twigg, William	Works at Darley mill	Bath street	
Twigg, John	Twisthand	Liversage street	
Twigg, John	Twisthand	Bloom street	
Tyce, William	Foreman to Mr. Beeland, tailor	Orchard street	
Tyler, James	J. jeweller	Union buildings	
Udall, Miss		Agard street	
Ufton, John	Butcher	Bloom street	
Underwood, William	Framework knitter	Litchurch street	
Unsworth, William	Silk manufacturer	Rose cottage	B
Unsworth, Mrs.		Siddals lane	
Unsworth and Williamson	Manufacturers of sewing silks, twists, purse twists, cords, braids, and laces—agents Bennoch and Twentyman, 33, Wood street, Parker street, London	Siddals lane	
Unwin, Rev. Edward	Vicar of St. Werburgh's	Parkfield, Kedleston road	F,B
Upton, Ann	Butcher	37, Sadler gate	
Upton, William	Butcher	Walker lane	B
Vallack, James	Solicitor, office Full street	Normanton road	B
Vallance, Richard	Framework knitter	Talbot street	Fr
Vanstone, Francis	J. turner	Wilmot street	
Varley, Thomas	Shoemaker	Bradshaw street	
Vernon, Catherine	Cork cutter	Iron gate	
Vessey, Thos. Staley	Solicitor	Leaper street	Fr
Vessey, John	Joiner	Ct. 5, St. Peter's st.	
Waddams, Elizabeth	Grocer and tea dealer	Victoria street	
Wade, Rev. E.	Minister of Trinity church	London road	
Wade, Mrs.	Straw bonnet maker	Green lane	
Wade, John	Stonemason	Talbot street	F
Wade, James	Builder	Brook street	
Wade, Edw. Mich.	Schoolmaster	Liversage street	B
Wain, Robert	Beer seller, and dealer in all kinds of herbs	Canal street	F
Wain, Robt. & Thos.	Sawyers	River street	
Wain, William	Sawyer	Albion street	
Wain, Samuel	Beer seller and shopkeeper	Bloom street	
Wainwright, Thomas	Bookbinder	Albion street	
Wainwright, Alfred	Butcher	Queen street	F
Wait, Francis	Timber merchant, and circular saw mills, Chester road	Mansfield road	B
Wakefield, John	Shopkeeper	5, Lodge lane	F

Wakefield, Mark	Inspector of engines	North street
Wakefield, Thomas	Framework knitter	Ct. 3, St. Mary's gate
Wakefield, Mark	Inspector of engines	North street
Walcup, Richard	J. silk throwster	Union workhouse Fr
Walcup, Robert	J. silk throwster	Brook street Fr
Wales, Hugh	Tea dealer	Devonshire street
Walker, Thomas	Shopkeeper	River street B
Walker, William	Shopkeeper	25, Bridge street B
Walker, Elizabeth	Straw hat manufacturer	21, Devonshire street
Walker, William	Engine driver	Leeds place
Walker, William	Shoemaker	Fingal street
Walker, John	Coal dealer	Bridge gate F
Walker, John	J. carpenter	Union buildings
Walker, Wm. Thos.	Gentleman	Grove street F,B
Walker, Sarah	Milliner, dress maker, and straw hat manufacturer	Friar gate
Walker, Charlotte	Straw hat manufacturer	62, Devonshire street
Walker, Thomas	Livery stable keeper	River street
Walker, Thomas	Foundry man	Erasmus street
Walker, John	Butler at Mr. Joseph Strutt's	15, Burton road
Walker, James Wm.	Dealer in flour and bacon	Green street
Walker, Thomas	J. joiner	21, Devonshire street
Walker, Richard	Patent mangle	3, Bath street
Walker, Joseph	Silk throwster, mill Bold lane	8, St. Alkm. ch. yd. B
Walker, John	Weaver	Albion street
Walker, William	Wood turner	22, Nun's street
Walker, Edward	Vict., Cock Inn	15, Cockpit hill B
Walker, John	Dealer in flour	Traffic street B
Walker, Edward	Shopkeeper	Eagle street
Walker, William	J. joiner	Bloom street
Walker, John	J. whitesmith	Bloom street
Walker, Joseph & Co.	Dealers in flour, &c.	Exeter street
Walker, John	Shopkeeper & dealer in coals	Duke street B
Walker, Mrs.	Schoolmistress Infant school	Walker lane
Walkerdine, James	Framework knitter	Markeaton lane
Walkerdine, William	Shoemaker	Brook street
Walkerdine, Nehem.	Slater	Ct. 3, Bridge street
Walkerdine, David	Stonemason and slater	Upper Brook st. F,B
Walkerdine, Joseph	Silk framework knitter, and beadle at St. Peter's ch.	Leonard street
Walkerdine, William	Slate yard	Upper Brook st. F,B
Walklake, J. William	Shoemaker	22, Goodwin street
Wall, John	Book-keeper	Large's street B
Wall, William	Labourer	Ashbourn road
Walley, John	Moulder	Duke street B
Wallis, Henry	Horsebreaker and trimmer	
Wallis, Thomas	Porter at Station	Litchurch street Fr
Wallis, Joseph	Gardener	87, Bridge street B
Wallis, Robert	Vict., Green Man Inn	Ashbourn F
Wallis, William	Tailor	27, Wardwick B
Wallis, John	J. boiler maker	Queen street F,Fr
Wallis, Edward	Grocer and flour dealer	20, Bradshaw st. F,B

Wallis, George	King's Head, family and commercial hotel, and general posting house	10, Corn market	F,Fr
Wallis, William	Vict., Milton's Head	Hill street	B
Wallis, William Wallace	Coach proprietor, general carrier by railway, and royal mail coach office—offices King street & Sadler gate	Friar gate	Fr
Wallis, Samuel	Bookbinder	Traffic street	
Walplate, William	Labourer	Darley lane	Fr
Walston, George	J. printer	William street	
Walston, Thomas	J. printer	William street	
Walters & Greensmith	Corn millers	Darley abbey	
Walters, John	Ironmonger, 10, Iron gate	Normanton terr.	F,B
Walters, Charles	Dealer in coal	Bridge gate	Fr
Walters, William	Alms houses	Full street	Fr
Walters, John	Corn miller	Darley Abbey	F
Walters, John, jun.	Shopkeeper	Darley abbey	F
Walters, Joseph	Butcher	King street	B
Walters, George	Policeman at Station	1, Bradshaw street	
Walters, Henry	Coal merchant	Bridge gate	B
Walthall, Richard		Duffield	Fr
Walthall, Peter, esq.		Darley Dale	F
Walton, Samuel	Cabinet maker, and parish clerk at All Saints' church	37, Parker street	F,Fr
Walton, Joseph W.	Shoemaker	Ford street	Fr
Walton, Thomas Wedgwood	Wholesale and retail chemist and druggist, Corn market	Cross lanes	F,B
Walton, John	Baker, flour dealer, & grocer	48, Bridge street	F,Fr
Walton, Joseph	Farmer	Stockbrook field	Fr
Walton, Thomas	Cowkeeper	Ford street	Fr
Ward, William	Dealer in smallware	Queen street	
Ward, Elizabeth	Vict., Lord Hill	Short street	
Ward, Josepha and Jemima	Ladies' boarding school	Sacheverel street	
Ward, Abraham, jun.	Framework knitter	Albion street	Fr
Ward, John, jun.	Framework knitter	Albion street	Fr
Ward, George	Builder, joiner, and carpenter	Osmaston street	F,B
Ward, John		Richmond, Surrey	F
Ward, John	J. jeweller	Liversage street	Fr
Ward, James	Tailor	Traffic street	
Ward, James		St. Mary's row, Birmingham	F
Ward, Thomas	Framework knitter	Wilmot street	
Ward, William	Hosier	Willow row	
Ward, Rev. Richard	Rector of Brandon	Suffolk	F
Ward, Robert	Jeweller	40, Bridge street	B
Ward, Richard	Beer seller	69, Eagle street	B
Ward, William	Shopkeeper	22, Willow row	B
Ward, William	Maltster	Friar gate	B
Ward, Whitehall	Alms houses	Etwall	Fr
Ward, Richard	Framework knitter	Bloom street	Fr

Ward, Robert	Gentleman, silk dyer and lace manufacturer	5, Full street	F,Fr
Ward, Thomas	Vict., Saracen's Head Inn	St. James's lane	B
Ward, Benjamin, esq.	Surveyor of assessed taxes	Bridge street	
Warner, Ann	Schoolmistress, National school	Curzon street	
Warren, Mary	Straw hat manufacturer	Osmaston street	
Warren, William	Gentleman	London road	F,B
Warren, Thomas	Weighing machine proprietor	Liversage street	F
Warren, Stephen	Flour dealer	King street	B
Warren, John	Foreman to Messrs. Frost and Stevenson	5, Exeter place	B
Warrington, Moses	Clothier	Sacheverel street	
Warrington, Joseph	Shopkeeper	13, Green street	B
Waterfall, William	Labourer	Brook street	
Waterfield,Thos.,sen.	Jeweller	Osmaston road	F,B
Waterfield, Joseph	Jeweller	Friar gate	
Waterfield, William	Higgler	Duke street	
Waters, Henry	Joiner	St. Mary's gate	B
Wathall, Leonard	Joiner and cabinet maker	Morledge	B
Wathall, Lark	Tailor	Bag lane	
Wathey, Samuel	Brass modeller	Sheffield place	
Watson, John		Mickleover	F
Watson, John	Porter and pale ale brewery	New Uttox. road	F,B
Watson, Thomas	Confectioner and baker	22, Sadler gate	F,B
Watson, John	Grocer	South street	F,B
Watson, Joseph		Quorndon	F
Watson, Joseph	Baker and flour dealer	13, Sadler gate	F,B
Watson, Samuel	Chemist and druggist, and wine and spirit merchant	St. Peter's street	B
Watson, William	Labourer	Spring gardens	
Watts, William	Locomotive department	Osmaston road	
Watts, Samuel	Stonemason	Sacheverel street	
Watts, Mary	Shopkeeper	Nun's street	
Waudby, William	J. plasterer	31, Leonard street	
Weare, William	Gentleman	Iron bridge, Shropshire	F
Weatherby, Henry	Shoemaker	Ct. 6, Bold lane	
Weatherhead,Samuel	Gentleman	11, Iron gate	B
Weatherhead, Walters, and Co.	Silversmiths, furnishing iron-mongers, flax dressers, gun-smiths, oil and colour men, rope and twine manufactu-rers, wholesale and retail	Iron gate	
Webb, Thomas	Grocer	Traffic street	
Webster, Thomas M.	J. cooper	Sadler gate	Fr
Webster, Joseph	Apothecary	Infirmary	Fr
Webster, William	Governor of workhouse	Osmaston road	B
Webster, Mrs. Wm.	Governess of workhouse	Osmaston road	
Webster, John	J. smith	Parker street	Fr
Webster, Joseph	J. smith	Parker street	Fr
Webster, Benjamin	Warehouseman	Corn market	Fr
Webster, John	Works at lace factory	Curzon street	Fr
Webster, John	Looker over at factory	Castle street	

Webster, George	Inspector of weights & measures for the Borough of Derby and Hundreds of Repton and Gresley, Morleston and Litchurch, and Appletree	Darwin terrace	Fr
Webster, John	Sawyer	Castle street	
Webster, John	Dyer	Albion street	
Webster, Robert	J. weaver	Grove street	F
Webster, John	J. joiner	Albion street	
Webster, John	Traveller for Cox and Co.	Sacheverel street	B
Webster, Benjamin	Dyer	9, Bridge gate	F,B
Webster, John	Alms houses	Bridge gate	F,Fr
Webster, Joseph	Lace manufacturer, fancy lace depôt	9, Rotten row	
Webster, Isaac	Tailor	Ashbourn road	B
Webster, Thomas	Iron moulder	Sacheverel street	
Webster, John	Surgeon	14, Tenant street	F,B
Webster, William, jun.	Boot and shoemaker	5, Victoria street	Fr
Webster, Moses	Artist	Darwin terrace	B
Webster, William, sen.	Boot and shoemaker	51, Friar gate	F,Fr
Webster, John	Labourer	Agard street	
Webster, Jeremiah	Cooper and basket maker	Sadler gate	F,Fr
Webster, William	J. chandler	18, Green street	
Webster, Joseph	Butcher	Corn market	Fr
Webster, Isaac	Book-keeper	Summer hill	B
Webster, Henry	J. whitesmith	Parker street	Fr
Wedge, Moreton Chas.	Ale and porter brewery	Wardwick	F,B
Welbourne, Robert	Maltster, and agent to Schweppe and Co., soda water manufacturers	Friar gate	B
Welch, David	Solicitor	22, St. Mary's gate	F
Welch, John	House, sign, and furniture painter	Abbey barns	B
Welch, William	House and furniture painter	Friar gate	B
Welch, Henry		Spondon	F
Welldale, Sarah	Dressmaker	Osmaston street	
Wells, Richard	Labourer	Bradshaw street	
Wells, George	Framework knitter	Cannon street	Fr
Wells, John	Tailor	Thorntree lane	B
Westcott, James	Vict., Golden Eagle	Agard street	B
West, Robert	Blacksmith	Bradshaw street	
West, Henry	Colour works and chemist	William street	B
Westmoreland, John	Engine cleaner	Leeds place	
Weston, Anthony	Butcher and victualler	Swanwick	F
Wetton, John	Labourer	Bag lane	
Wetton, George	Tape weaver	Cannon street	
Wharton, Elizabeth	Dyer	Sadler gate	
Wheatcroft and Company	Furnishing ironmongers, wholesale and retail	16, Corn market	
Wheatcroft, Wm., sen.	Vict., Star Inn	Siddals lane	F,Fr
Wheatcroft, Wm., jun.	Solicitor's clerk	Siddals lane	Fr

Wheatcroft and Son	General carriers by canal and railway to all parts of the kingdom	Siddals lane
Wheatcroft, Mrs.		North parade
Wheatcroft, William	Shopkeeper	Bridge street
Wheatley, William	Framework knitter	Parker street
Wheatley, John	Organ builder	Uttoxeter road
Wheatley, Georgiana	Dressmaker	Uttoxeter road
Wheeldon, Thomas	Shopkeeper and wharfinger, Morledge	28, Eagle street F,B
Wheeldon, George	Labourer	Ashbourn road
Wheeldon, John	Hosier and lace manufacturer	Chester road F
Wheeldon, William	Grocer and flour dealer	22, Bridge gate F,Fr
Wheeldon, George	Baker and flour dealer	2, Mansfield road F,Fr
Wheeldon, Samuel	Wheelwright	Chapel street F,B
Wheeldon, William	Cow keeper	Notting. road F,Fr
Wheeldon, Joshua	Butcher	Bag lane
Wheeldon, Thomas	Farmer	Notting. road F,Fr
Wheeldon, Joseph	Book-keeper	Parker street
Wheeldon, Joseph	Farmer	Radbourn F
Wheeldon, William	Gardener	High street
Wheeldon, John	Wheelwright	Ct. 3, Full street
Wheeldon, William	Framework knitter	19, Willow row
Wheeldon, Fred. Rich.	Book-keeper	Exeter street F,B
Wheeldon, Samuel	Grocer, &c.	7, Albion street B
Wheeler, Hannah	Lodging house	Liversage street
Whegwell, James	Draper	Eagle street B
Wheldal, John	Vict., Bee Hive	Devonshire st. F,B
Whetton, John	Earthenware dealer	Willow row
Whiston and Son	Solicitors	St. Peter's street
Whiston, Wm., sen.	Solicitor, and clerk to the magistrates	St. Peter's street F,B
Whiston, Wm., jun.	Solicitor, coroner for the County of Derby, & high constable for the Hundred of Repton and Gresley, and clerk to the magistrates	Office St. Pet. st., res. Osmaston road F,B
Whiston, Rev. Robert	Head master of Proprietary school	Rochester in Kent F
Whitaker, William	Framework knitter	Agard street Fr
Whitaker, Samuel	Secretary to Derby Infirmary	Cross lanes F,Fr
Whitaker, John	Furniture broker	Cross lanes Fr
Whitaker, Thomas	Painter	Cross lanes Fr
Whitehead, James	Shoemaker	Grove street
Whitehead, John	Butler to Rich. Arkwright, esq.	Willersley castle F
White, John	Coal dealer	25, Exeter street B
White, William	Higgler	Queen street
White, Abraham	Whitesmith	St. Peter's ch. yard
White, Joseph	Turnkey at gaol	Uttoxeter road
White, John	J. silk throwster	Canal street
White, Joseph	Labourer	6, Agard street
White, George	Shopkeeper	24, Burton road

White, Jeremiah	Shopkeeper	Park street	
White, Joseph	J. bricklayer	Litchurch street	
White, William	Framework knitter	High street	
White, Frederick	Policeman	North street	
White, Martha	Baker and flour dealer	Ashbourn road	
Whiting, Joseph, jun.	Beer seller and butcher	26, Eagle street	B
Whitehurst, Squire	Watch manufacturer	24, Exeter street	B
Whitehurst, Francis	Whitesmith	St. Werburgh's ch. yd.	
Whitehurst, John	Manufacturer of church turret clocks and house clocks, regulators & cottage clocks, watchman's time-pieces & egg clocks, &c., gold and silver watches of every description, chronometers, &c., sun, wind, and miners' dials, barometers, thermometers, and mathematical instruments; improved roasting jacks, with single or double spits; brass and bell founder	1, Cherry street	B
Whitehurst, Charles	Higgler	Ct. 2, St. Mich. lane	
Whiteman, Joseph	Baker and flour dealer	Eagle street	B
Whitmore, Samuel	Postboy	Leeds place	
Whitmore, Edward	Plasterer and shopkeeper	Bag lane	Fr
Whitmore, Samuel	Labourer	Brook street	
Whittaker, John	Works at china factory	25, Erasmus street	B
Whittaker, James	Bookseller, stationer, printer, and dealer in patent medicines	Corn market	
Whittaker, Richard	Vict., Coach and Horses	King street	
Whittingham, Thos.	Labourer	Grove street	
Whitworth, John	J. tailor	Green lane	
Whyman, William	Cornfactor and flour dealer	Uttoxeter road	B
Wibberley, Joseph	Higgler	Grove street	
Wibberley, William	Labourer	Litchurch street	
Wickham, Thomas	Carpenter and bendware manufacturer	Agard street	F,B
Widdowson, Joseph	Shopkeeper and vict., the Old Britannia	10, River street	F,B
Wightman, Sarah	Vict., Bell, commercial inn and posting house	Sadler gate	
Wigley, Robert	Sawyer	Castle street	
Wigley, William	Shoemaker	Fingal street	
Wigley, Samuel	J. weaver	Hill street	
Wilcockson, Daniel	Porter	Leeds place	
Wilcockson, George	Vict., Buck-in-the-Park	Curzon street	
Wilcockson, Mrs. Elizabeth		Wilmot street	
Wild, George	Tea dealer, coffee roaster, and spice merchant	17, Corn market	B
Wild, James	Gardener	Bag lane	

Wild, Henry	J. dyer	Agard street	B
Wild, George	Gardener	Traffic street	
Wilkes, Gilbert Bull	Farmer, and bailiff to the Rev. W. Spilsbury	Willington	F
Wilkes, Solomon	Gentleman	Burton road terrace	
Wilkes, Thomas	Compositor	Sadler gate	Fr
Wilkins, George and Son	Booksellers, printers, bookbinders, and music sellers	18, Queen street	F,B
Wilkins, George	Bookseller	Duffield road	F,B
Wilkins, William	Bookseller	Duffield road	B
Wilkins, Henry	Umbrella manufacturer	Friar gate	B
Wilkinson, William	Tailor	Leeds place	
Wilkinson, Henry	Eating house	Sadler gate	B
Wilkinson, Mrs.	Clergymen's widows' alms houses, Friar gate		
Willder, Samuel	Grocer, tea dealer, and tallow chandler	St. Peter's street	F,B
Williams, Charles John	Historical, landscape, and architectural engraver on steel and copper, & printer and bookseller	Sadler gate	B
Williams, Edward	J. painter	Searl street	B
Williams, John	Framework knitter	Burton road	
Williams, John	Painter	10, Uttoxeter road	
Williams, Emma	Milliner and dressmaker	Railway terrace	
Williams, Harriet	Shopkeeper	Railway terrace	
Williams, German	Shopkeeper	10, Brick street	B
Williams, William	Pig jobber and beer seller	Drewry lane	B
Williams, Henry	Shopkeeper	Friar gate	B
Williams, John Jones and Company	Grocers & tea dealers—golden canister tea warehouse	Corn market	B
Williamson, Thomas	Labourer	Bag lane	Fr
Williamson, Thomas	Traveller	16, Exeter street	B
Williamson, Charles	Framework knitter	High street	
Williamson, John	Vict., Green Dragon	St. Peter's street	Fr
Williamson, Richard	Saddler, collar & harness maker	Talbot yard	
Williamson, William	Clerk at Messrs. Strutt's, haberdasher, and dealer in smallware	8, Friar gate	F,Fr
Williamson, John	Shopman	Friar gate	Fr
Williamson, William	Solicitor, and commissioner of bankruptcy	Corn market and Littleover	F,B
Williamson, Jane	Register office	22, King street	
Williamson, Benjamin	Gentleman	16, North parade	B
Williamson, Thomas	Vict., Rose and Crown	Corn market	F,Fr
Williamson, Samuel	Labourer	Parker street	
Williamson, John	J. weaver	8, Goodwin street	B
Williamson, Edward	Vict., Dog and Duck	Haarlem street	B
Williamson, John	Draper	Wilmot street	B
Williamson, Mrs.		George street	
Willisford, Wm. & Co.	Cork cutters	Corn market	B
Willoughby, Richard	Schoolmaster	45, Friar gate	B
Willson, Robt. Wm.		Nottingham	F

Willson, William	Traveller	Agard street	
Wilmot, Mrs. Elizab.		Friar gate	
Wilmot, James Sebastian, esq.		12, Wardwick	B
Wilson, Joshua	Landscape gardener	Sitwell street	
Wilson, William	Gardener and seedsman	32, King street	B
Wilson, Sarah	Beer seller	Bridge gate	
Wilson, Joseph, John, and Isaac	Silk hosiers	St. Helen's street	
Wilson, John	Gentleman	Osmaston road	F
Wilson and Sadler	Nursery and seedsmen	Cheapside	
Wilson, William	Framework knitter	22, Bridge street	B
Wilson, William	Brush manufacturer	23, Bridge gate	B
Wilson and Dunn	Braziers & tin plate workers	King street	
Wilson, Moore, & Co.	Silk manufacturers	Devonshire street	
Windle, Edwin	Fitter	North street	
Winfield, Thomas	Gentleman	William street	F,B
Winfield, Richard	Shopkeeper	18, Nun's street	B
Winfield, William	J. cooper	Leonard street	
Winfield, Thomas	Shoemaker	Devonshire street	
Winfield, Richard	J. joiner	Agard street	
Winfield, Elizabeth	Baker and flour dealer	St. Peter's street	
Winfield, John	Works at china factory	40, Erasmus street	
Wingfield, George	Wharfinger	Morledge	B
Wingfield & Wheeldon	Carriers by water to Gainsbro', Stafford, and Shropshire	Morledge	
Winson, Joseph		Full street	F
Winstanley, Israel	Joiner and vict., Boar's Head	King street	
Winter, Ann	Dress and straw hat maker	St. Peter's street	
Winter, Henry	Draper	St. Peter's street	F,B
Winter, James	Beer seller	Park street	
Winterton, Henry	Builder	Summer hill	F,B
Wintle, John, Grocer & provision warehouse		30, Queen st. & Tenant st.	B
Witton, Samuel	Beer seller	Canal street	
Wolstenholme, Adam	Officer of Excise	York street	
Wood, Daniel	Higgler	Bath street	
Wood, William	J. joiner	William street	Fr
Wood, Eli	Last maker	Willow row	
Wood, James	Four dealer	King street	
Wood, Joseph	Shopkeeper	20, Parker street	B
Wood, Samuel	Gardener	Eagle street	
Wood, Joseph	Schoolmaster, National school	Traffic street	
Wood, Richard	Bricklayer	37, Full street	F,B
Wood, Thomas	Tailor	Cockpit hill	Fr
Wood, Thomas	Basket maker	Bath street	F
Wood, Thomas	Labourer	Albion street	
Wood, Robert	Painter	Ashbourn road	B
Wood, John	Cowkeeper	Burton road	
Wood, George	Needlemaker	St. Helen's street	F,B
Wood, John	Framework knitter	13, Brook street	
Wood, John	Builder, and stone and marble mason	Liversage street	B
Wood, William	Labourer	Eagle street	

Wood, George	Spar manufacturer	16, St. Helen's st.	B
Wood, William	Schoolmaster, Full street	Amen alley	
Wood, Timothy	Cornfactor and corn miller	Bridge gate and Duke street	F,B
Wood, George	Cabinet maker	Green lane	
Wood, Samuel	Framework knitter	Hill street	
Wood, John	Cornfactor and flour dealer	King street	B
Woodford, John	Solicitor	25, St. Mary's gate	
Woodhead, George	Supervisor of Excise	Darwin terrace	
Woodhouse, Joseph	Labourer	St. Michael's lane	Fr
Woodhouse, Abraham	Labourer	Ct., St. Mich. lane	B
Woodhouse, Samuel	Labourer	Litchurch street	
Woodhouse, Thomas	Beadle and sexton at Saint Michael's church	St. Michael's lane	Fr
Woodroffe, Richard	Vict., Pheasant	Bridge street	
Woodruff, William	Butcher	Brook street	
Woods, John		Ireton farm, Mugginton	F
Woodward, George	Beerseller, Rising Sun	Osmaston street	B
Woodward, William	Shoemaker	41, Bridge street	B
Woodward, Francis	Labourer	Litchurch street	
Woodward, Cornelius	Currier and leather cutter	Sadler gate	
Woodward, John	Beerseller and shopkeeper	Castle street	B
Woodward, Francis	Vict., the Leopard	Grove street	B
Woodward, Joseph	Gardener	Canal street	F,B
Woodward, Joseph	Watchmaker	18, Notting. road	B
Woodward, John	Shoemaker	Ford street	
Woodward, William	Shoemaker	Goodwin street	B
Woodward, Samuel	Bell hanger and locksmith	Full street	B
Woodward, Francis	Shopkeeper	Park street	B
Woodward, Francis	Shoemaker	Ford street	B
Woodward, Thomas	Vict., Black's Head	29, Devonshire street	
Woodward, William	Organist at Catholic church	Nottingham road	
Woodward, James	Framework knitter	Bridge street	Fr
Woodward, John	Framework knitter	63, Bridge street	B
Woodward, Joseph	Framework knitter	High street	
Woodward, Isaac	Shoemaker	Goodwin street	Fr
Woolhouse, Richard	Sacking, rope, twine, & tarpauling manufacturer	25, King street	B
Woolhouse, John	Manufacturer of sacking, rope, twine, tarpauling, oil cloth, Roman cement and plaster, St. Mary's mill	44, Sadler gate	B
Woolhouse, Ruth & Hannah	Milliners and dress makers	Sadler gate	
Woolley, Thomas		Allestree	F
Woolley, Thomas	Music master, piano forte and music repository	46, Full street	B
Woolley, Samuel	Builder and cabinet maker	Curzon street	B
Woolley, Michael	Framework knitter	Ct. 1, Bridge street	B
Wooler, Wm. Moore	Surgeon	St. Mary's gate	B
Wooler & Hamilton	Surgeons	St. Mary's gate	
Woollatt, Samuel	Warehouseman	Kensington street	

Woollatt, Samuel	Butcher	Kensington street	
Woollatt, Joseph	Butcher	St. Peter's street	F,B
Woollatt, Samuel	Butcher	17, Albion street	B
Woollatt, William	J. dyer	Sitwell street	
Woollatt, Joseph	Cabinet maker & upholsterer, plate glass warehouse and dealer in piano fortes	Iron gate	B
Wombles, Joseph	Framework knitter	St. Peter's street	Fr
Wragg, James	Engine tenter	Burton road	B
Wragg, William	Policeman	St. Peter's ch. yard	
Wragg, William	Provision warehouse	36, Sadler gate	B
Wreford & Company	Silk hosiery manufacturer, Aldermanbury, London— James Squire, agent	14, Bridge street	
Wright, Munday	China painter	Rivet street	Fr
Wright, Samuel	J. baker	Green street	Fr
Wright, Thomas	Farmer	Old Uttoxeter road	B
Wright, John & Co.	Lace manufacturers	Siddals lane	
Wright, Samuel	Framework knitter	Osmaston street	B
Wright, Joseph		Dalton Hackney, Middlesex	F
Wright, Samuel Job	Silk throwster and alderman	43, Friar gate and Mickleover	F,Fr
Wright and Baker	Silk merchants	Agard street	
Wright, Thomas	Silk merchant, Agard street; Iron founder and manufacturer of slide lathes, locomotive engine, tender, and carriage wheels, turn tables, &c., Britannia foundry	53, Friar gate	F,Fr
Wright, Isaac	Moulder	Bath street	
Wright, Robert	Framework knitter	Lodge lane	
Wright, George	J. wheelwright	Osmaston road	B
Wright, Joseph	Vict., Thorntree Inn	St. Peter's street	B
Wright, Edward	Weaver	Brook street	
Wright, Philip	Painter	Ct., Sadler gate	B
Wright, William	Cabinet maker	71, Eagle street	
Wright, William	Tailor	Sacheverel street	
Wright, John		Kibworth, Leicestershire	F
Wright, John & Son	Cheesefactors	19, Market place	B
Wright, Thomas	Gentleman	40, Osmaston road	B
Wright, Thomas	Beer seller	20, St. Mary's gate	B
Wright, John	J. shoemaker	Agard street	
Wright, John	Surgeon	9, Friar gate	F,B
Wright, Mary	Stay maker	Market head	
Wright, Mrs.		Friar gate	
Wright, Miss		North parade	
Wright, George	Milk seller	17, Green street	B
Wright, Rev. Charles	Vicar of St. Peter's church	Bosworth	F
Wright, Edmund	Cabinet maker, broker, appraiser, & auctioneer, clerk at St. John's church	King street	F,B
Yates, David	Manager at water works	St. Michael's lane	

Yates, Thomas	Railway coach builder	Park street	B
Yates, Edward	Grocer	2, Castle street	Fr
Yates, James	Stonemason	31, Bath street	B
Yates, John	Tailor	23, Drury lane	B
Yates, John	Framework knitter	Kensington	
Yeamans,Jos.&Thos.	Butchers and graziers	42, Corn market	F,B
Yeamans, Samuel	Butcher	32, St. Ma. gate	F,Fr
Yeamans, Charles	Grocer	Bridge street	Fr
Yeates, Eliza	Ladies' boarding & day school	Wilmot street	
Yeaverley, William	Framework knitter	Kensington	
Yeaversley, Joseph	Dealer in rags	Parker street	
Yeomans, James	Coal merchant and letter of pleasure boats	Duke street	
Yeomans, John	Weaver	Litchurch street	
Yeomans, Thomas	Tailor	St. Peter's street	F
Yeomans, Robert	Tailor	Ct. 1, Victoria st.	B
Yeomans, Joseph	Butcher	Old shambles	B
Yeomans, Richard	Weaver	Nun's street	B
Yeomans, John	Vict. and coal merchant	Bradshaw street	B
Yeomans, John	Shoemaker	Castle street	
Yeomans, Charles	Tanner	14, Lodge lane	F,Fr
Yeomans, Thomas	Labourer	Friar gate	B
Yeomans, Samuel	Grocer	Ct. 4, Bridge street	B
Yeomans, William	Gentleman	Borrowash	F
Yeomans, Mary	Milliner and dressmaker	Corn market	
Yeomans, Thomas	J. coach builder	Bag lane	
Yeomans, William	Silk weaver	Burton road	
Yeomans, George	Butcher	St. Mary's gate	Fr
Young, John	Labourer	Bag lane	B
Young, William	Labourer	15, Leeds place	

ADDITIONS AND ALTERATIONS

NOT INCLUDED IN THE FOREGOING ALPHABETICAL LIST.

Adams, John	Shopkeeper	41, Brook street
Adams, John	Beer seller	Lodge lane
Allen, William	Wheelwright	Mansfield road
Annable, John	Shopkeeper	Liversage street
Annable, William	Vict., Devonshire Arms	Devonshire street
Ault, John	Timber merchant	Rivett street
Baggaley, George	Fitter	21, North street
Baggaley, John	Fishmonger	Rivett street
Bailey, Mary	Shopkeeper	Bridge gate
Baldwin, David	Grocer	60, Bridge street
Ball, Harriet	Shopkeeper	St. James's lane
Ball, James	Shoemaker	John street
Ball, Thomas	Shoemaker	Orchard street

Bancroft, William	Baker	8, Burton road
Barber, William	Baker and grocer	25, North street
Barker, Thomas	Hairdresser	Morledge
Barnard, Ruth	Schoolmistress	4, Brook street
Barnsdall, Elizabeth	Straw hat manufacturer	Friar gate
Bartlett, Sarah	Schoolmistress, National school	Curzon street
Bateman, Sarah	Baker	Morledge
Batkin, William	Hairdresser	24, North street
Bennett, William	Iron turner	Rivett street
Berrisford, Charlotte	Staymaker	8, King street
Bettison, Joseph	Beer seller	Canal street
Birkin, James	Sinker maker	Bridge gate
Born, William	Book-keeper	12, Railway terrace
Borrey, Saml.&James	Framesmiths	Sacheverel street
Bottom, James	Shopkeeper	5, Erasmus street
Boulderstone, Thos.	Shoemaker	Brook street
Brett, William	Goods department	16, Railway terrace
Bretnor, Elizabeth	Straw hat manufacturer	Victoria street
Briley, Benjamin	Inspector of coaches	34, North street
Brookes, Ann	Crape flower manufacturer	Osmaston street
Brown, Charles	Livery stables	Siddals lane
Brown, George	Butcher	33, Friar gate
Burgen, Francis	Porter	2, Sheffield place
Butler, Edward	Provision warehouse	Ford street
Burrows, James	Sinker maker	Sacheverel street
Camp, Thomas	Shopkeeper	Erasmus street
Camp, Charles	Labourer	23, North street
Cartland, Abel	Guard	36, North street
Chadburn, Thomas	Painter	6, Sheffield place
Chadwick, William	Policeman	3, Midland terrace
Chambers, Reuben	Fitter	19, North street
Chester, Robert	Labourer	16, North street
Clarke, John	Porter	3, Sheffield place
Clay, Wentworth	Superintendent of luggage department	Osmaston road
Clays, Joseph	Butcher	Leonard street
Cleever, William	Beer seller	34, Nun's street
Clements, John	Fitter	9, North street
Clulow, Edward	Book-keeper	8, Midland terrace
Coke, Edward	Shopkeeper	6, Jury street
Collier, Richard	Vict., Crown and Mitre	Amen alley
Cooke, John	Joiner	5, Sheffield place
Cooke, Janet	Milliner	Traffic street
Cooke, C.	Milliner and straw bonnet manufacturer	St. James's lane
Cooling, John	Porter	5, North street
Cope, Joseph	Shoemaker	10, Eagle street
Copestake, Edward	Butcher	41, Nun's street
Copestake, Elizabeth	Milliner	Wilmot street
Copestake, Mary	Shopkeeper	Burton road
Cowlishaw, James	Wheelwright	London road

Crawford, John	Tailor	Back Sitwell street
Cuff, John	Midland hotel	Railway terrace
Davidson, Rev. Thos.	Wesleyan minister	4, Railway terrace
Dawes, Captain		Friar gate
Dawson, Joseph	Chemist and druggist	Iron gate
Dewe, C. T. R.	Solicitor	Abbot's Terrace
Dicken, Elizabeth	Milliner	Friar gate
Dobson, Ralph	Book-keeper	6, Midland terrace
Dobson, John Thomp.	Turner	2, Midland terrace
Dodson, George	Striker	17, North street
Doland, Bryan	Labourer	32, Midland terrace
Domleo, William	Butcher	Old Shambles
Doubleday, William	Butcher	1, North street
Dunn, John	Foreman over Smiths	13, North street
Eley, John	Vict., Old White Hart	Bridge gate
Elliott, Edward	Beer seller	Brook street
Eyre, Arabella	Fancy repository	Friar gate
Fernley, William	Hairdresser and umbrella manufacturer	Ford street
Field, Mrs. T.	Ladies' day school	Carrington street
Fletcher, Henry	Smith	Chester road
Fogg, John	Tailor	27, Bold lane
Ford, William & Co.	Manufacturing chemists	Uttoxeter road
Fox, Henry W.	Solicitor	Friar gate
Freeman, John	Postboy	5, Leeds place
Gardiner, Robert	Train guard	Midland terrace
Garner, William	Shopkeeper	Ashbourn road
Garratt, Mary	Milliner	Friar gate
Gibson, Henry	Fitter	North street
Gilbert, James	Shopkeeper	Siddals lane
Gill, Thomas	Clothes dealer	Bold lane
Gill, John	Book-keeper	Railway terrace
Gladwin, Mrs. Henry	Milliner and straw hat manufacturer	Queen street
Grafton, Henry	Guard	10, Leeds place
Greasley, Charlotte	Schoolmistress	Osmaston street
Green,	Guard	7, Sheffield place
Green, William	Tailor	Rivett street
Greenah, John	Engine driver	30, North street
Griffiths, Richard	Vict., Brown Bear	Lodge lane
Hackett, Eliza	Schoolmistress	Brook street
Harby, M.	Milliner	Erasmus street
Harland, Robert	Joiner	Railway terrace
Harper, John	Maltster	Green lane
Harrison, George	Sawyer	12, North street
Hawksworth, Mary	Stay maker	Rivett street
Hawksworth, Hannah	Milliner	Rivett street
Headland, Isaac	Shopkeeper	Queen street
Heald, George	Gentleman	Sacheverel street
Heath, Thomas	Gardener	London road
Hebb, Francis	Silk dyer	Green lane
Hill, Thomas	Corn miller	Ford street

Henshaw, Henry & Company	Coal merchants	Exeter street and St. Mary's bridge
Hill, Robert	Time keeper	Railway terrace
Hill, Mary Anne	Schoolmistress	Railway terrace
Hines, Charles	Warehouseman	Railway terrace
Hinks, William	Joiner	37, North street
Howel, Richard	Porter	28, North street
Hodgkinson, John	Twisthand	Rivett street
Hope, William	Labourer	10, North street
Horsley, William	Engine driver	12, Leeds place
Hoskins, Edward	Surgeon	London terrace
Houghton, David	Shopkeeper	Bag lane
Hoyle, Martha	Shopkeeper	1, Midland terrace
Hudson, James	Switchman	1, Sheffield place
Hungerford, Julia	Milliner	St. Mary's gate
Hunt, John	Labourer	14, Leeds place
Hunt, Edward	Carpet warehouse	Market place
Hutchinson, William	Agent	Uttoxeter road
Illsley, William	Sawyer	North street
Inman, John	Book-keeper	Osmaston road
Ironmonger, Mary	Shopkeeper	20, Orchard street
Irons, Thomas	Last maker	Talbot yard
Jackson, John	Goods department	15, Railway terrace
Jackson, George	Shoemaker	Hope street
Jackson, Henry	Solicitor	London terrace
James, Miss Elizabeth		Friar gate
James, John	Schoolmaster	George street
Jay, Caroline	Professor	Becket well lane
Jennings, Ellen	Stay warehouse	St. Peter's street
Jepson, Joseph	Labourer	North street
Johnson, Thomas	Fitter	11, North street
Jolley, John	Hairdresser	Bag lane
Jones, Thomas	Furniture broker	35, Goodwin street
Jones, John	Policeman	Leeds place
Jordan, Mrs. Ann		Exeter street
Keeling, Eliza	Straw hat manufacturer	Queen street
Keoh, M. M.	Shopkeeper	Albion street
Kinsey, James, Executors of	Maltster	Friar gate
Kirby, William	Basket maker	St. Peter's street
Kirkup, Robert	Engineer	10, Midland terrace
Lane	Vict., Brunswick hotel	Railway terrace
Lee, George	Needle maker	55, Bridge street
Lees, William	Waiter	13, Railway terrace
Lewis, Mary and Elizabeth	Milliners and straw hat manufacturers	St. Peter's street
Ling, William	Vict., Coach and Horses	Little Chester
Lister, Thomas	Agent to Ames and Co.	Siddals lane
Livesay, John	Silk weaver	Rivett street
Lloyd, Sarah	Stay maker	31, Friar gate
Lomas, Samuel	Locomotive department	9, Midland terrace
Lomas, Henry	Locomotive department	Railway terrace

Lowe, John	Locomotive department	Railway terrace
Longdon, William	Shopkeeper	13, Bridge street
Lucas, John	Surgeon and druggist	John street
Marples, Matthew	Pork butcher	Osmaston street
Marshall, William	Hairdresser	27, Sadler gate
Marshall, Charles	Turner and smith	Rivett street
Mart, Mary Anne	Milliner	28, St. Helen's street
Martin, Thomas	Fitter	18, North street
Martin, John	Butcher	Sitwell street
Mason, John	Copper smith	22, North street
Meakin, Thomas	Baker	Nun's street
Meakin, William	Beer seller	Sacheverel street
Mellor, Jane	Schoolmistress	Bridge street
Melrose, James	Smith	14, North street
Milling, Miss	Milliner	Liversage street
Mitchell, Henry Jas.	Book-keeper	20, Railway terrace
Moorley, Joseph	Schoolmaster	29, St. Peter's street
Mottram, Thomas	Surgeon and apothecary	Charles street
Mycock, Joseph	Porter	29, North street
Nevill, Francis	Inspector of mail guards, general post office, London	5, Midland terrace
Ordish, Eliz. & Ann	Milliners	Bridge street
Orgill, Joseph	Luggage guard	7, North street
Palmer, Mary Anne	Ladies' boarding school	42, Friar gate
Parker, John	Beer seller	Bag lane
Payne, James	Hostler	3, Leeds place
Pearse, Augustus John	Book-keeper, goods departmt.	Railway terrace
Pedley, Mary	Milliner	Tenant street
Pegg, Charles	Shopkeeper and engineer	Park street
Pemberton, Sarah	Beer seller	Friar gate
Pescud,* John	Schoolmaster	Siddals lane
Pescud,* Amy	Schoolmistress	Siddals lane
Pickersgill, Charles	Shopkeeper	Canal street
Pitman, Jane	Schoolmistress	Chapel street
Portmore, Charles Broadhurst	Solicitor	Market place
Potter, John	Joiner	Siddals lane
Potts, Benjamin	Chair maker	Nottingham road
Poulton, Ellen	Shopkeeper	Railway terrace
Pountain, John	Book-keeper	21, Railway terrace
Raisin, George	Warehouseman	Rivett street
Redfern, John	Butcher	Siddals lane
Ridgeway, John	Schoolmaster	Traffic street
Riggott, Elizabeth	Shopkeeper	13, Goodwin street
Roberts, Elijah	Coach proprietor, Nag's Head,	Derby & Newcastle
Robinson, Jonathan	Fireman	13, Leeds place
Robinson, George	Shopkeeper	Albion street
Ross, John	Framesmith	Normanton street
Rowley, John	Tailor	Hope street
Scotton, William	Baker	Rivett street

* Instead of *Prescud,* as before.

Sedgwick, Hepsiban	Milliner	Ford street
Shenton, Mary	Milliner and dressmaker	Siddals lane
Shenton, Edward & Sons	Slaters, and head and tomb-stone engravers	3, George street and Siddals lane
Shipley, Thomas	Twisthand	Rivett street
Siddal, John	Portrait painter	Cheapside
Slater, Jeremiah	Bricklayer	20, North street
Smedley, James	Plumber	101, Friar gate
Smeeton, Robert	Fitter	3, North street
Smith, James	Porter	4, Sheffield place
Smith, John	Cooper	Rivett street
Smith, Edward	Shopkeeper	Osmaston street
Smith, Joseph & Co.	Cornfactors	Nottingham road
Soar, John	Turner	Darley lane
Spencer, James	Fireman	4, Leeds place
Stanton, James	Shopkeeper	26, Bridge gate
Stevenson, Leonard	Fireman	15, North street
Stevenson, Mrs.		6, Leeds place

CLASSIFICATION

OF

TRADES AND PROFESSIONS.

GENTRY AND CLERGY.

Abney, Rev. Edward Henry, the Firs

Ayrton, Rev. Samuel, Baptist minister, Sitwell street

Bateman, Alleyne Sacheverel, esq., Litchurch villa

Bateman, Mrs. Elizabeth, Litchurch villa

Bacon, Mrs. Susannah, Ashbourn road

Bainbrigge, Thomas Parker, esq., J.P., Corn market

Baker, William, esq., M.D., Friar gate

Baker, William, esq., Friar gate

Bakewell, Miss, Iron gate

Barber, John, esq., Queen street

Barker, Miss Harriet, Vernon st.

Bell, Horace, gentleman, Duffield road

Bent, Thomas, esq., M.D., Friar gate

Bennett, Miss, Friar gate

Binger, J. O., esq., Osmaston road

Bingham, John, esq., Rose cottage

Bingham, Miss Martha, Vernon st.

Boden, Henry, esq., Grove terrace

Boden, Thomas, gentleman, Curzon street

Bridgett, Mrs. Sarah, North parade

Briggs, Thomas, gentleman, Litchurch

Brooks, Rev. Ley, Full street

Brown, Richard, esq., St. Helen's st.

Burroughs, Thomas, gentleman, Osmaston road

Calvert, Edward, esq., Full street

Chatterton, John, esq., Alvaston

Clay, Wentworth, gentleman, Osmaston road

Clay, Miss Mary, Tenant street

Coke, Thomas, gentleman, Wilmot street

Cooper, Thomas, gentleman, Victoria street

Cooper, John, gentleman, Traffic st.

Corbin, Rev. John, 35, Friar gate

Corn, John, gentleman, Wilmot st.

Cox, Thomas, esq., Friar gate

Cox, George, esq., Grove terrace

Cox, Roger, esq., Spondon

Cox, Henry, esq., Park Fields

Cox, Samuel Walker, esq., Brailsford lodge

Cracroft, Miss Sophia, Ashbourn road

Crompton, John Bell, esq., Milford house and Iron gate

Curzon, Admiral Henry, Ashbourn road

Curzon, John, esq., Full street

Darby, Thomas, sen., gentleman, Wilmot street

Dawes, Captain, Friar gate

Dean, Rev. James, Osmaston road

Dixon, Captain Francis, Cherry st.

Drewry, Mrs., Ashbourn road

Emery, Mrs. Alice, 5, Friar gate

Etches, Charles, gentleman, Wilmot street

Evans, William, esq., M.P., Allestree hall

Evans, Samuel, esq., Darley Abbey

Evans, the Misses, Darley hall

Evans, Rev. Richard, Normanton terrace

Collumbell, William, gentleman, Cherry street

Copestake, James, gentleman, Old Uttoxeter road

Copestake, John, gentleman, Wilmot street

Corn, John, gentleman, Wilmot st.

Ferguson, George, esq., M.D., London road

Fisher, Rev. William, Grove terrace

Fitchett, Robert, gentleman, Mount Carmel

Fletcher, Rev. William, St. Peter's st.

Flewker, Mrs., Park place, Burton road

Ford, Rev. John, Baptist minister, North parade

Forester, Richard Forester, esq., M.D., J.P., Green hill

Fox, Samuel, jun., esq., J.P., North parade

Fox, Mrs. Catherine, Wardwick

Fox, Douglas, esq., J.P., Wardwick

Fox, Francis, esq., M.D., Wardwick

Fox, Archibald, gentleman, Wardwick

Fox, Edward, esq., Green lane

Frear, Benjamin, esq., Friar gate

French, Miss, Ashbourn road

Fritche, George, gentleman, Victoria street

Frost, R., esq., Secretary to North Midland Railway Company

Fuller, Mrs. Maria, Wilmot street

Fulton, Andrew, gentleman, Sacheverel street

Gamble, Stephen, esq., Duffield road

Gamble, John, gentleman, Full st.

Gawthorne, Rev. James, Calvinist minister, Victoria street

Gell, Rev. Philip, Friar gate

Gell, Thomas, esq., Friar gate

German, John, gentleman, Osmaston road

Gibson, Miss Frances, 18, St. Mary's gate

Goodall, John, esq., Normanton

Haden, Richard Wright, esq., J.P., St. Michael's church yard

Handford, Joseph, gentleman, Osmaston road

Hadley, Mrs. Susannah, 13, Ashbourn road

Hall, Mrs., North parade

Hall, Lorenzo Kirkpatrick, esq., J.P., Milford

Harrison, Miss Louisa, Little Chester

Harrison, William, gentleman, Sitwell street

Harrison, Mrs. Mary, 36, Friar gate

Hart, William, gentleman, St. John's terrace

Haslam, Richard Canaway, gentleman, North parade

Hewitt, Benjamin, gentleman, St. Helen's street

Heygate, James, esq., M.D., the College

Hill, John, esq., St. Alkm. ch. yard

Hoare, Mrs., Litchurch Grange

Holbrooke, Charles, esq., Boulton house

Holden, the Misses, Ashbourn road

Hope, Rev. Charles Robert

Hope, Robert John, gentleman, London terrace

Hope, Mrs. Elizabeth, London road terrace

Hope, Rev. Rich. Mellor, Duffield

Hope, Miss Susannah Ellen, 3, North terrace

Horsfield, Rev. Abraham, Litchurch Grange

Horsley, Nathaniel, gentleman, Queen street

Howard, Rev. John Garton, Lodge lane

Jessopp, Francis, esq., Wardwick

Jessopp, Francis Johnson, esq., Wardwick

Johnson, John, gentleman, Albion street

Jones, Rev. Noah, North parade

Killer, John E., esq., Friar gate
Lewis, Josiah, esq., Osmaston parsonage
Latham, Rev. John, the Elms
Leacroft, Richard Becher, esq., Osmaston road
Lillingston, Rev. Edward, Ashbourn road
Locket, William, esq., J.P., Wardwick
Macklin, Rev. Roseingrave, Wardwick
Mather, Mrs., Rose cottage
Mellor, Mrs. F., Vernon street
Meynell, Miss Mary, 41, Friar gate
Middleton, Mrs. Hannah, London road
Morley, Edward, gentleman, Wilmot street
Morley, Joseph, gentleman, Duffield road
Morley, William, gentleman, London road
Morris, Mrs. Ann, Litchurch lodge
Moss, John, esq., St. Peter's street
Mousley, William Eaton, esq., Exeter house
Mousley, John Hardcastle, esq., Exeter house
Mousley, Rev. William Eaton, Exeter house
Mozley, Henry, sen., esq., Friary
Mozley, Henry, jun., esq., Wardwick
Mozley, John, gentleman, Friar gate
Mozley, Charles, gentleman, Friary
Mundy, William, esq., Markeaton hall
Newton, William Leaper, esq., Leylands
Newton, Robert, esq., Leylands
Pegg, Thomas, gentleman, Litchurch hollies
Perry, Miss Mary, Kedleston road
Pickering, Rev. George, Mackworth
Pike, Rev. John G., D.D., Baptist minister, Parker street
Ratcliff, Mrs. Mary, London terrace
Redfern, Mrs. Mary, Grove terrace
Ronald, Robert, esq., Corn market
Sandars, John, esq., Market place
Sandars, Francis, gentleman, Friar gate

Sandars, Charles, gentleman, Friar gate
Severne, Mrs. Louisa, Grove terrace
Shaw, William, gentleman, Vernon street
Simpson, James, esq., St. Mary's gate
Simpson, Charles, gentleman, Iron gate
Simpson, Frederick, gentleman, College place
Simpson, Edwd., gentleman, Bridge gate
Simpson, William, esq., M.D., Hilton cottage
Sing, Rev. Thomas, Bridge gate
Smith, George Warwick, gentleman, the Elms
Smith, Miss Elizabeth, Ashbourn rd
Smith, Mrs. Margaret, Friar gate
Stephenson, John, gentleman, Ashbourn road
Storer, Captain J., Full street
Strutt, Edward, esq., M.P., St. Helen's house
Strutt, Joseph, esq., J.P., St. Peter's house
Strutt, Jedediah, esq., J.P., Green house, Belper
Strutt, John, esq., J.P., Bridge hill
Strutt, Anthony, esq., J.P., Makeney cottage
Strutt, the Misses, the Grove
Taylor, Mrs., Kedleston road
Trafford, Thomas, gentleman, Vernon street
Turner, William, gentleman, Green lane
Unwin, Rev. Edward, Park field
Walker, William Thomas, gentleman, Grove street
Ward, Robert, gentleman, Full st.
Williamson, Mrs. Mary, George st.
Wilmot, Mrs. Elizabeth, Friar gate
Wilmot, Sir Robert, bart., Osmaston hall
Wilmot, Henry Sacheverel, esq., J.P., Chaddesden hall
Wright, Mrs. Elizabeth, Friar gate
Wright, Thomas, esq., Friar gate
Wright, Samuel Job, esq., Mickleover
Wright, Miss Sarah, North parade

Wright, Mrs. Sarah, Friar gate
Wright, John, gentleman, Market place
(See also Solicitors, Manufacturers, &c., not included here.)

ACADEMIES.

Aldridge, Richard G., Traffick street
Ayrton, Rev. Samuel (day) Sitwell street
Barnard, Ruth (day) 4, Brook street
Bartlett, Sarah (National) Traffic st.
Birkin, William (day) Full street
Bennett, Joseph (boardg) Parker st.
Brentnall, Hannah (boarding) St. Mary's gate
Britton, Alexander (Lancastrian) Orchard street
Cragg, William Preston (National) Curzon street
Fletcher, Rev. William (boarding and free grammar) St. Peter's st.
Greasley, Charlotte (day) Osmaston street
Hackett, Eliza (day) Brook street
Haslam, Mary Eleanora, North parade
Hill, Mary Anne (day) Railway terrace
Holbrooke, Charlotte (Infant) Mill street
Hopkinson, Eliza (day) Erasmus st.
Hudson, John (boarding) Full street
James, John (day) George street
Jay, James (boardg) Mount pleasant
Johnson and Pratt (day) Agard st.
Kirkland Mrs. (day) Duke street
Lallemands, Aïméé, Ann, & Caroline (boarding) Green lane
Mather, John (boardg) Osmaston st.
Moorley, Joseph (day) St. Peter's st.
Newsome, Henry, Uttoxeter road
Oliver, Elizabeth (boarding & day) St. Helen's street
Osborne, Sarah Ann (boarding and day) St. Mary's gate
Pescud, Amy (Infant) Siddals lane
Pescud, John (National) Traffic st.
Sherwin, John, Litchurch street
Simpson, Mary (Wesleyan) Green lane

Smallwood, the Misses, Green lane
Stubberfield, Thomas (Wesleyan) Chapel street
Thompson, Mary Anne (boarding) London street
Yeates, Eliza (boarding and day) Wilmot street
Ward, Josepha and Jemima (day) Sacheverel street
Warner, Ann (National) Curzon st.
Wilson, Sarah Frances (boarding) St. Alkmund's vicarage
Willoughby, Wm. (day) Bridge st.
Willoughby, Richard, Bridge street
Wood, William (day) Full street

ACCOUNTANTS.

Ashby, George, South street
Ashby, Thomas, Sitwell street
Bailey, John, Parker street
Bowring, Charles, St. John's terrace
Bromley, John, St. Mary's gate
Glover, Stephen, Derby
Edwards, Peter Turner, Agard st.
Eyre, Samuel, Full street
Sheppard, Thomas, John street
Stone, Richard, Curzon street

AGENTS.

Brearey, Rowland Amcotts (Church of England Fire and Life Assurance) Corn market
Brearey and Eyre (House & Land) Corn market
Bretnor and Co. (Birmingham Fire and Eagle Life Assurance Companies) Friar gate
Bromley, Robert (Land) London st.
Bromley, John (Land, and to the Economical Life and Fire Assurance Company) St. Mary's gate
Cockayne, John (House) Parker st.
Earp, Thomas (Estate, House, Land, Canal, and Railway, &c.) 4, London terrace
Edge, Thomas (to Beasley and Champion, Carrington brewery) Full street
Eyre, Samuel (York and London Fire and Life Assurance, and Plate Glass Company) Full street

Featherston, Charles W., 5, Amen alley

Freake, J. F. (House) Market place

Gamble and Co. (Union Fire and Life Assurance) Iron gate

Gardner, Wm. (Cheese) London st.

Glover, Stephen (Estate, House, Canal, Railway, and Turnpike-share) Derby

Goodwin, Thos. & Francis (Cheese) Cockpit hill

Griffin, E. (to Sutton & Co.) Cockpit hill

Hallam, Michael (to District Society for promoting Christian Knowledge) 17, Sadler gate

Hobson, William (for South Australian Emigration) Iron gate

Holmes, Godfrey (to Wheatcroft & Sons) Cockpit hill

Hood, George (County Fire and Provident Life Assurance Companies) George street

Humpstone, Joseph (to Curtis and Harvey, gunpowder manufacturers) Wardwick

Hutchinson, William, Uttoxeter road

Lackington, James (House) Osmaston road

Lamb, George (Land) St. Peter's bridge

Lister, Thomas (to Ames and Co.) Siddals lane

Marshman, William (for Roads) Traffic street

Merrey, Thomas (to Tunley and Hodson) Siddals lane

Moseley, Robert and Nephew (for British Plate Glass Company) Corn market

Price, John, general agent (Yorkshire Fire and Life Office) Victoria street

Roberts, Thomas (for all London newspapers) St. James's lane

Robotham, John (to J. and W. Soresby) Morledge

Rowbottom, William (British Fire and Westminster Life Assurance, and for London newspapers) St. Mary's gate

Rice, Richard (to Pickford and Co.) Siddals lane

Rickard, George (to Canal company) Cockpit hill

Sandars, John (Pelican Life and Phœnix Fire) Market place

Simpson, Frederick (Land) College place

Spencer, William (to the National Assurance office) Green lane

Smith, William and Son (Land, and Nottinghamshire and Derbyshire Fire and Life Assurance) St. Alkmund's church yard

Stevenson, William (British Empire Life Assurance) Corn market

Stone, Richard (Land) Curzon st.

Swanwick, John T. (Land, and Sun Fire and Life) St. Mary's gate

Welbourne, Robert (for Schweppe and Co.'s soda water) Friar gate

Williamson, J. (Globe Fire & Life) Corn market

ALE and PORTER MERCHANTS & DEALERS.—See also BREWERS.

Allsop, Samuel and Sons (Burton) vaults Corn market.

Beasley and Champion (Carrington) vaults Full street, agent T. Edge

Meakin, J. (Burton) vaults Sadler gate.

Mason and Gilbertson (Burton) vaults Town hall, agent Christopher Smithson

Sale, Charles, Iron gate

ARCHITECTS.

Keeling, Francis, Ashbourn road

King, Samuel, Queen street

Mason, John, London street

Price, John, Victoria street

Stevens, Henry J., Full street

Thompson, Francis, Osmaston road

ARTISTS.

Brassington, John (portrait) Friar gate

Eyre, James, Derwent street
Kirk, Samuel (animal) St. Peter's st.
Hughes, John (miniature) King st.
Moore, Henry, Green hill
Roebuck, Thos. (animal) Corn mkt.
Siddal, John (portrait) Cheapside
Webster, Moses, Derwent street

APPRAISERS.

Cartlich, Thomas, Sadler gate
Glazebrook, Paul, Eagle street
Smith & Son, St. Alkmund's ch. yd.

AUCTIONEERS and VALUERS.

Brearey and Son, Victoria street
Brearey and Eyre, Corn market
Freake, J. F., Market place
Glover, Stephen, Derby
Moore, H., St. Alkmund's church yd.
Wright, Edmund, King street

BAKERS and FLOUR DEALERS.

Allsop, Richard, Ashbourn road
Allsop, Isaac, Green lane
Bancroft, William, 8, Burton road
Barber, John, Queen street
Barker, William, Morledge
Barker, John, Burton road
Bate, Henry, St. Peter's street
Bateman, Sarah, Morledge
Beer, Richard, Bath street
Beer, James, Nun's street
Boden, Francis, Leonard street
Bradbury, Thomas, Burton road
Brentnall, James, Iron gate
Broomhead, William, Queen street
Burnett, John, Friar gate
Campion, Thomas, Eagle street
Carrington, Richard, Bag lane
Clarke, Mary, Bridge gate
Cooper, George, Bridge street
Copestake, Charles, Morledge
Denman, William, Osmaston road
Denstone, William, Sacheverel st.
Denstone, Joshua, Cheapside
Earp, George, Curzon street
Fletcher, William, Willow row
Freckleton, John, Hill street
Hanson, Thomas, Sadler gate

Harrison, Thomas, York street
Hodgkinson, Richard Earle, Lodge lane
Holmes, William, London road and Osmaston street
Hoult, Jacob, Brook street
Hunt, Joseph, Green lane
Hunt, Edward, Park street
Hunt, Samuel, Old Uttoxeter road
Hunt, Joseph, Nun's street
Johnson, Charles, Charles street
Johnson, William H., Siddals lane
Jerram, Thomas, Leonard street
Lees, Alfred, Walker lane
Locker, Ann, Green lane
M'Corsie, William, Bold lane
Marsden, Joseph, London road
Mather, William, Fowler street
Meakin, Thomas, Nun's street
Morledge, William, Siddals lane
Orenshaw, George, Sadler gate
Osborne, Joseph, St. Peter's street
Owen, James, St. Peter's street
Parker, Richard, Devonshire street
Page, Henry, Burton road
Peake, Samuel, Burton road
Pearson, William, Bridge street
Pearson, Peter, Bridge street
Prince, John, St. Alkmund's ch. yd.
Pike, Washington, Cheapside
Radford, John, Corn market
Rimington, George, Park street
Robotham, George, Corn market
Salt, Sarah, Burton road
Simpson, John, Walker lane
Smith, George Slater, Friar gate
Smith, Charles, Friar gate
Smith, Charles, Bridge gate
Sowter, Thomas, Willow row
Sowter, Charles, Friar gate
Sowter, William, Friar gate
Sowter, Joseph, Brook street
Spencer, Charles, Old Uttoxeter road
Steer, Samuel, Exeter street
Storer, Thomas, Bridge street
Tempest, John, Talbot street
Turner, William, Eagle street
Turner, William, Albion street
Walton, John, Bridge street
Warren, Stephen, King street, flour dealer only
Watson, Joseph, Sadler gate

Watson, Thomas, Sadler gate
Wheeldon, George, Mansfield road
Whiteman, Joseph, Eagle street
White, Martha, Ashbourn road
Winfield, Elizabeth, St. Peter's street
Winfield, Thomas, Market place
Wintle, Thomas, Tenant street and Queen street
Wood, Timothy, Sadler gate
Wood, John, flour dealer, King st.

BANKERS.

Cox, William and Sons, Tenant st.
Crompton, Newton, and Co., Iron gate ; draw on Smith, Payne, and Smith, London
Derby and Derbyshire Banking Company, Corn market ; draw on Williams, Deacon, & Co. ; Robert Ronald, esq., manager
Evans, William and Samuel, St. Mary's gate ; draw on Jones, Lloyd, and Co., London
Smith, Samuel & Co., Rotten row ; draw on Smith, Payne, & Smith.
Savings Bank, Friar gate ; John Watson, actuary

BASKET MAKERS.

Ford, Thomas, King street
Horsley, John, Grove street
Kirby, William, St. Peter's street
Hudson, William, Green lane
Leedham, Ann, Bradshaw street
Smith, Lewis, Morledge
Webster, Jeremiah, Sadler gate
Wood, Thomas, Bath street

BEER SELLERS.

Adams, John, Bridge street
Allsop, Joseph, Park street
Anthony, Joseph, Normanton road
Appleby, John, Bradshaw street
Ashmole, Charles, Devonshire st.
Austin, William, York street
Barber, Ann, Jury street
Bennett, William, St. Helen's street
Bentley, William, South street
Bentley, Samuel, Sadler gate
Bentley, Richard, Bridge gate
Bettison, Joseph, Canal street
Bland, John, Albion street
Bowmer, Joshua, Ashbourn road
Britt, David Caleb, Hope street
Broadhurst, George, Bridge street
Brookes, Francis, Kensington st.
Brookes, John, Parker street
Brownsword, William, Brook street
Brunt, William, Darley lane
Bull, Thomas, Park street
Camp, William, Chester place
Cholerton, Sarah, London road
Clayson, Mary, Willow row
Cleever, William, Nun's street
Collier, John, Leaper street
Cooper, Thomas, Darley lane
Cope, John, Sadler gate
Cotton, John, Devonshire street
Cowlishaw, John, Traffic street
Dexter, Samuel, Liversage street
Dimock, James, Victoria street
Douge, Philip, Park street
Eley, Samuel, Bridge gate
Elliott, Edward, Brook street
Endsor, Thomas, Siddals lane
Fletcher, John, Liversage street
Falconer, Abraham, City road
Fitchett, Thomas, Green street
Ford, James, Fowler street
Foster, Thomas, Cheapside
Frost, John, Ashbourn road
Gray, John, Walker lane
Greatorex, Luke, John street
Gregory, Thomas, Queen street
Gunnell, William, Canal street
Hadfield, Mary, Willow row
Hand, Joseph, Nottingham road
Hardy, Joseph, Normanton road
Harrison, James, Duke street
Hewitt, James, Nun's street
Hewitt, Thomas, Willow row
Hodgkinson, George, Bold lane
Holmes, Henrietta, Eagle street
Hudson, William, London road
Hunt, Hannah, Osmaston street
Ingham, Thomas, Bridge gate
Jankinson, Joseph, Bridge street
Johnson, Joseph, Mill street
Kershaw, Richard, Upper Brook st.
Lees, William, John street
Lomax, George, Walker lane

Marriott, Thomas, John street
Marshall, Thomas, St. Alkm. ch. yd.
Manlove, Thomas, Canal street
Meakin, William, Sacheverel street
Moss, John, Bridge gate
Nadin, John, Canal side
Nightingale, Thomas, Sacheverel st.
Pattyson, Thomas, John street
Page, Charles, Bourne street
Parker, John, Bag lane
Pegg, John, William street
Ratcliffe, Elizabeth, Wright street
Redfearn, Joseph, Mundy street
Redfearn, John, Nun's street
Riding, Joseph, Eagle street
Robinson, John, Bold lane
Roworth, John, Chapel street
Rushton, John, Eagle street
Sephton, William, Nottingham road
Shepherd, Thomas, Sitwell street
Simpson, William, Albion street
Simpson, Samuel, Siddals lane
Smith, John, Bath street
Smith, Thomas, King street
Spendlove, John, Eagle street
Statham, John, John street
Storer, Thomas, Traffic street
Tantum, Edward, Burton road
Taylor, Eliza, Canal street
Thompson, Stephen, Canal street
Wain, Samuel, Bloom street
Wain, Robert, Canal street
Ward, Richard, Eagle street
Whiting, Joseph, jun., Eagle street
Widdowson, Joseph, River street
Williams, William, Drewry lane
Wilson, Sarah, Bridge gate
Witton, Samuel, Canal street
Woodward, Thomas, Devonshire st.
Woodward, George, Osmaston st.
Wright, Thomas, St. Mary's gate

BENT TIMBER MANUFAC-TURERS.

Cholerton, Harvey & Co., Albion st.
Smith, William & Son, King street

BELL HANGERS.

Halbard, John, Devonshire street
Harrison, John, Bridge gate

Haslam, William, St. Helen's street
Hunt, Joseph, St. Peter's street
Parkes, Marmaduke, Friar gate

BLACKSMITHS.

Bentley, Samuel, Corn market
Bentley, William, Sadler gate
Bentley, Samuel, George yard
Bentley, James, Thorntree lane
Botham, Henry, Queen street
Brown, Thomas, Talbot street
Coxon, Jacob, Devonshire street
Gibson, John, Parker street
Mawe, Thomas, Wright street
Moorley, William, Albion street
Priest, John, Bag lane
Priest, William, Bag lane
Shaw, John, Canal street
Smith, Samuel, Corn market
Stone, John, Park street
Thorley, William, Queen street
Thorley, Thos., St. Michael's lane
West, Robert, Bradshaw street

BLACKING MANUFACTURERS.

Bullock, William, Bath street
Clifford, John, Thorntree lane
Locker, John, Devonshire street
Pegg and Co., Goodwin street
Soar, John, Walker lane
Soar, Thomas, Bridge street

BOARDING HOUSE (Commercial.)

Gawthorne, W. R., St. Mary's gate

BOAT AND BARGE BUILDERS.

Sephton, William, Nottingham road
Street and Thompson, Exeter st.

BOOKBINDERS.

Bolton, William, St. Mary's gate
Bolton, John, Friar gate
Horsley, Charles, York street
Roberts, William, Willow row
Smith, James, Liversage street
Wainwright, John, Albion street
Wallis, Samuel, Traffic street

BOOKSELLERS, BOOKBINDERS, STATIONERS, & PRINTERS.

Bamford, John, Osmaston street
Bemrose, William, Iron gate
Chadfield, Joseph, Friar gate
Dobson, Ralph, Traffic street
Glover, Stephen, Derby
Hobson, William, Iron gate
Hill, John, Morledge
Horsley, William, Sadler gate bridge
Lindley, Richard, Rotten row
Locker, Joseph, Jury street
Mozley, Henry and Sons (wholesale) Friar gate
Pike, William & Walter, Corn mkt.
Porter, Henry, Park street
Richardson and Son (wholesale) Ashbourn road
Roberts, Thomas, St. James's lane
Rowbottom, Wm., St. Mary's gate
Smith, John, Liversage street
Stenson, Wm. John, Corn market
Storer, James, St. Peter's street
Whittaker, James, Corn market
Wilkins and Son, Queen street
Williams, Charles John, Sadler gate

BOOT AND SHOEMAKERS.

Adams, Ann, Burton road
Adcock, George, Nottingham road
Anthony, George, Duke street
Austin, Thomas, Burton road
Bacon, Thomas, St. Peter's street
Baker, Sarah, Rotten row
Baker, Joseph, Corn market
Baker, William, Bag lane
Bailey, George, Litchurch street
Ball, Thomas, Orchard street
Bannister, Charles J., Bold lane
Barber, Henry, Castle street
Barker, Elijah, Burton road
Barker, John, Union buildings
Barker, Stephen, Agard street
Barlow, Benjamin, Agard street
Barlow, Matthew, Cross lanes
Barnes, Thomas, St. Peter's street
Bartlet, John, Castle street
Bassendine, George, Cheapside
Beeson, Thomas, sen., Eagle street
Beeson, Thomas, jun., Eagle street

Bestwick, J., Lodge lane
Bigsby, Benjamin, Grove street
Bland, Joseph, Albion street
Bland, William, Friar gate
Bland, James, Bold lane
Blood, William, Osmaston street
Bostock and Sons, Sadler gate and Queen street
Boulderstone, Thomas, Brook street
Bradbury, Thomas, Sadler gate
Bradshaw, Edward, Eagle street
Bratby, William, Nottingham road
Brierley, Richard, Willow row
Britton, William, Bridge street
Broughton, Henry, Bridge gate
Brown, William, St. Michael's lane
Bryan, Samuel, Queen street
Budworth, Thomas, Siddals lane
Burrows, William, Bridge street
Chaplin, J., St. Peter's street
Chaplin, Samuel, Brook street
Cockayne, Charles, Duke street
Cooper, Thomas, St. Helen's street
Cope, John, Devonshire street
Cope, Joseph, Eagle street
Corden, Joseph, Friar gate
Cotton, William, Ashbourn road
Drew, Isaac, St. Mary's gate
Drew, William, Osmaston street
Eaton, John, Parker street
Endsor, Thomas, Siddals lane
Etches, John, Bold lane
Evans, George, Bloom street
Fallows, John, Cockpit hill
Ford, Thomas, Green street
Ford, Joshua, Kensington street
Gadsby, Peter, Grove street
Gadsby, Enoch, Wardwick
Gee, Thomas, Union buildings
Gillam, William, Iron gate
Godwin, Thomas, King street
Gray, George, Bridge street
Gray, John, Walker lane
Harding, Thomas, Friar gate
Harrison, R. T., Wardwick
Harrison, John, Morledge
Hawkridge, John, Waterloo street
Heathcoat, Thomas, Hill street
Hefford, John, Queen street
Heming, John, Agard street
Heskett, Thomas, Bag lane
Holme, George, Market head

Hoon, Isaac, Bloom street
Hunt, John, Goodwin street
Hughes, Thomas, Nun's street
Jackson, George, Hope street
Johnson, William, King street
Kerry, Joseph, Cheapside
Keys, Thomas, Brook street
Knowles, John, Bridge street
Lee, George, Sadler gate
Lester, William, Green lane
Litchfield, John, Sadler gate
Lloyd, J., Bold lane
Lowe, Thomas, Ashbourn road
Legg, John, Grove street
Martin, Joseph, Orchard street
Martin, Charles, Goodwin street
Maskrey, James, Willow row
Meakin, William, River street
Meakin, George, Brook street
Meakin, William, Exeter street
Meakin, James, Goodwin street
Meakin, Thomas, Brook street
Moore, William, Castle street
Moore, William, William street
Mountford, Benjamin, Kensington
Musgrove, Joseph, Kensington
Neal, Nathaniel, Sadler gate
Newham, William, Walker lane
Palmer, George, Wright street
Parr, Benjamin, Bag lane
Peat, Richard, Park street
Percival, John, Sacheverel street
Pipes, Thomas, Darley lane
Pipes, Thomas, St. Peter's street
Pool, Thomas, Albion place
Poyser, John, Devonshire street
Poyser, Henry, Brook street
Preston, Ann, 5, Victoria street
Ratcliffe, Joseph, Morledge
Richardson, Peter, Walker lane
Roe, William, Grove terrace
Rosigh, M. de, Irongate
Rushton, John, Lodge lane
Sandars, Joseph, Sadler gate
Shepherd, Thomas, Sitwell street
Simpson, Joseph, St. Peter's street
Sparks, James, St. Peter's street
Stevenson, Thomas, Bold lane
Summer, William, Green lane
Swindell, Joseph, Darwin row
Thompson, William, Green lane
Tooth, Richard, Full street

Tracey, Michael, Bridge street
Varley, Thòmas, Bradshaw street
Walker, William, Fingal street
Walklate, J., Goodwin street
Weatherby, Henry, Bold lane
Webster, William, Friar gate
Whitehead, James, Grove street
Wigley, William, Fingal street
Winfield, Thomas, Devonshire st.
Woodward, Francis, Bridge street
Woodward, William, Goodwin st.
Woodward, Isaac, Goodwin street
Woodward, John, Ford street
Yeomans, John, Castle street

BRAZIERS AND TIN PLATE WORKERS.

Beeson, William, Iron gate
Brodhurst, George, Victoria street
Ingham, Henry, Brook street
Maskrey, John, Willow row
Parker and Son, Sadler gate
Pemberton, George, St. Peter's st.
Richardson, J., Bridge gate
Sandars & Haywood, Market place
Smith, Samuel (and vapour bath manufacturer) Corn market
Smith, Samuel, London road
Smith, Thomas, St. Peter's street
Wilson and Dunn, King street

BRASSFOUNDERS.

Haywood, George, Willow row
Haywood, James, Phœnix foundry, Exeter street
Hollins, Sarah, Cavendish street
Hollins, Joseph, London street
Page, Thomas, Corn market
Whitehurst, John (and bell) Cherry street

BROKERS AND FURNITURE WAREHOUSE.

Blackwell, Henry, Queen street
Brown, John, Bag lane
Cartlich, Thomas, Sadler gate
Cole, William, St. Peter's street
Glazebrook, Paul, Cockpit hill
Knight, Rhoda, Nun's street

Wathall, Leonard, Morledge
Whitaker, John, Cross lanes
Wright, Edmund, King street

BREWERS.

Allsopp, Samuel and Sons, vaults Corn market
Beasley and Champion (Carrington brewery) vaults Full street
Hagen, Benjamin, South street
Hunt, Henry, Nottingham road
Meakin, J. (Burton) vaults Sadler gate
Porter, John, Ashbourn road
Watson, John, Curzon street
Wedge, Moreton Charles, Wardwick

BRUSHMAKERS.

Ford, George, Victoria street
Glover, Thomas, London road
Mason, John and Son, Ashbourn road
Smith, George, Sadler gate
Wilson, William, Bridge gate

BRICKLAYERS.
Those marked * are Journeymen.

Buxton, Thomas, Parker street
*Buxton, James, Parker street
*Buxton, John, Brook street
*Harlow, John, Brook street
*Harlow, Charles, sen., Mundy st.
*Harlow, Charles, jun., Brook st.
Moody, George, Chapel street
Moss, Henry, Traffick street
Mozley, Burrows, Albion street
*Neville, George, Litchurch street
Pegg, Jacob, Sitwell street
Percival, William, Bradshaw street
*Pierce, John, Uttoxeter road
*Pool, John, Devonshire street
*Redfearn, Joseph, Mundy street
*Riding, John, Sitwell street
Riley, Samuel, Charles street
*Roome, William, Devonshire street
Sims, James, Traffick street
*Slinn, Thomas, Cross lanes
*Slinn, James, Friar gate
Stevenson, Henry, Sitwell street

Stothard, Robert, Sacheverel street
*Stroud, Robert, St. Peter's street
Tate, John, Large's street
Wade, James, Brook street
Wade, Joseph, Bridge street
Wood, Richard, Full street

BRICKMAKERS.

Bennett, Thomas, Uttoxeter road
Gascoyne and Son, St. Peter's st.
Harpur, John, Talbot street
Harpur, Joseph, Uttoxeter road
Holmes, William, Uttoxeter road
Holmes, John, Uttoxeter road
Pool, Benjamin, Goodwin street
Redfearn, John, Nun's street
Redfearn, Joseph, Mundy street
Woollatt, Joseph, Burton road

BUILDERS, STONEMASONS, AND BRICKLAYERS.

Cooper, Thomas, Brook street
Gascoyne, Joseph and Son, Babington lane
Redfearn, John, Nun's street
Swinnerton, Steph., Mansfield road
Thompson, George, Devonshire st.
Wood, John, Liversage street

BUILDERS AND CARPENTERS.

Adin, John, Friar gate
Bennett, Charles (and Printer's joiner) Curzon street
Bennett, William, St. Helen's street
Bridgart, John and Robert, Friar gate
Bridgart, George, King street
Brown, William, Large's street
Cooper, William Mansfield, St. Mary's gate
Cowlishaw, John, Sacheverel street
Eaton, John, Chapel street
Gadsby, Thomas, Wardwick
Harvey, Samuel, George street
Malin, James, Forester street
Marriott and Garratt, Derwent st.
Orme, Benjamin, Bridge street
Orme, Frederick, Bridge street
Orme, William, Siddals lane

Pool, William, Friar gate
Potter, Samuel, Devonshire street
Slater, Robert Gilman, Vernon st.
Slater, William, Fowler street
Smith, Edward, Queen street
Sowter, William, Castle street
Swain, John, Traffick street
Thompson, Edwin, London road
Ward, George, St. Peter's street
Winterton, William, Summer hill
Woolley, Samuel, Curzon street

BUILDING SURVEYORS.

Cooper, William Mansfield, St. Mary's gate
Grace, Robert, Sitwell street
Mason, John, London street
Smith and Son, St. Alkm. ch. yard

BUTCHERS.

Archer, Henry, London road
Ashby, Abraham, Queen street
Bailey, John, sen., Queen street
Bailey, John, jun., St. Peter's street
Bamford, Robert, Market place
Bancroft, Gervas, Traffic street
Barker, William, Bold lane
Beardsley, William, Brick street
Beasley, Edward, Bridge gate
Bennett, Paul, Friar gate
Boam, Christopher, Burton road
Boam, Daniel, Burton road
Boam, John, Castle street
Bowmer, Joshua, Ashbourn road
Bowmer, James, Willow row
Bridges, Richard, Goodwin street
Brown, George, Friar gate
Bryer, Benjamin, Old shambles
Chambers, Gervas, Burton road
Clay, John, jun., Traffick street
Clay, Thomas, Leonard street
Clays, Joseph, sen., Leonard street
Collumbell, Charles, Drewry lane
Copestake, Edward, Nun's street
Dalby, Samuel, Osmaston road
Dallison, John, Hill street
Dallison, Gilbert, Corn market
Domleo, William, Old shambles
Doubleday, William, North street

Dreher, John Frederick (pork) Morledge
Dunnicliff, John, St. Peter's street
Dunnicliff, William, Market place
Dunnicliff, John, Bridge street
Dunnicliff, William, Dunkirk
Egard, Charles, Ashbourn road
Eyre, Timothy, Mansfield road
Fluid, Thomas, Old Shambles
Gilbert, Josiah, Old shambles
Glue, Henry, Hope street
Greatorex, William, Osmaston road
Greatorex, Joseph, Friar gate
Greatorex, Edward, Iron gate
Greaves, John, Goodwin street
Gretton, John, Osmaston street
Gutteridge, Thomas, Park street
Howkins, Samuel, Ford street
Haynes, Thomas, Green street
Haynes, William, Bag lane
Haynes, George, Parker street
Hodgkinson, John, St. Peter's street
Houghton, John, Bloom street
Holloway, Thomas, Victoria street
Hughes, John, London road
Hudson, William, Park street
Hurd, William (pork) Bold lane
Kramer, F. (pork) Iron gate
Lewis, John, Canal street
Longdon, Henry, jun., Queen st.
Lowe, Richard, Sadler gate
Maddocks, Richard, Osmaston st.
Mansfield, John, Canal street
Marples, Matthew (pork) Osmaston street
Marriott, Christopher, Bridge gate
Martin, John, Old shambles
Martin, Joseph, Old shambles
Mead, William, Brook street
Morley, Samuel, Parker street
Pegg, Elizabeth, Bridge gate
Potter, Charles, Friar gate
Potter, James, Ashbourn road
Radford, Henry, Old shambles
Radford, John, Sitwell street
Radford, John, Iron gate
Radford, Francis, Corn market
Radford, William, Burton road
Radford, Joseph, Liversage street
Ramsall, Edwin, St. Peter's street
Redfearn, Philip, Grove street

I

Redfearn, William, Goodwin street
Redfern, John, Siddals lane
Salisbury, Richard, King street
Shaw, Samuel, Sacheverel street
Shaw, Christopher, Sitwell street
Sheppard, Slater, Brook street
Simms, William, Burton road
Simpson, James, Devonshire street
Simpson, Thomas, Nun's street
Slater, John, Brook street
Smith, Thomas, Queen street
Smith, Thomas, Litchurch street
Smith, Thomas, Morledge
Steele, Thomas, sen., Willow row
Steele, Thomas, jun., Sadler gate
Taylor, Thomas, Bag lane
Tinsley, Edward, Devonshire street
Tomlinson, Joseph, William street
Topham, Thomas, St. Mary's gate
Tunnicliff, John, Sadler gate
Ufton, John, Bloom street
Upton, Anne, Sadler gate
Upton, William, Walker lane
Wainwright, Alfred, Queen street
Walters, Joseph, King street
Webster, Joseph, Corn market
Wheeldon, Joshua, Bag lane
Whiting, Joseph, Eagle street
Woodruff, William, Brook street
Woollatt, Samuel, Kensington st.
Woollatt, Joseph, St. Peter's street
Woollatt, Samuel, Albion street
Yeamans, Samuel, St. Mary's gate
Yeamans, Joseph & Thomas, Corn
  market
Yeomans, Joseph, Old shambles
Yeomans, George, St. Mary's gate

CABINET MAKERS.
Those marked thus * are UPHOLSTERERS.

Barker, Edward, St. Mary's gate
*Barnett, George and Son, Market
  place
Bennett, William, St. Helen's street
*Blackwell, Henry, Queen street
*Botham, Robert, Friar gate
Bowler, Joseph, Jury street
Brierley, Thomas, Wilmot street
Brierley, Joseph, Upper Brook st.
Brown, Thomas, Osmaston street
*Cartlich, Thomas, Sadler gate

*Cholerton, Matthew, Victoria st.
Cooper, William Mansfield, St.
  Mary's gate
*Cole, William, St. Peter's street
Cunliffe, Henry, Siddals lane
Fitchett, Samuel, Ashbourn road
Footit, Richard, London street
*Gamble, Stephen & Co., Iron gate
Glazebrook, Paul, Cockpit hill
Hobson, James, South street
Hughes, John, King street
How, Thomas, Market place
*Knight, William, Friar gate
Manuel, Anthony, Full street
Northwood, George, Talbot street
Pickering, William, King street
*Radford, Francis, Brook street
Smith, Edward, Queen street
Wathall, Leonard, Morledge
Wood, George, Green lane
*Woollatt, Joseph, Iron gate
Woolley, Samuel, Curzon street
Wright, Edmund, King street

CARPENTERS AND JOINERS.

Bennett, Charles (and printer's fur-
  niture) Curzon street
Bennet, William, St. Helen's street
Eaton, Joseph, Chapel street
Freeman, William, Upper Brook st.
Harvey, Samuel, George street
Husband, William, Exeter street
Jackson, Francis, St. Peter's ch. yd.
Jay, John, Bradshaw street
Littlewood, William, Osmaston st.
Marshall, Samuel, St. Alkm. ch. yd.
Miers, Robert, Nun's street
Milner, Edward, Bloom street
Moore, William, Traffick street
Moore, William, Bag lane
Moore, John, Normanton road
Moorley, James, Osmaston street
Morley, William, Parker street
Morley, Thomas, Green lane
Ordish, Thomas, Nun's street
Platts, William, Queen street
Poyser, Michael, Osmaston street
Potter, Samuel, Siddals lane
Robottom, George, Upper Brook st.
Smith, John, Old Uttoxeter road
Smith, John, Darley lane

Swain, John, Traffick street
Taylor, George, Wilmot street
Walker, Thomas, Devonshire street
Wickham, Thomas, Agard street

CARPET WAREHOUSE.

Hunt, Edward, Market place

CARVERS AND GILDERS.

Bancroft, Thomas, Devonshire st.
Bonsor, Alexander, Ford street
Bregazzi, Mary (and barometer and thermometer manufacturer) Cheapside
Coleman, John, King street
Fisher, John, Sadler gate
Moseley and Nephew, Corn market
Sutherland, James, Friar gate

CEMENT AND PLASTER MANU-FACTURERS.

Brookhouse, Joseph, St. Mary's mill and Morledge
Brookhouse, Thomas, Morledge
Brookhouse, Robert, Morledge
Martin, Thomas (patent cement) City road
Pegg, Robert and Co., Goodwin st. mill and Uttoxeter road
Searl, William, Wardwick
Woolhouse, John, Sadler gate

CHAIRMAKERS AND TURNERS
(See TURNERS.)

Baldwin, David, George street

CHEESEFACTORS.

Cox, William, Sons, & Co., Tenant street
Duesbury, William, Cheapside
Etches, William Jeffery, St. Peter's bridge
Goodwin, Thomas and Francis, Cockpit hill
Orton and Arnold, St. Alkmund's church yard

Simpson, Charles, Iron gate
Wright, John and Son, Mkt. place

CHEESE AGENTS.

Gardner, William, London road
Goodwin, Thomas, Devonshire st.
Goodwin, Francis, Cockpit hill
Taylor, Ambrose, Wilmot street

CHEESEMONGERS AND BACON FACTORS.

Barber, Samuel, St. Peter's street
Brindley, John, Corn market
Bowler, John, Albion street
Brockelsby, Robert, Sitwell street
Hatch, Samuel, Victoria street
Stone, Richard, Curzon street
Stone, John, Willow row
Trusswell, John, Corn market

CHEMISTS AND DRUGGISTS.

Brookes, Philip, Cheapside
Bryer, Richard, Corn market and Friar gate
Dawson, Joseph, Iron gate
Flower, Henry, Queen street
Goodall, Henry, Victoria street
Hart, Edward, Sadler gate
Hollingworth, James, Queen street and St. Peter's street
Jones & Hewitt, dispensing chemists, Iron gate
Moorcroft, Henry, Rotten row
Shaw, John, Corn market
Sherwin, William, Queen street
Stevenson, William, Corn market
Walton, Thomas W., Corn market
Watson, Samuel, St. Peter's street

CHEMISTS (Manufacturing.)

Challinor, William, City road
Pegg, Robert and Co., Goodwin street and Uttoxeter road
Ford, William and Co., Uttoxeter road
West, Henry, William street

CHINA MANUFACTURER.

Bloor, Robert, Nottingham road, and 34, Old Bond street, London

COACH BUILDERS.

Dagley and Smith, London road
Holmes, Herbert and Alfred (and harness makers by appointment to Her Majesty Queen Adelaide and His Royal Highness Prince Albert) London road
Moore, Thomas, Curzon street

COACH WHEEL MAKER.

Bateman, George, Morledge

COAL MERCHANTS & DEALERS.

Birchall, Minshul, Duke street
Bowler, Jacob, Parker street
Butler, Herbert, Mansfield road
Byatt, Joseph, Siddals lane
Cockayne and Slack, London road and Nottingham road
Dyche, Samuel, Bag lane
Ford, Joseph, Short street
Henshaw, Henry and Co., Exeter street
Jerum,   Railway station
Johnson, William, Cockpit hill
Ludlam, Henry, Cockpit hill
Pegg, Charles, Nun's street
Rice, Benjamin, sen., Cavendish st.
Stephenson, John, esq. (and lime merchant) London road
Walters, Henry, Duke street
White, John, Nottingham road

COLOUR MANUFACTURERS.

Challinor, William, City road
Cox, Brothers, and Co., Morledge
Ellam, William, Markeaton lane
Eyre, Beebe, Island place
Ford, William and Co., Uttoxeter road
Mason, John and Son, London road
Mason, Joseph and Co., Derwent street

Mason, Robert, Exeter street
Pegg, Robert & Co., Uttoxeter road

CONFECTIONERS.

Brentnall, James, Iron gate
Briggs, William, Traffick street
Cowlishaw, R. P., Liversage street
Duesbury, William O., Cheapside
Eggleston, Matthias, Iron gate
Hollingshead, Edmund, Iron gate
Hunt, Joseph, St. Peter's street
Lander, Thomas, Ford street
Locker, Ann, Green lane
Orenshaw, George, Sadler gate
Robotham, George, Corn market
Smith, Charles, Friar gate
Watson, Thomas, Sadler gate
Winfield, Elizabeth, St. Peter's st.

COOPERS.

Bannister, Thomas, Sadler gate
Burton, John, King street
Clark, John, Willow row
Smith, William, Tenant street
Stanesby, Thomas, St. Peter's st.
Stanesby, Richard, Full street
Webster, Jeremiah, Sadler gate

CORK CUTTERS.

Vernon, Catherine, Iron gate
Willisford, William and Co., Corn market

CORNFACTORS.

Blood, Thomas, Darwin row
Boden, Richard, Corn market
Clark, Mary and Henry, Nottingham road
Harrison, John, Morledge
Henshaw, Henry, Bridge gate
Hodgkinson, Joseph, Brook street
Mousley, Benjamin, jun., Traffick st.
Pike, Washington, Cheapside
Thorpe, John and Co., Morledge
Shaw, Francis, Cherry street
Smith, Joseph and Co., Nottingham road

Wheeldon, William, Bridge gate
Wood, Timothy, Duke street

CORN MILLERS.

Barber, John, Siddals lane
Burrows, Richard, Borrowash
Denstone, Joshua, Cheapside
Hill, Thomas, St. Mary's mill
Meakin, Henry, Nun's mill
Meakin, Benjamin, St. Michael's mill
Miller,   Markeaton mill
Shaw, Francis, Duke street
Sowter, William, Darwin terrace
St. Michael's Steam Mill Company, St. Michael's lane
Walters and Greensmith, Darley
Wood, Timothy, Duke street

COTTON MANUFACTURERS.

Evans, Walter & Co., Darley mill
Strutt, William, George, & Joseph, Corn market and Belper

COTTON WASTE MANUFAC-TURER.

Mellor, John, Agard street

CURRIERS & LEATHER CUTTERS.

Argill, Samuel, Bridge gate
Brookes, Samuel, Queen street
Cock, John Henry, Friar gate
Elliott, James, Sadler gate
Richardson, William and John, St. Peter's street
Shepherd, John, Bag lane
Woodward, Cornelius, Sadler gate

DENTIST.

Murphy, James B., St. Peter's st.

DYERS.

Baxter, Harvey, Bloom street
Cope, Henry, St. Michael's lane
Evans, Joseph, St. Michael's lane
Garrick, Thomas, Victoria street
Hebb, Francis, Green lane

Henchley, Samuel, Derwent street
Mead, George, St. James's lane
Tunaley, Thomas, sen., Tenant st.
Tunaley, Thomas, jun., Derwent st.
Tunaley, William, Upper Brook st.
Tunaley, Samuel, Derwent row
Unsworth and Williamson, Siddals lane
Ward, Robert, Full street
Wharton, Elizabeth, Curzon street
Webster, Benjamin, Bridge gate

DEALERS IN GAME.

Cope, William, Sadler gate
Field, Thomas, London road
Mason, Thomas, Iron gate
Wood, John, Market place

DRAPERS, LINEN & WOOLLEN.

Bannister, C. J. and R., Rotten row
Barnes, William, St. Peter's street
Beeland, William, Iron gate
Bennett, Robert, Iron gate
Briggs and George (wholesale) St. Peter's bridge
Brindley, William (woollen) Tenant street
Draper, Sarah, Corn market
German and Holmes, Corn market
Green, Lawrence, City road
Hackett, Thomas, Market place
Hellaby, Edward, Corn market
Hodgkinson and Co., Iron gate
Kent and Askew, Iron gate
Lowe, Samuel, Corn market
Massey, Jonathan and Elijah, Corn market
Sale, William, Corn market
Sheppard and Co., Market head
Shilcock and Hipworth, Iron gate
Sperrey, Edward, Queen street
Stevenson, George, Iron gate
Winter, Henry, St. Peter's street

EATING HOUSES.

Bailey, Robert, Bridge gate
Cox, Samuel, Bridge street
King, Samuel, Queen street
Orenshaw, George, Sadler gate
Price, George, sen., Sadler gate

Wilkinson, Thomas, Sadler gate
Wragg, William, Sadler gate

ENGINEERS AND MACHINE MAKERS.

Abell, William, George street
Bates, Edward, Parker street
Carr and Smith, Liversage street
Crump, Thomas, Friar gate
Dobson, Thomas, Wilmot street
Duncan, David, Nun's street
Fox, Joseph and James (and manufacturers of lathes) City road
Frost, William, City road
Harrison, John (and boiler manufacturer) Bridge gate
Macintyre, James, Bradshaw street
Mosedale, William, Nun's street
Pegg, Charles, Park street
Yates, David, St. Michael's lane

ENGRAVERS.

Garforth, John, Fox's cottage, New Uttoxeter road
Moore, Henry, Green hill
Williams, Charles John, Sadler gate

FANCY REPOSITORIES.

Cubley, Anne, Queen street
Eyre, Arabella, Friar gate
Holmes, Jonathan, Friar gate

FELLMONGERS.

Cooper and Son, Uttoxeter road
James, Thomas, St. James's lane

FIRE OFFICE AGENTS, &c.
(See AGENTS.)

FISHMONGERS.

Baggaley, John, John street
Cope, John (and oyster rooms) Sadler gate
Jackson, William (& oyster rooms) Full street
Mason, Thomas (and oyster rooms) Iron gate
Wood, John, Market place

FISHING TACKLE MANUFACTURERS.

Milward, William and Son, Market place
Peach, Joseph, St. Peter's street

FLAX DRESSERS.

Milward, William and Son, Market place
Weatherhead, Walters, and Co., Iron gate

FRAMESMITHS.

Borrey, Samuel and James, Sacheverel street
Hirst, John, Osmaston street
Hornshaw, John, Bridge gate
Ross, John, Normanton street

FURNITURE BROKERS.

Brown, John, Victoria street
Cartlich, Thomas, Sadler gate
Cole, William, St. Peter's street
Glazebrook, Paul, Cockpit hill
Knight, Rhoda, Nun's street
Mc'Guire, Charles, Morledge
Whitaker, John, Cross lanes
Wright, Edmund, King street

FURRIERS.

Fleming, Queen street
Roberts, Market place
Sale, William, Corn market

GARDENERS, SEEDSMEN, AND GREEN GROCERS.

Birkin, James, Bridge gate
Brookhouse, Milicent, Friar gate
Burnett, John, Friar gate
Calow, Joseph, John street
Cash, William, Cheapside
Cash, Stephen, Queen street
Cash, Thomas, Morledge
Chadwick, William, London road
Cooling, Edward, Uttoxeter road
Cooper, J., Darley lane
Dakin, John, Burton road
Dean, William, Cannon street

Fearn, John, Upper Brook street
Fletcher, William, Bold lane
Fletcher, John, Willow row
Foster, William, St. Peter's street
Foster, William, Sadler gate
Gaunt, Joseph, St. Peter's street
Gaunt, Joseph, Bridge street
Greaves, William, Castle street
Hall, John, Burton road
Hazledine, William, Willow row
Heath, Thomas, London road
Hickham, Thos., Siddals lane
Holland, Joseph, Grove street
Holland, John, Green lane
Jennings, James, Leonard street
Kidney, John, Bag lane
Lowe, Richard, New street
Marshall, George, Kensington st.
Marshall, J., John street
Millington, Joseph, Bag lane
Millington, Henry, St. Helen's st.
Millington, Joseph, Osmaston road
Moore, John, Siddals lane
Nash, William, Kensington
Palmer, John, Iron gate
Philip, William, Parker street
Purdy, Thomas, Bag lane
Riley, John, Parker street
Rose, Joseph, Cannon street
Shaw, John Vicars, Wright street
Shaw, John, Cockpit hill
Shaw, Griffith, Wright street
Simpson, John, Castle street
Standley, Thomas, Bridge gate
Stanley, Thomas, Friar gate
Sutliffe, John, Green lane
Teat, William, Bridge street
Wallis, Joseph, Bridge street
Wheeldon, William, High street
Wild, James, Bag lane
Wild, George, Traffick street
Wilson and Sadler, Cheapside
Wilson, William, King street
Wood, Samuel, Eagle street

GAS WORKS.

Crump, Thomas, Friar gate, manager

GAS FITTERS.

Crump, Thomas, Friar gate
Hood, George, George street

GLASS MERCHANTS.

Chatterton, John, jun., Morledge
Cox, Brothers, & Co., Morledge

GLASS AND CHINA DEALERS.

Clavey, Philip, Sadler gate
Downes, Charles Jackson, Canal street
Humphreys, Ellen, Full street
Jackson, John, St. Peter's street
Johnson, John, Tenant street
Mellor, Sarah Ann, Victoria street
Shepherdson, John, Queen street
Whetton, John, Willow row

GLOVERS.

Bamford, James, Wardwick
Hunt, William, Friar gate
Smith, Henry, St. Mich. ch. yd.

GROCERS AND TEA DEALERS.

Bailey, Thomas, Iron gate
Bakewell & Son, Market head
Bond, Joseph, Traffick street
Branton, Thos. & Wm., Queen st.
Bretnor, Bernard & Co., Friar gate
Brookes, Philip, Cheapside
Butler, Thos., Grove street
Cadman, John, Sadler gate
Cholerton, John, Willow row
Collumbell, Sarah, King street
Cooke & Co., Corn market
Eaton, Francis, Friar gate
Furniss, William, Bridge street
Furniss, Alfred W., London street
Gadsby, William, St. Peter's street
Greatorex, Jeremiah, St. Peter's st.
Hodgkinson, Thos., Queen street
Hodgkinson, Henry, Brook street
Holbrook, Edward, Green lane
Ironmonger, Eli, Friar gate
Keenan, Thomas, Wardwick
Lancashire, George, Carrington st.
Lees, Alfred, Walker lane
Marsden, William, Market place
Morley, J., Iron gate & St. Peter's st.
Merry, William, Bridge gate
Pick, Abraham, Queen street

Redgate, Robert, Bridge street
Sandars, John, Market place
Slater, Thomas, Brook street
Smith & Co., London road
Stafford, Joseph, London road
Stone, Richard, Wardwick
Storer, James, Corn market
Swift, Thomas, Sadler gate
Waddams, Elizabeth, Victoria st.
Walton, John, Bridge street
Wheeldon, George, Mansfield road
Wheeldon, William, Bridge gate
Wild, George, Corn market and
    Traffick street
Willder, Samuel, St. Peter's st.
Williams, John Jones & Co., Corn
    market
Wintle, John, Queen street
Yates, Edward, Castle street
Yeamans, Charles, Bridge street
Yeomans, Samuel, Bridge street

GUNSMITHS.

Holmes, John & Sons, Rotten row
Weatherhead, Walters, & Co., Iron
    gate

HAIRDRESSERS & PERFUMERS.

Abbott, Henry, Sadler gate
Allen, John, Bold lane
Blundstone, Samuel, St. Peter's st.
Barker, Thomas, Morledge
Boden, George, Corn market
Clarke, Alfred, St. Peter's street
Dawson, George, St. James's lane
Fernley, William, Ford street
Goulding, Thomas, Bridge gate
Inott, Robert C., 2, Market head
Jackson, Charles, Bridge street
Jolley, John, Bag lane
Knight, James, Bridge street
Marshall, William, Sadler gate
Morley, William, Bridge gate
Pegg, William, Friar gate
Perkins, Henry, Corn market
Porter, Robert, Brook street
Randall, George, Rotten row
Rewcastle, David, Queen street
Rewcastle, John, Green lane
Rewcastle, Nathaniel, Willow row

Richardson, John, King street
Sadler, Charles, Iron gate
Short, Thomas Wilkins, Traffick st.
Simpson, Henry, Osmaston street
Smithard, John, Morledge
Tooby, Thomas, Bridge street

HATTERS.

Bolus, Joseph & Co., Market head
Eyre, Thomas, Sadler gate
Fearn, George, St. Helen's street
Potter, Joseph, Bold lane
Roberts, Samuel Charles, Mkt. place
Sale, William, Corn market
Storer, Thos. & Son, Corn market
Stanesby, James, Queen st.
Thompson, John, Willow row

HARNESS MAKERS.—See also
    SADDLERS.

Holmes, Herbert & Alfred, Lon-
    don road

HOP & SEED MERCHANTS.

Cooke & Co., Corn market
Forman, Robert, Corn market
Sandars, John, Market place

HORSETRAINERS&TRIMMERS.

Broughton, Thomas, Siddals lane
Kirk, Thomas, Summer hill
Pepper, Francis, York street
Wallis, Henry, Derby

HOSIERS, GLOVERS. AND
    HABERDASHERS.

Buckley, Elizabeth, St. Peter's st.
Eyre, Thomas, Sadler gate
Haslam, Francis, Cheapside
Heathcoat, Thomas, Brook street
Holmes, Jonathan, Friar gate
Hunt, William, Friar gate
King, Sarah, St. Peter's street
Platts, Ann, Iron gate
Sperrey, Frances, Rotten row
Steel, Mary, Burton road
Swain, William, Grove street

Tatem, James, Queen street
Vernon,   St. Peter's street
Williamson, William, Friar gate

HOSIERY MANUFACTURERS.

Cotton, John, Fowler street
Cramond, William (silk) George st.
Fox, Samuel, jun. (silk) Wardwick
Harrison, John, Cherry street
Longdon, Robert (silk) Friar gate
Lewis, Samuel (silk) Willow row
Wreford & Co. (silk) Bridge street,
　(J. Squire, agent)

HOTELS, COMMERCIAL INNS, AND POSTING HOUSES.*
Those marked * are POSTING HOUSES.
Those marked † keep FLYS.

*Bell, Sadler gate, Sarah Wightman
Brunswick Inn, Harvey Lane,
　Railway terrace
Bull's Head, Hannah King, Queen
　street
Fox and Owl, Leech, Ann & John,
　Bridge gate
King's Arms & County Hotel,
　Thomas Neale, St. Mary's gate
*King's Head, Corn Market, George
　Wallis
*Midland Hotel and Refreshment
　Rooms (and Family Hotel and
　Posting house) John Cuff, Rail-
　way Station
†Nag's Head, Henry Cantrill, St.
　Peter's street
*New Inn, Hannah Spencer, King
　street
Old Angel Inn, John Reeves, Corn
　market
*Royal Hotel and Commercial Inn,
　Francis Huggins, Victoria street
Royal Oak, John Lillie, Market
　place
Saracen's Head, Thomas Ward, St.
　James's lane
†Talbot, and Nottingham house,
　Joseph Glue, Iron gate
†Tiger, Tryphena Taylor, Corn
　market

HORSE DEALERS.

Denham, William, Siddals lane
Hind, Robert, Traffick street
Roe, John, Curzon street

IRON AND BRASS FOUNDERS.

Falconer and Peach, City road
Haywood, George, (brass) Willow
　row
Haywood, James, Phœnix Foundry,
　Nottingham road
Hollins, Sarah (brass) Cavendish
　street
Hollins, John, (brass) London road
Page, Thomas, Morledge
The Derwent Foundry Co., Exeter
　place
Wright, Thomas, Britannia Foun-
　dry, Duke street

IRON MERCHANTS.

Evans, Wm. & Samuel, Morledge
Morley, William, Wardwick
Robinson, Thomas (nail iron) Bridge
　street
Sandars & Haywood, Market place

IRONMONGERS.

Holmes & Sons, Rotten row
Hunt, Joseph, jun., St. Peter's st.
Ratcliffe, Wm. & J., Corn market
Sandars & Haywood, Market place.
　(wholesale)
Weatherhead, Walters, & Co., Iron
　gate (wholesale)
Wheatcroft and Co., Corn market

JEWELLERS (Working.)

Bateman, Henry, Sadler gate
Gregory, John, Hill street
Moore, James, London road
Page, William, Sacheverel street
Peach, Joseph, St. Peter's street
Roberts, Wolstan, Sadler gate
Severne, De Milt, Osmaston road

JOINERS.—See CARPENTERS.

LACE DEALERS.

Aldred, George, Sacheverel street
Bunting, Lydia & Jane, St. Peter's bridge
Gregory, William, Victoria street
Haslam, Francis, Cheapside
Mills, James, Friar gate
Webster, Joseph, Rotten row

LACE MANUFACTURERS.

Boden & Morley, (merchants) Castle street
Dallison, William and Son, Devonshire street
Wreford & Co., (J. Squire, agent) Bridge street
Wright, John and Co., Siddals lane

LAMP MANUFACTURER.

Evans, William, Kensington street

LAND SURVEYORS.

Bromley, Robert, St. Mary's gate
Bromley, John, London street
Lamb, George, Corn market
Price, John, Victoria street
Roe, William, Grove terrace
Simpson, Frederick, College place
Smith, William and Son, St. Alkm. church yard
Spencer, William, Green lane
Stone, Richard, Curzon street
Swanwick, John Thos., St. Mary's gate

LAW STATIONERS.

Eyre, Beeby, Piazza
Featherstone, C. W., Amen Alley
Keightley, Jonathan W., St. Peter's street

LAST MAKERS.

Irons, Thomas, Talbot yard
Mart, Samuel, Talbot street
Poyser, William, Sadler gate
Wood, Eli, Willow row

LIBRARIANS.

Avery, Mrs., King street
Bailey, Edward, Amen Alley
Dewar, David, Mechanics' Institution
Locker, Joseph, Jury street
Roberts, Thomas, St. James's lane

LEAD MERCHANTS.

Chatterton, John, Morledge
Cox, Brothers and Co. (and patent shot manufacturers) Morledge
Holbrook, Charles, St. Peter's street

LEAD WORKS.

Cox, Brothers & Co., Morledge and Mill hill
Goodale, Wm. and John, Normanton road
Holbrook, Charles, St. Peter's st.

LICENSED TO LET POST HORSES.

Briggs, Joseph, Osmaston street
Broughton, Thomas, Siddals lane
Brown, Charles, Siddals lane
Garrick, Thomas, Wardwick
Glue, Joseph, Iron gate
Kirk, Thomas, Summer hill
Newham, John, Agard street
Pepper, Francis, York street
Price, George, sen., Sadler gate
Roe, John, Curzon street
Spencer, John, St. Peter's street
Swindell, James, Goodwin street

LINT MANUFACTURER.

Harcourt, John, Kensington street

MACHINE MAKERS.—See ENGINEERS.

Robinson, Joseph, Wright street
Shaw, Thomas, Wright street
Shaw, Charles, Willow row

MALTSTERS.

Beeson, Thos., St. Mary's gate
Clarke, James, Sadler gate
Clarke, Mary, Nottingham road
Davis, James, Uttoxeter road

Dimock, Thos., St. Helen's street
Denstone, James, Bold lane and Huffin Heath
Denstone, Joshua, Cheapside
Ford, James, Agard street
Forman, Robert, jun., Curzon st.
Gregory, Thomas, Queen street
Harper, John, Green lane
Hunt, Henry, Nottingham road
Kinsey, James, Executors of, Friar gate
Kniveton, Robert, Siddals lane
Leech, John, Bridge gate
Longdon, William, Queen street
Longdon, Henry, Queen street
Lowe, William, Brook walk
Mansfield, George, King street
Mansfield & Moreton, St. Michael's lane
Mansfield, William, King street
Mead, George, Bloom street
Neale, John, Albion street
Oliver, Elias, Old Uttoxeter road
Reeves, John, Corn market
Roberts, William, Short street
Sowter, Charles, Short street
Sowter, William, Darwin Terrace
Symons, Mydhope William, North parade
Ward, William, Friar gate
Wedge, M. C. Wardwick
Welbourne, Robert, Friar gate

MARBLE MASONS.

Blore, Joseph, Bridge street
Hall, Joseph, King street
Henley, John, Parker street
Swinnerton, Stephen, Mansfield road
Wood, George, Liversage street

MILLINERS & DRESSMAKERS.

Aldridge, Hannah, Albion street
Ashby, Mrs. T., Sacheverel street
Bacon, Emma, Nun's street
Bailey, Hannah, Queen street
Beeland, Mary, (show rooms) Iron gate
Blundstone, Fanny, Osmaston st.
Botham, Mary, Friar gate

Buckley, Elizabeth, Friar gate
Bull, Mary Ann, Morledge
Bunting, Lydia and Jane, St. Peter's street
Burnett, Elizabeth, Friar gate
Calliner, Eliza, Castle street
Cay, Mary, Traffick street
Cluer, Mary, Market place
Cooke, Janet, Traffick street
Copestake, Elizabeth, Wilmot st.
Cox, Harriet, Tenant street
Cross, Ann Sophia, St. Helen's st.
Dallison, Ann, Sadler gate
Dicken, Elizabeth, Friar gate
Drabwell and Benson, Sadler gate
Dudley, Sarah, Osmaston street
Eaton, Sophia, Queen street
Evans, Ann, Friar gate
Eyre, Sarah, Derwent street
Falconer, Ann, Mansfield road
Farnsworth, Mary, Bold lane
Fearn, Georgiana, St. Helen's street
Fletcher, Hannah, Ford street
Frost, Charlotte, Traffick street
Garratt, Miss, Full street
Gill, Susan, Jury street
Green, Elizabeth, George street
Gregory, Frances, Victoria street
Hall, Elizabeth, Bridge street
Harlow, Mary, Green lane
Harrison, Miss, St. Mary's gate
Harrison, Hannah, St. Peter's st.
Hatter, Mary, Tenant street
Hinckley, Elizabeth, Full street
Holmes, Mary Ann, Friar gate
James, Elizabeth, St. Peter's church yard
Jarvis, Ann, Sadler gate
Jennings, Miss, Parker street
Keeling, Eliza, Queen street
Knight, Elizabeth, Duke street
Lakin, Miss, St. Mary's gate
Lassells, Sarah, Bold lane
Lindley, Julia, St. Mary's gate
Marler, Sparks, and Ashby, Queen street
Mart, Mary Ann, St. Helen's street
Millington, Eliza, Amen Alley
Moran, Maria, Sadler gate
Ordish, Elizabeth Ann, Lodge lane
Pedley, Sarah, Tenant street
Potter, Mary, Bold lane

Roe, Mary Ann, London road
Salt, Lucy, Bridge street
Sedgwick, Hepsibah, Ford street
Sharp, Mary, Friar gate
Slater, Elizabeth, Brook street
Sparks, Lydia, Full street
Spencer, Harriett, Bridge gate
Thorpe, Mary, Osmaston road
Toplis, Elizabeth, Bridge gate
Walker, Sarah, Friar gate
Welldall, Sarah, Osmaston street
Wilson, E., Green lane
Winter, Ann, St. Peter's street
Woolhouse, Ruth Hannah, Sadler
   gate
Yeomans, Mary, Corn market

MILK SELLERS.

Brown, Francis, Burton road
Cantrell, Mrs., Ford street
Caladine, George M., Agard street
Chadwick, Samuel, Grove street
Crosby, William, Dog-kennel lane
Dallison, Daniel, Friar gate
Fox, William, Mundy street
Garton, Stephen, Burton road
Garton, Thomas, Burton road
Hanson, Joseph, Sadler gate
Haynes, Richard, Bridge street
Haynes, Thomas, Brook street
Haynes, Thomas, St. Peter's street
Hill, William, Castle street
Jolley, John, Ashbourn road
Mellor, John, Devonshire street
Slack, Samuel, Kedleston road
Slater, Jacob, Uttoxeter road
Smith, Thomas, Canal street
Smith, William, Darley lane
Stubbs, Large, Albion street
Taylor, John, Nottingham road
Wright, George, Green street

MILLWRIGHTS & ENGINEERS.

Abell, William, Cavendish street
Carr and Smith, Liversage street
Frost, William, City road
Mosedale, William, Nun's street
Topham, Snowden, St. Alkmund's
   church yard

MODELLER AND SCULPTOR.

Barton, William, Parker street

NAILMAKERS.

Eley, Samuel, Bridge gate
Eley, George, Bridge gate
Eley, William, Lodge lane
Gibson, William, Bridge street
Ottewell, Thomas, Nottingham rd.
Pitt, William, Bag lane
Ride, Thomas, Green lane
Robinson, Thomas, Bridge street
Shaw, Thomas, Agard street
Smith, Thomas, Devonshire street

NEEDLE MAKERS (for Stocking Weavers.)

Church, John, St. Helen's street
Cockayne, John, Parker street
Hall, William, Parker street
Hawley, William, Parker street
Jackson, Charles, Bridge gate
Kirk, William, St. Helen's street
Lee, George, Bridge street
Martin, S., Bridge gate
Taft, Elizabeth, Bridge gate
Wood, George, St. Helen's street

NEWSPAPERS.

Derby Mercury (Wednesday) Thos.
   Burroughs, Iron gate
Derby and Chesterfield Reporter
   (Thursday) Walter Pike, Corn
   market
Derbyshire Courier (Saturday) Wil-
   liam Rowbottom, St. Mary's gate
Derbyshire Chronicle (Saturday)
   James Storer, St. Peter's street

NURSERY AND SEEDSMEN.

Cash, Stephen, Queen street
Palmer, John and Son, Iron gate
Wilson and Sadler, Cheapside
Wilson, Joshua (landscape garden-
   er) Sitwell street

OIL AND COLOURMEN.—See also IRONMONGERS.

Bridgart, William (and artists' repository) Sadler gate
Challinor, William, City road

OPTICIANS & MATHEMATICAL INSTRUMENT MAKERS.

Davis, J., St. Mary's gate
Steer, John, Market head

PAINTERS.

Allkin, Robert, Osmaston street
Bowden, Richard, St. Peter's street
Bullock, James, Upper Brook street
Buxton, James, Derwent street and Nottingham road
Coxon, Robert Eaton, Curzon street
Emmerson, Thomas, Sacheverel st.
Fisher, John, Sadler gate
Ford, John, Devonshire street
Gamble and Cubley, Queen street
Gamble, John, jun., North parade
Hemingway, Benjamin, Full street
Hill, George, St. Peter's church yd.
Holmes, William, Sadler gate
Hughes, Duke, St. Peter's street
Longdon and Basford, Talbot yard
Longdon, Thomas, Ashbourn road
Mason, Robert, Exeter street
Moseley, William W., Friar gate
Pedley, John, Tenant street
Price, James, St. Mary's gate
Robinson, George, King street
Simpson, Isaac, Cockpit hill
Simpson, J., Devonshire street
Simpson, Benjamin, Albion street
Simpson, Thomas, Rivett street
Simpson, Charles, Siddals lane
Simpson, William, Castle street
Simpson, Isaac, jun., Cockpit hill
Simpson, George, Devonshire st.
Thompson, Henry, Parker street
Welch, William, Friar gate

PAPER HANGERS.

Bamford, John, Osmaston street
Barnett and Son, Market place

Cholerton, Matthew, Victoria street
Chadfield, Joseph, Friar gate
Gamble and Co., Iron gate
Knight, William, Friar gate
Rowbottom, William, St. Mary's gate
Woollatt, Joseph, Iron gate

PAPER MANUFACTURERS AND WHOLESALE STATIONERS.

Chadwick, Robert, Queen street
Evans and Co., Queen street— mill Darley.
Tempest and Son, Little Eaton mills

PATTEN, CLOG, AND PATTEN RING MAKERS.

Page, Benjamin, Eagle street
Page, John, Fingal street
Page, David, Willow row
Page, Edward, Walker lane
Page, Henry, Willow row
Pipes, Thomas, St. Peter's street
Poyser, William, Sadler gate

PAWNBROKERS AND GENERAL SALESMEN.

Eames, Francis, Victoria street
Hall and Goodwin, Old Piazzas, Market place
Lomax, William, Corn market
Prince and Bolsover, Queen street
Shaw, William, Cockpit hill

PHYSICIANS.

Baker, William, Friar gate
Bent, Thomas, Friar gate
Ferguson, George, London street
Forester, Richard Forester, Green lane
Fox, Francis, Wardwick
Heygate, James, College, Full st.

PIPE (TOBACCO) MAKERS.

Cleever, William, Willow row
Needham,   Agard street
Salisbury, Henry, Willow row

Strong, Thomas, Willow row
Strong, Sampson, Willow row

PLATE GLASS WAREHOUSES.

Eyre, Samuel, Full street
Moseley and Nephew, Corn market

PLUMBERS AND GLAZIERS.

Borrington, James, Friar gate
Brewer, George Henry, Agard st.
Broomhead, E. and G., Bridge gate
Brown, George, London road
Chatterton, John (wholesale) Morledge
Cooper, Mary and Robert, Thorntree lane
Crump, Thomas, Friar gate
Forman, Elijah, Wardwick
Gunn, Thomas, Devonshire street
Haslam, Benjamin, Queen street
Hodgkinson, George, Bold lane
Holmes, William, Sadler gate
Hood, George, George street
Keeling, George, St. Mary's gate
Keeling, Thomas, Market place and Osmaston street
Lord, Joseph, Iron gate
Rice, Benjamin, Friar gate
Roberts, Walter, Bold lane
Sidebottom, Joseph, Derwent street
Smedley, James, Friar gate
Thompson, Henry, Parker street
Tomlinson, Edward, Old George yard

PORTER AND ALE DEALERS.—
See ALE and PORTER MERCHANTS.

Cox and Malin, Corn market
Cox, Haden, and Pountain, Market place

POULTERERS.

Cope, John, Sadler gate
Wilkinson, Henry, Sadler gate
Wood, John, Market place
Wragg, William, Sadler gate

PRINTERS (See also BOOKSELLERS.)

Smith, George, Victoria street

PLASTERERS.

Brassington, Thomas, Brook street
Bridgart, Thomas, South street
Brookhouse, Joseph, Morledge
Brookhouse, Thomas, Morledge
Brookhouse, James, Thorntree lane
Brookhouse, Robert, Eagle street
Brookhouse, John, Ford street
Cook, John, Sitwell street
Johnson, Isaac, Cockpit hill
Pike, Isaac, Parker street
Pike, Isaac, Sadler gate bridge
Shaw, James, Green street
Simpson, Joseph, Cockpit hill
Simpson, Thomas, Devonshire st.
Simpson, Benjamin, Albion street
Simpson, Joseph, Hill street
Simpson, Thomas, Walker lane
Simpson, Robert, Bag lane
Simpson, John, Burton road
Simpson, Francis, Eagle street
Simpson, Samuel, Siddals lane

PROFESSORS AND TEACHERS.

Blake, Daniel (music) Cavendish st.
Fritche, George, jun., (dancing) Rose cottage
Fritche, Froude (music) North parade
Gover, Edward William (music) Friar gate
Gover, William E. (music and dancing) Ford street
Gover, William (music) Ford street
James, H. W. (dancing) Bridge gate
Jay, Caroline (French) Mount pleasant
Norton, Josiah (music) Darwin terrace
Shiers, Mary (music and dancing) London street
Tunaley, Thomas (dancing) Full st.
Woolley, Thomas (music) Full st.

REGISTER OFFICES FOR SERVANTS.

Bull, Samuel, Friar gate
Butler, Edward, Ford street
Keenan, Thomas, Victoria street
Williamson, Jane, King street

ROPE AND TWINE MAKERS.

Those marked * are also SACKING MAN-
UFACTURERS.

*Milward and Son, Market place
Mitchell, J. and T., Fowler street
Weatherhead, Walters, and Co., Iron
   gate
*Woolhouse, John, Sadler gate
*Woolhouse, Richard, King street

SADDLERS AND HARNESS MAKERS.

Garner, Robert, Victoria street
Gilbert, George, Bridge gate
Holmes, Herbert and Alfred, Lon-
   don street
Lindley, James, St. Peter's street
M'Clair, George, Queen street
Moore, Thomas, Curzon street
Needham, Edward, Bridge gate
Nicklinson, Henry, Rotten row
Tummond, Charles Thomas, Lodge
   lane, & manufacturers' box maker

SAW MILLS (CIRCULAR.)

Dyche, J. and R., Cockpit hill
Roe and Oakley, Siddals lane
Wait, Francis, Mansfield road

SHOPKEEPERS.

Adams, John, Brook street
Adams, Thomas, Parker street
Allen, Richard, Hill street
Allen, William, Upper Brook street
Annable, William, Eagle street
Annable, John, Liversage street
Armstrong, Joseph, Walker lane
Austin, Thomas, Burton road
Bailey, Alice, Ashbourn road
Bainbridge, Elizabeth, City road
Baldwin, David, Bridge street
Ball, James, John street
Barker, Elijah, Burton road
Barker, John, High street
Barker, William, Morledge
Barnett, Joseph, Walker lane
Bassano, John, Darley lane
Bassano, Anthony, Nottingham road
Bateman, George, Morledge
Beer, Richard, Bath street
Blundstone, William, Osmaston st.
Bond, Joseph, Traffick street
Bottom, James, Erasmus street
Bradbury, Sarah, Erasmus street
Brain, Thomas, Burton road
Brentnall, John, Uttoxeter road
Briggs, William, Leonard street
Briggs, Amos, Sitwell street
Britain, James, Bag lane
Bull, John, Albion street
Butler, Edward, Ford street
Butler, Thomas, Grove street
Camp, Thomas, Erasmus street
Cay, George, Ashbourn road
Chadwick, Samuel, Normanton road
Cholerton, Edward, Eagle street
Clulow, William, Osmaston road
Cockayne, Mary, Duke street
Colburn, George, Bridge gate
Cooke, Edward, Jury street
Copestake, Charles, Morledge
Copestake, John, Talbot street
Copestake, Mary, Burton road
Copestake, William, Nun's street
Cowlishaw, R. P., John street
Dakin, William, Eagle street
Dallison, Richard, Devonshire st.
Denman, William, Osmaston street
Dobson, Ness, Canal street
Duncan, William, Parker street
Fasom, Joshua, Kensington street
Elliott, Edward, St. Alkmund's
   church yard
Endsor, Thomas, Siddals lane
Evans, John, Sadler gate
Fearn, John, William street
Field, Thomas, London road
Gibson, William, Bridge street
Gilbert, James, Siddals lane
Goodwin, William, Friar gate
Goodson, John, Walker lane
Green, Lawrence, Goodwin street
Hage, Mary, Traffick street
Hanson, Joseph, Sadler gate
Harper, William, Parker street
Harrison, Mary, Agard street
Harrison, Hannah, Burton road
Haslam, Henry, Bag lane
Hazledine, William, Willow row
Hazledine, Thomas, Leonard street

Heathcoat, John, William street
Hill, John, Morledge
Hill, Thomas, High street
Hill, Joseph, Park street
Hodgkinson, Henry, Brook street
Hodgkinson, Thomas, Nottingham
    road
Hoggatt, William, Sitwell street
Holmes, Joseph, Grove street
Holmes, Edward, Walker lane
Houghton, David, Bag lane
Hudson, Moses, Eagle street
Ironmonger, Mary, Orchard street
Johnson, Joseph, Willow row
Jones, Dorothy, Walker lane
Keenan, Thomas, Victoria street
Keeton, Francis, Friar gate
Keoh, M. M., Albion street
Kirkland, Thomas, Mansfield road
Kirkland, Mary, Brook street
Knight, Thomas, Bridge street
Lander, Thomas, Ford street
Leech, Elizabeth, Bag lane
Lees, Alfred, Walker lane
Lilley, George, London road
Longdon, William, Bridge street
Lucas, William, St. Helen's street
Marler, Susan, St. James's lane
Marshall, Sarah, St. Helen's street
Mather, Ann, Brook street
Matthews, Ann, Upper Brook st.
Mayer, Charles, Exeter street
Mellor, John William, Devonshire
    street
Meynell, Thomas, Goodwin street
Moore, John, Goodwin street
Moore, Samuel, Osmaston street
Moore, William, Bag lane
Moore, Samuel, Bradshaw street
Murfin, George, Bag lane
Nadin, William, Traffick street
Nall, William, Bridge street
Neale, John, Eagle street
Needham, Ann, High street
Noble, Godfrey, Eagle street
Norton, David, Morledge
Oakley, James, Siddals lane
Osborne, Joseph, St. Peter's street
Osborne, Richard, Brook street
Page, Edward, Walker lane
Parker, John, Parker street

Pattison, Thomas, John street
Pearson, William, Bridge street
Pegg, Samuel, City road
Pegg, Charles, Park street
Pegg, William, Nottingham road
Percival, John, Sacheverel street
Pickersgill, Charles, Canal street
Potts, Robert, Fowler street
Pratt, John, Siddals lane
Radford, John, Bag lane
Redgate, Robert, Bridge street
Riggott, Elizabeth, Goodwin street
Robinson, George, Albion street
Rowbottom, Richard, Willow row
Shaw, Mary, Ford street
Shaw, John, Canal street
Simpson, John, Walker lane
Simpson, William, Bridge street
Slater, Thomas, Upper Brook st.
Smith, Thomas, Burton road
Smith, Charles, Talbot street
Smith, John, Goodwin street
Smith, Edward, Osmaston street
Smith, Elizabeth, Osmaston street
Smith, Charlotte, Agard street
Smith, Samuel, Grove street
Sparks, James, South street
Spencer, Charles, Nun's street
Sproat, Robert, Goodwin street
Stanton, James, Bridge gate
Steel, Catharine, Leonard street
Steer, Samuel, Exeter street
Stevenson, William, Willow row
Stone, Richard & Mary, Wardwick
Stone, George, Bradshaw street
Storer, William, Willow row
Swindell, Charlotte, Normanton rd.
Tattershaw, William, Parker street
Timperley, Elizabeth, London road
Tivey, Edward, Traffick street
Topham, Snowden, Goodwin street
Turner, Samuel, Burton road
Wakefield, John, Lodge lane
Walker, Thomas, River street
Walker, John, Duke street
Walker, William, Bridge street
Walker, Edward, Eagle street
Wallis, Edward, Bradshaw street
Ward, William, Willow row
Warrington, J., Green street
Watts, Mary, Nun's street

Wheeldon, Thomas, Eagle street
Wheeldon, William, Bridge gate
Wheeldon, George, Mansfield road
Wheeldon, Samuel, Albion street
White, Jeremiah, Normanton road
Widdowson, Joseph, River street
Williams, German, Brick street
Williams, Henry, Friar gate
Winfield, Robert, Nun's street
Wood, Joseph, Parker street
Woodward, Francis, Park street
Yeamans, Charles, Bridge street

SILK MANUFACTURERS AND MERCHANTS.
Those marked * are SILK THROWSTERS.

Bridgett, Thomas & Co. (sewings, velvets, ribands, laces, &c.) Bridge street
Davenport and Humpstone (laces and smallwares) Morledge mill
Frost and Stevenson (galloons, doubles, &c.) City road
Madeley, Thomas and Co. (smallwares, silk and cotton) George street
Peet, James and Charles Septimus (galloons, doubles, &c.) Brook street and Nun's street
Robinson, John and Thomas (silk velvets, &c.) Sacheverel street
*Simpson, Turner, & Co., Canal st.
Taylor, William (sewings, velvets, ribands, laces, &c., original mill) Silk mill lane
Topham and Fawcett (sewings, ribands, smallwares, &c.) Green lane
Unsworth and Williamson (sewings, twists, purse twists, cords, braids, laces, &c.) Siddals lane. Agents Bennock and Twentyman, 78, Wood street, Cheapside, London, and D. Miller, 17, Rook street, Manchester
Wilson, Moore, & Co. (silk velvets, &c.) Devonshire street
*Wright and Baker, Agard street
*Wright, Samuel Job, Agard street
*Wright, Thomas, Agard street

SILVERSMITHS & JEWELLERS.

Holme and Smithard, Corn market

Mackenzie, Henry, Corn market
Moseley, Robert and Nephew, Corn market
Randall, George, Rotten row
Roberts, Wolstan, Sadler gate
Steer, John, Market head
Stevens, James, Sadler gate
Weatherhead, Walters, and Co., Iron gate

SINKER MAKERS.

Bentley, John, Duke street
Birkin, James, Bridge gate
Burrows, James, Sacheverel street

SLATERS AND SLATE MERCHANTS.

Coulson, Robert (& tomb & headstone engraver) Siddals lane
Coulson, Nathaniel (and tomb and headstone engraver) Nottingham road
Shenton, E. and Son (and tomb and headstone engravers) George street and Siddals lane
Walkerdine, D. & W., Upper Brook street

SMALLWARE AND TAPE MANUFACTURERS.

Hackett & Son (tape) Talbot street
Hunt, George (boot lace and trimming) City road

SOAP BOILERS.

Pick, Abraham, Queen street
Sandars, John, Market place

SOLICITORS.

Balguy, Bryan Thomas, Town clerk
Barber, John, Queen street
Birch, R. W., Wardwick
Borough, William, Corn market
Cox, G. H. R., Tenant street
Curzon, John, Full street
Dewe and Fox, Iron gate
Dunnicliff and Severne, St. Mary's gate

K

Flack, Edward, Friar gate
Flewker, John, Wardwick
Fox, Henry William, Grove street
Frear, Benjamin, Friar gate
Goodale, John, Corn market
Huish, J. and M., St. Michael's church yard
Jackson, Henry, London terrace
Jessopp, Francis & Son, Wardwick
Jessopp, F. J., Wardwick
Khars, J. N., St. Mary's gate
Leech, Robert, Queen street
Massey, John S., Full street
Moss, John, St. Peter's street
Mousley, Wm. Eaton & Son, Full st.
Mozley and Flack, Victoria street
Portmore, Charles Broadhurst, Market place
Rowbottom, William, College place
Sale, Joseph, St. Peter's street
Simpson and Frear, St. Mary's gate
Smith, S. G., Full street
Vallack, James, Full street
Vessey, Thomas Staley, Leaper st.
Welch, David, St. Mary's gate
Whiston, William, sen., St. Peter's street
Whiston, William, jun., St. Peter's street
Williamson, William, Corn market
Woodford, John, St. Mary's gate

SPAR & MARBLE ORNAMENT MANUFACTURERS.

Blore, Joseph, Bridge gate
Green, Thomas, Upper Brook st.
Green, Edward, Upper Brook st.
Green, Bernard, Nun's street
Green, William, Parker street
Hall, Joseph, King street
Shepherdson, John, Queen street
Spinks, Thomas, King street
Thompson, William, Markeaton st.

STATIONERS (WHOLESALE.)

Chadwick, Robert, Queen street
Evans, Wm. & Sam., St. Mary's gate
Mozley, Henry & Sons, Friar gate
Richardson, Thomas and Son, Ashbourn road

STAYMAKERS.

Baxter, William, Haarlem street
Berrisford, William, King street
Hawksworth, Mary, Rivett street
Lloyd, Sarah, Friar gate
Mills, James, Friar gate
Moran, Maria, Sadler gate
Torr, Lydia, Bold lane
Wright, Mary, Market head

STONE AND MARBLE MASONS.

Bateman, William, Brook street
Cooper, Thomas, Brook street
Hall, Joseph (marble and statuary) King street
Swinnerton, Stephen, Mansfield rd.
Thompson, George, Devonshire st.
Wood, John (and statuary) Liversage street

STRAW HAT MAKERS.

Barber, Mary Ann, London road
Barnsdall, Mary and Elizabeth, Bridge gate
Berresford, Charlotte, King street
Bonam, Elizabeth, St. Peter's street
Bretnor, Elizabeth, Victoria street
Cooper, Elizabeth, Bridge street
Eccleshare, Matilda, Willow row
Fryer, William, Friar gate
Gaunt, Mary, St. Peter's street

SURROGATES.

Fisher, Rev. William, Osmaston terrace
Lillingstone, Rev. E., Ashbourne road

SURGEONS.

Bennett, William, Friar gate
Borman, Allan, London road
Borough, Charles, St. Peter's street
Butler, Joseph, Bridge street
Buxton, Thomas, St. Alkm. ch. yd.
Fearn, Samuel, St. Peter's street
Fisher, Thomas, Lunatic asylum, Cross lanes
Fox and Rudkin, Ford street

Fox, Douglas, Wardwick
Gisborne, Henry F., Tenant street
Greaves, A. G., Friar gate
Hamilton, Robert, St. Mary's gate
Harwood, Thomas, St. Peter's st.
Hill, John, St. Alkmund's ch. yd.
Johnson, John, St. Alkm. ch. yd.
Johnson, John W., St. Mary's gate
Jones, John, Friar gate
Lindley, John, St. Mary's gate
Lucas, John (and druggist) John street
Rudkin, John Charles, Friar gate
Webster, John, Tenant street
Wooler and Hamilton, St. Mary's gate
Wright, John, Friar gate

TAILORS AND WOOLLEN
DRAPERS.
Only those marked * are WOOLLEN
DRAPERS.

Alexander, Thomas, Upper Brook street
Allen, William, Willow row
Ault, Joseph, Goodwin street
Bacon, John, Bridge gate
Bailey, John, Parker street
Bancroft, William, Sadler gate bridge
Barker, James, Traffick street
Barker and Son, Bridge street
*Beeland, William, jun., Iron gate
*Bembridge, James, London street
Bembridge, George, Nun's street
Brown, John, Agard street
Bullock, Joseph & Son, Wardwick
Bullock, James, Sadler gate
Chaplin, Joseph, Mill street
Collumbell, Richard, Goodwin st.
*Darby and Sons, Market place
Denstone, James, London street
Dyche, Charles, Sadler gate
*Edwards, Thomas, Queen street
Ellaby, William, Brook street
*Fearn, Henry, St. Peter's street
*Fernyhough, William, Sadler gate
*Fletcher, J. M., Victoria street
Fogg, John, Bold lane
Ford, John, Friar gate
*Guylee, Joseph, Full street
Harris, William, Chester road
Harris, Joseph, Friar gate

Hawkridge, Thomas and Son, St. Mary's gate
Hawkridge, Henry, Bridge street
Heathcoat, John, William street
Hind, Joseph, Eagle street
Hogg, John, Bag lane
*Hollingworth, Francis, St. Peter's street
*Hunt, William, Friar gate
Huss, Samuel, Bridge street
*Leese, William, St. Mary's gate
Maggay, Charles, Hill street
Marson, John, Devonshire street
*Moorcroft, William, Jury street
Norton, John, Osmaston street
Norton, Thomas, Tenant street
Norton, William, Green lane
Odery, James, Ford street
Owen, Samuel, St. Alkm. ch. yd.
*Parkins, Thomas & Son, Sadler gate
Pipes, Samuel, Osmaston road
Poyser, Edwin, St. Helen's street
Poyser, George, Market place
Prince, Mrs. G., Cheapside
*Quin, James, St. James's lane
Redfearn, Benjamin, Osmaston st.
*Redfern, Philip, St. James's lane
Redfearn, Godfrey, St. Werburgh's church yard
Richardson, James, Osmaston street
Robinson, William, Nun's street
Rowley, John, Hope street
Sandars, William, Leonard street
Sedgwick, William, Ford street
*Shaw, William, Cockpit hill
Slack, Joseph, Eagle street
Smith, David, Morledge
Smith, James, Bridge gate
Smith, James, Siddals lane
Smitherd, Joseph, Tenant street
*Spencer, Henry, Friar gate
*Storer, James, Corn market
*Suddall, William, Sadler gate
Tetley, John, Traffick street
*Thelen, Franz. W., Iron gate
Thumpstone, Charles, St. Peter's st.
Towle, Thos., Willow row
Turner, Henry, Brook street
Turner, John, Canal street
*Wallis, Wm., Wardwick
Ward, James, Traffic street
Wathall, Lark, Bag lane

Webster, Isaac, Ashbourn road
Wells, John, Thorntree lane
Wood, Thos., Cockpit hill
Yates, John, Drewry lane
Yeomans, Thos., St. Peter's street
Yeomans, Robert, Victoria street

TALLOW CHANDLERS.

Pick, Abraham, Queen street
Sandars, John, Market place
Storer, James, Corn market
Willder, Samuel, St. Peter's street

TANNERS.

Cooper & Son, Uttoxeter road
Cooper, John, Green street
Goodale, J. & W., Friar gate and
    Normanton road
Oliver, Thos., Full street

TAVERNS & PUBLIC HOUSES.

Abbot, Eliz., Cross Keys, Corn mkt.
Allen, Charles, Lion and Tigress,
    Bradshaw street
Allsop, Samuel, Sitwell Arms, Sa-
    cheverel street
Alton, James, Seven Stars, King st.
Annable, Wm., Devonshire Arms,
    Devonshire street
Appleby, John, Hawk & Buckle,
    Bradshaw street
Ault, Ann, Exeter Arms, Exeter
    place
Ault, Samuel, Brown Bear, Green
    lane
Ault, William, Stag & Thorn, Traf-
    fic street
Bagnall, George, Black Swan, Sid-
    dals lane
Bailey, William, Eagle & Child, St.
    Alkm. church yard
Bates, John, Fountain Inn, Osmas-
    ton road
Beeson, Thomas, Star and Garter,
    St. Mary's gate
Blackwall, James, Black Boy, Sad-
    ler gate
Bloor, Joseph, Britannia, River st.

Bloor, Thomas, Druids' Arms,
    Traffic street
Bonell, James, Golden Lion, Bridge
    gate
Boulton, William, Lord Nelson,
    Wardwick
Bartlett, John, Eagle, London st.
Bradbury, Edward, Tailors' Arms,
    Green lane
Brassington, James, Half Moon,
    Sadler gate
Brentnall, John, Earl Grey, Uttox-
    eter road
Brocklesby, Joseph, Roebuck,
    Bridge gate
Brown, Philip, Green Man, Ken-
    sington street
Buckley, Edmund, Old Plough, St.
    Peter's street
Bull, Samuel, Noah's Ark, Mor-
    ledge
Bull, John, Greyhound, Market
    head
Bull, Thomas, Lamb, Park street
Bull, John, Black Boy, Albion st.
Burke, Frederick, Marquis of An-
    glesea, St. Peter's street
Cantrill, Henry, Nag's Head Com-
    mercial Inn, St. Peter's street
Carrington, Richard, Bird-in-Hand,
    Morledge
Carson, John, City Arms, Osmas-
    ton street
Cave, Mary, Fox & Goose, Friar gate
Cholerton, Sarah, Black Swan,
    London street
Collier, Richard, Crown & Mitre,
    Amen alley
Cuff, John, Midland Hotel, Rail-
    way terrace
Davis, Thomas, Old Neptune, St.
    Peter's street
Davis, William, Three Jolly Butch-
    ers, Traffic street
Dawson, John, George the Fourth,
    Leonard street
Dimock, Thomas, Old Spot, St.
    Helen's street
Dolman, John, Jolly Toper, Not-
    tingham road
Dyche, William, Woodman's Stroke,
    Bag lane

Eley, John, Old White Hart, Bridge gate

Falconer, Abraham, Old Tiger, City road

Flude, Thomas, Anchor, St. Peter's street

Frost, William, Greyhound, Friar gate

Glue, Joseph, Talbot Inn, Iron gate

Gover, William Edwd., The Apollo, Ford street

Green, Thomas, Queen's Head, Victoria street

Gregory, James, Wheat Sheaf, Walker lane

Griffiths, Richard, Brown Bear, Lodge lane

Hadfield, Mary, Golden Ball, Willow row

Harrison, David, Crown, Morledge

Harrison, William, George and Dragon, Walker lane

Haynes, Henry, Peacock, Nottingham road

Haynes, Thomas, White Swan, St. Peter's street

Hemingway, Richard, Dog and Partridge, Tenant street

Hill, John, Brick and Tile, Brick street

Hollis, William, Coach and Horses, St. James's lane

Holmes, Thomas, Vine Inn, Ford street

Hornshaw, John, Nottingham Arms, Bridge gate

Hunt, Francis, Black Horse, Nun's street

Hurd, William, Robin Hood, Iron gate

Huggins, Francis, Royal Hotel, Victoria street

Ingham, Thomas, British Arms, Bridge gate

Johnson, Mary, The Bird, Jury street

Jolley, William, Tap House, Rotten row

Keeton, Thos., Duke of York, Burton road

King, Hannah, Bull's Head, Queen street

Kinsey, Francis, Nottingham Castle, Queen street

Kirk, William, Horse and Trumpet, Full street

Kirk, William, Bunch of Grapes, Green lane

Lane, Harvey, Brunswick Inn, Railway terrace

Leech, Ann and John, Fox & Owl, Bridge gate

Lewis, Rice, Old Boat, Morledge

Lilley, John, Royal Oak, Market place

Ling, William, Coach and Horses, Little Chester

Longdon, William, Old Tiger, Queen street

Longdon, Roger, Seven Stars, Upper Brook street

Longdon, Henry, sen., Old Dolphin, Queen street

Lowe, Joseph, Old Flower Pot, King street

Lowe, William, Ram Inn, Bridge street

Ludlam, Henry, Castle and Falcon, Cockpit hill

Maddocks, Joseph, Bay Horse, Uttoxeter road

Manlove, Thomas, Black Bull, Canal street

Mansfield, William, Canal Tavern, Cockpit hill

Mayer, Thomas, Punch Bowl, Nottingham road

Merry, John, Three Nuns, Nun's street

Moore, Samuel, Mason's Arms, Albion street

Moore, F., Green Man, St. Peter's street

Moore, Peter, Railway Tavern, Canal street

Moreton, Henry, Coach and Horses, Sadler gate

Morley, Samuel, Devonshire Arms, Queen street

Neale, Thomas, King's Arms and County Family Hotel, St. Mary's gate

Norris, Henry, Duke of Wellington, Brook street

Orme, Samuel, Dusty Miller, Cockpit hill

Payne, James, Wagon and Horses, Ashbourn road

Pearson, John, White Lion, Friar gate

Pegg, John, Tanner's Arms, William street

Piggin, Thomas, Bishop Blaze, Morledge

Pitman, Richard, Hen & Chickens, Walker lane

Platts, William, Duke of Clarence, Mansfield road

Prince, John, Telegraph, Morledge

Radford, William, Bell and Castle, Burton road

Ramsell, Edwin, Durham Ox, St. Peter's street

Reeves, John, Old Angel, Corn market

Ride, Samuel, Goat's Head, Willow row

Riding, Peter, Freemason's Arms, Albion street

Rodgers, Thos., Old Three Crowns, Bridge gate

Rowley, Sarah, Stag and Pheasant, Brook street

Rowley, William, Sun Inn, Friar gate

Russell, John, Barley Mow, St. Peter's street

Sephton, William, Boat, Nottingham road

Shaw, Adam, Flower Pot, King st.

Simpson, Edward, Lord Byron, Bold lane

Simpson, William, Holly Bush, Bridge street

Sison, Michael, Shakspeare, Bold lane

Smedley, William, White Bear, Derwent row

Smedley, Samuel, Castle Fields Inn, Traffic street

Smedley, Mary, Wheel, Friar gate

Smith, Joseph, Swan with Two Necks, St. James's lane

Smith, H. F., Plough, London st.

Smith, Charles, Windmill, Willow row

Smith, Ralph, Shakspeare, Sadler gate

Smith, John, Bowling Green Inn, Nottingham road

Smith, Joseph, Royal Telegraph, London road

Snow, Walter, Plumber's Arms, Bag lane

Spencer, Hannah, New Inn, Coach and Railway office, and Posting house, King street

Steer, Aaron, Odd Fellows' Arms, King street

Stone, Edward, Three Tuns, Sadler gate

Summerfield, Thomas, Duke of Devonshire, Goodwin street

Tarr, William, Noah's Ark, Morledge

Taylor, Henry, Angel, Burton road

Taylor, John, White Horse, Friar gate

Taylor, Tryphena, Tiger, Commercial Inn, Corn market

Tomlinson, Thos., Old Oak, Agard street

Tunnicliff, John, Horse and Jockey, Sadler gate

Turner, Thomas, Hare & Hounds, Erasmus street

Wallis, George, King's Head, Family and Commercial Inn, and Posting house, Corn market

Wallis, William, Milton's Head, Hill street

Walker, Edward, Old Cock Inn, Cockpit hill

Ward, Elizabeth, Lord Hill, Short street

Ward, Thomas, Saracen's Head, St. James's lane

Westcott, James, Golden Eagle, Agard street

Watson, Samuel, Sir Walter Scott, Wardwick

Wheatcroft, William, Star, Siddals lane

Wheldal, John, Bee Hive, Devonshire street
Whittaker, Edward, Coach and Horses, King street
Widdowson, Joseph, Old Britannia, River street
Wightman, Sarah, Bell, Family and Commercial Inn, and Posting house, Sadler gate
Wilcockson, George, Buck-in-the-Park, Curzon street
Williamson, William, Green Dragon, St. Peter's street
Williamson, Thomas, Rose & Crown, Corn market
Williamson, Edward, Dog & Duck, Haarlem street
Winstanley, Israel, Boar's Head, King street
Witton, Samuel, Red Lion, Canal street
Wood, John, Fox and Grapes, Castle street
Woodruffe, Richard, Pheasant, Bridge street
Woodward, Francis, the Leopard, Grove street
Woodward, John, Fox and Grapes, Castle street
Wright, Joseph, Thorntree Inn, Thorntree lane
Yeomans, John, Hawk and Buckle, Bradshaw street

TIMBER MERCHANTS.

Ault, John, Rivett street
Dyche, J. and R., Cockpit hill
Roe and Oakley, Cockpit hill and Siddals lane
Smallwood, William Thomas, Exeter street
Wait, Francis, Mansfield road

TIMBER BENDERS FOR GIG SHAFTS, &c.

Cholerton, Harvey and Co., Albion street
Smith, William and Son, King st.

TOBACCONISTS AND TOBACCO MANUFACTURERS.*

*Bullock, George, Iron gate
Fley, Richard, Rotten row
Forman, Robert, Corn market
*Smith, Joseph, St. Peter's street

TOY DEALERS.

Bateman, Henry, Sadler gate
Hawgood, Henry, Cheapside
Perkins, Henry, Corn market
Randall, George, Rotten row
Steer, John, Market head
Stevens, James, Sadler gate

TRUNK AND BOX MAKERS.

Simms, Mary, St. Mary's gate
Tummond, Charles Thomas, Lodge lane
Thorley, John, Walker lane

TURNERS & CHAIRMAKERS.
Those marked * are CHAIRMAKERS.

*Baldwin, David, George street
*Clap, Edward, Kensington street
Cooper, William, London street
Dudley, Charles, Willow row
*Gorse, Joseph, Ashbourn road
Lowe, John, Bold lane
Potter, David, sen., Curzon street
Potter, David, Talbot yard
Robinson, James, Wright street
*Roe, William, Nottingham road
*Smith, George, London road
Wait, Francis, City road

UMBRELLA AND PARASOL MAKERS.

Fernley, William, Ford street
Rewcastle, David, Queen street
Steer, John, Market head

VETERINARY SURGEONS.

Atherstone, Edwin, Tenant street
Atherstone, Hugh, Sadler gate
Statham, William, Derwent street

WATCH AND CLOCKMAKERS.

Bancroft, Isaac, Bridge gate
Barber, Charles, Bridge street
Brookhouse, J., St. Peter's street
Brownsword, Peter, Bourne street
Cook, Thomas, St. James's lane
Cooper, William, London street
Edwards, William, Rotten row
Holme and Smithard, Corn market
Johnson, Thomas, London road
Jolliffe and Son, St. Peter's street
Mackenzie, Henry (dealer) Corn
    market
Poole, William, Devonshire street
Roberts, Wolstan, Sadler gate
Shipley, James, Bold lane
Soar, John, Darley lane
Thoma, Joseph, Sadler gate
Whitehurst, John, Cherry street
Woodward, Joseph, Nottingham
    road

WHEELWRIGHTS.

Allen, William, Mansfield road
Briand, Thomas, Parker street
Burton, Thomas, Tenant street
Cowlishaw, James, London street
Ford, George, Nottingham road
Hodgkinson, George, Friar gate
Hodgkinson, Charles, Friar gate
Taylor, John, Mansfield road
Wheeldon, Samuel, Chapel street

WHARFINGERS.

Pickford and Co., Cockpit hill
Soresby, James and W., Morledge
Sutton and Co., Cockpit hill
Tunley and Hodson, Siddals lane
Wheatcroft, David, Cockpit hill

WHITESMITHS.

Allen, J., St. Peter's church yard
Allsop, Charles, Jury street
Busher, Joseph, King street
Coxon, James, Osmaston road

Eyre, James, Full street
Freckleton, John, Bridge street
Harrison, John, Bridge gate
Haslam, William, St. Helen's street
Haynes, Ann, St. Werburgh's
    church yard
Hornshaw, John, Bridge gate
Hornshaw, Lewis, Brook street
Hunt, George, Duke street
Hunt, Joseph, sen., St. Peter's
    street
Hunt, John, St. Mary's gate
Kirk, John, Jury street
Maw, Thomas, Wright street
Moore, Henry, Sadler gate
Newbold, William, Sadler gate
Parkes, John, Brook street
Parkes, Marmaduke, Friar gate
Shaw, Charles, Willow row
Shaw, Thomas, Wright street
Smith, Samuel, Corn market
Smith, Thomas, Willow row

WINE & SPIRIT MERCHANTS.

Baxter, Robert, Iron gate
Chell, John, Full street
Cox and Malin, Corn market
Cox, Haden, and Pountain, Market
    place
Edwards and Hallam, Iron gate
Pountain, Benjamin, Rotten row
Ratcliff, John, Corn market
Sandars and Clarke, Market place
Watson, Samuel, St. Peter's street

WIRE WORKERS.

Steel, Samuel, St. Peter's street
Torr, James, sen., Bold lane
Torr, James, jun., Morledge

WOOLLEN DRAPERS.—See also
DRAPERS and TAILORS.

Briggs, George, and George (and
    linen drapers) St. Peter's bridge
Brindley, William, Tenant street

MEMBERS OF PARLIAMENT FOR THE BOROUGH

E. Strutt, Esq. and the Hon. J. G. B. Ponsonby,

RECORDER.

John Balguy, Esq., Duffield.

MAGISTRATES.

MAYOR.—J. B. Crompton, Esq., Milford.

T. P. Bainbrigge, Esq.
T. Bent, Esq., M.D.
J. B. Crompton, Esq., Milford
Henry Cox, Esq.
R. F. Forester, Esq., M.D.
D. Fox, Esq.
Samuel Fox. jun., Esq.

R. W. Haden, Esq.
W. Mundy, Esq., Markeaton Hall
W. L. Newton, Esq.
Joseph Strutt, Esq.
S. Gamble, esq. (late Mayor)
Sir Henry Sacheverell Wilmot, Bart.
Chaddesden Hall.

MEMBERS OF THE COUNCIL.

ALDERMEN.

Those in the first column were elected November 9th, 1838, and go out in 1844, and those in the second column were re-elected on 9th November, 1841, and go out in 1847.

John Bell Crompton, Esq.
Stephen Gamble, Esq.
John Johnson, Gent.
W. L. Newton, Esq.
John Sandars, Esq.
S. J. Wright, Gent.

John Barber, Esq.
Thomas Bent, Esq., M.D.
R. F. Forester, Esq., M.D.
Francis Jessopp, Esq.
Edward Strutt, Esq., M.P.
Joseph Strutt, Esq.

COUNCILLORS.

With the list of the Wards and the Names of the Councillors in each Ward.

The names in the first column are those elected on the 1st of Nov. 1842; those in the second were elected on the 1st of Nov. 1841, and those in the third column, on the 1st of Nov. 1840, and go out on the 1st of Nov. 1843.

BRIDGE WARD.

Stevenson, George	Taylor, William	Harrison, John
Wright, Thomas	Hollingworth, James	Hill, John

BECKET WARD.

Gadsby, Thomas	Goodwin, William	Etches, Charles
Porter, John	Mozley, Henry, jun.	Forman, Robert

CASTLE WARD.

Fox, Douglas	Lowe, Samuel	Burroughs, Thomas
Goodwin, Thomas	Moss, John	Gascoyne, Joseph

DERWENT WARD.

Sowter, William	Barton, William	Haywood, James
Ward, Robert	Gisborne, Henry	Mousley, William Eaton

FRIAR GATE WARD.

Dunnicliffe, John	Madeley, Thomas	Hood, George
Fox, Samuel	Walton, John	Pegg, Robert

KING'S MEAD WARD.

Hall, Joseph	Evans, William, M.P.	Cooper, Thos., Brook st.
Peet, James	Gamble, John	Tunaly, Thomas

CORPORATION COMMITTEES.

WATCH COMMITTEE.

Chairman. J. B. Crompton, Esq., Mayor.

Mr. Barton
Mr. Haywood
Mr. Hollingworth
Mr. William Leaper Newton
Mr. James Peet
Mr. Robert Pegg
Mr. William Sowter
Mr. Joseph Strutt
Mr. John Walton
Mr. T. Madeley

ESTATE COMMITTEE.

Chairman, J. Strutt, Esq.

Dr. Bent
John Barber, Esq.
Mr. Thomas Cooper, Brook Street
Dr. Forester
Mr. George Hood
Francis Jessopp, Esq.
Mr. Johnson
William Eaton Mousley, Esq.
S. Fox, Esq.
John Sandars, Esq.
Mr. John Wright

TOWN HALL BUILDING COMMITTEE.

The Members of the Estate Committee, and
Mr. T. Gadsby
Mr. J. Gascoyne

AUDIT COMMITTEE.

Chairman, J. Sandars, Esq.

Mr. Thomas Gadsby
Mr. William Goodwin
Mr. Haywood
Francis Jessopp, Esq.
Mr. Johnson
Mr. Peet
Mr. John Walton
Mr. Thomas Wright

BROOK-COURSE COMMITTEE.

Chairman, the Mayor.

Mr. John Gamble
Mr. Thomas Gadsby
Mr. John Harrison
Mr. Hood
Mr. Johnson
Mr. Thomas Madeley

QUARTERLY MEETINGS OF THE TOWN COUNCIL.

The quarterly meetings for the year are appointed to be held at the County Hall, at 11 o'clock in the forenoon, on the 1st Thursday in February, 1st Thursday in May, 1st Thursday in August, and 1st Thursday in November.

OFFICERS OF THE BOROUGH.

Town Clerk, Coroner, and Clerk of the Peace—B. T. Balguy, Esq.
Treasurer, Chamberlain, and Receiver of Corn Returns—Mr. Charles Pratt.
High Constable and Billet Master—Mr. W. H. Hodges.
Sergeants at Mace—Mr. Charles King, and Mr. H. Newton.
Superintendent of Police—Mr. J. A. Thompson.
Town Crier—Joseph Brown, Victoria street.
Tenter and Pinder—J. Parr, St. Alkmund's Church Yard.
Searchers of Flesh—Mr. Topham, and Mr. Steele.

DERBY POOR LAW UNION.

Chairman—John Sandars, Esq., Market Place.

Vice-Chairman—Mr. George Hood, George Street.

GUARDIANS EX-OFFICIO.

R. F. Forester, Esq., M.D.
Edward Strutt, Esq., M.P.

Thomas Bent, Esq., M.D.
William Locket, Esq.

BOARD OF GUARDIANS, ELECTED IN MARCH, 1842.

Bainbrigge, Thomas Parker
Baker, William, M.D.
Bingham, John
Bailey, Thomas
Bakewell, John
Bromley, John
Cooper, Thomas
Cox, Henry
Evans, Samuel
Fox, Douglas
Gadsby, William

Gamble, Stephen
Macconnell, Richard
Pegg, Robert
Radford, John
Sandars, John
Sadler, William
Steer, Samuel
Shaw, William
Watson, Samuel
Whiston, William, sen.

Greatorex, Joseph
Handford, Joseph
Hood, George
Hollingworth, James

Watson, Samuel
Chadwick, Robert
Abney, Rev. Edward Henry

OFFICERS OF THE POOR LAW UNION.

Clerk to the Board of Guardians, and Superintendent Regristrar—Mr. John Moody.
Auditor—Mr. J. Corden, Osmaston Road.
Relieving Officer—Mr. John Collumbell.
Master and Matron of the Workhouse— Mr. and Mrs. William Webster.
Collectors—Mr. W. H. Hodges, and Mr. G. Calladine.
Surgeon—Mr. Thomas Harwood.
Chaplain—
Registrars—Mr. Swanwick, and Mr. Jay.

PARISH OFFICERS.

ST. ALKMUND.

Churchwardens—Mr. George Bridgart, King St. and Mr. C. Yeamans, Bridge St.
Overseers—Mr. Joseph Bloor, River Street, and Mr. Williamson, North Parade.

ST. PETER.

Churchwardens—Mr. J. Ault, Rivett Street, and Mr. J. B. Murphy, St. Peter's St.
Overseers—Mr. R. Bryer, Corn Market, and Mr. Turner, Eagle Street.

ST. WERBURGH.

Churchwardens—Mr. W. Knight, Friar Gate, and Mr. Joshua Denston, Cheapside.
Overseers—Mr. John Mozley, Friar Gate, and Mr. John Welch, Friar Gate.

ALL SAINTS.

Churchwardens—Mr. H. J. Stevens, Full Street, and Mr. J. Chatterton, jun. Full St.
Overseers—Mr. Hollingshead, Iron Gate, and Mr. Rowbottom, St. Mary's Gate.

ST. MICHAEL.

Churchwardens—Mr. E. Smith, Queen Street, and Mr. J. Wintle, Queen Street.
Overseers—Mr. T. Stevenson, Queen Street, and Mr. S. King, Queen Street.

LITCHURCH.

Overseers—Mr. W. Stevenson, Litchurch Terrace, and Mr. Malin, Litchurch Ter.

LITTLE CHESTER.

Overseers—Mr. W. Prince, sen., Little Chester, and Mr. Birchall, Duke St. Derby.

PLACES OF WORSHIP.

ALL SAINTS' CHURCH.

Service in the Morning at half-past Ten, in the Afternoon, at a quarter before Three, and in the Evening, at half-past Six o'clock.

Perpetual Curate—Rev. E. Lillingstone.   *Beadle*—Mr. J. Marshall, Full street.
Organist—Mr. George Fritch.   *Sexton*—Mr. J. Harrison, Full street
Clerk—Mr. Walton, Parker street.

ST. PETER'S CHURCH.

In the Morning at half-past Ten, in the Afternoon at Three, and at half-past Six o'clock in the Evening.

Vicar—Rev. C. Wright.   *Clerk*—Mr. Dawson, St. Peter's street.
Curate—Rev. W. Fisher.   *Beadle*—Mr. J. Walkerdine, Leonard st.
Organist—Mr. Stenson, Corn market.   *Sexton*—Mr. Pratt, 31, Eagle street.

ST. WERBURGH'S CHURCH.

In the Morning at a quarter to Eleven, in the Afternoon at a quarter to Three, and in the Evening at half-past Six.

Vicar—Rev. Edward Unwin.
Curates—Rev. John Latham, and Rev. Gervase Wright
Organist—Mr. E. W. Gover, Friar gate.

Clerk—Mr. Harvey, George street.
Beadle and *Sexton.*—Mr. Redgate, Short street.

ST. ALKMUND'S CHURCH.

In the Morning at a quarter before Eleven, and in the Afternoon at a quarter before Three o'clock.

Vicar—Rev. E. H. Abney.
Organist—Mr. F. Fritche, North parade.
Clerk—Mr. E. Collumbell, King street.

Beadle—Mr. Charles Birch, Bridge gate.
Sexton—Mr. Thomas Marshall, St. Alkmund's church yard.

ST. MICHAEL'S CHURCH.

In the Morning at a quarter before Eleven, and in the Evening at half-past Six.

Vicar—Rev. John Garton Howard.
Curate—Rev. Mr. Howard, jun.
Clerk—Mr. James, Parker street.

Beadle and *Sexton*—Mr. T. Woodhouse, St. Michael's lane.

ST. JOHN'S CHURCH.

In the Morning at half-past Ten, in the Afternoon at a quarter before Three, and in the Evening at half-past Six o'clock.

Minister—Rev. Philip Gell.
Organist—Mr. J. Norton, Derwent terr.

Clerk—Mr. Wright, King street
Beadle—Mr. Redgate, Bridge street.

TRINITY CHURCH.

In the Morning at half-past Ten, and in the Evening at half-past Six.

Minister—Rev. E. M. Wade.
Clerk—Mr. R. P. Cowlishaw, John street, London road.

CHRIST CHURCH.

In the Morning at half-past Ten, and in the Afternoon at a quarter to Three.

Minister—Rev. Roseingrave Macklin.

CATHOLIC CHURCH.

In the Morning at half-past Ten, and in the Evening at half-past Six.

Priest—Rev. Thomas Sing.
Organist—Mr. William Woodward, Nottingham road.

DISSENTING MEETING HOUSES.

DENOMINATION.	PLACE.	MINISTERS' NAMES.
Baptists, General	Brook street	Rev. J. G. Pike.
Baptists, General	St. Mary's gate	Rev. J. G. Pike.
Baptists, General	Sacheverel st.	Rev. S. Ayrton.
Baptists, Particular	Agard street	Rev. J. Ford.
Congregationalists	Victoria street	Revds. J. Gawthorn and J. Corbin.
Methodists, Wesleyan	King street	Revds. J. Greeves, R. Keeling,
Methodists, Wesleyan	Green Hill	and T. Short.
Methodists, Primitive	Babington lane	Rev. J. Ellis.
Methodists, Primitive	Albion street	
Methodists, New Connexion	London road	Revds. P. Trewin, and G. Grundy.
New Jerusalem Temple, (Swedenborgians)	Duffield road	Rev. Mr. Knight.
Quakers	St. Helen's street.	
Unitarians	Friar gate	Rev. Noah Jones.

PUBLIC BUILDINGS, OFFICES, AND INSTITUTIONS.

Assembly and Concert Rooms, Market place.
Assessed Tax Office, 1, Curzon street —Receiving Inspector, George Chambers, esq. ; Surveyor, B. Ward, esq., Bridge street ; Clerk to the Commissioners, J. B. Simpson, esq., St. Mary's gate ; Assessor, Mr. R. Stone, 1, Curzon street.
Asylum for the Insane, Green hill house.—Thomas Fisher, Superintendent.
Athenæum, Museum, and News Room, Victoria street.
Baths, St. Helen's street.—Mr. Hall.
Corn Inspector's Office, Town Hall.—Inspector, Mr. Pratt.
County Court, St. Mary's gate.
County Gaol, South street.—John Sims, Governor ; Rev. George Pickering, Chaplain ; Douglas Fox, Surgeon.
Derby Town and County Library, Amen alley.—Edward Bailey, Librarian.
Derby Union Office, 19, Wardwick.—John Moody, Clerk and Superintendent Registrar ; John Collumbell, Relieving Officer ; John Corden, Auditor.
Excise Office, Mrs. Abbott, Cross Keys, Corn market.
Female British School, Chapel street.—Miss Simpson.
Free Grammar School, St. Peter's church yard ; Head Master, Rev. W. Fletcher ; Second Master, Mr. Rowell.
Gas Company's Offices, Cavendish street.—Thomas Crump, Manager.
Hawker's Licence Office, St. Mary's gate.—Mr. Kirk.
Infant Schools, Siddals lane, Mrs. Pescud ; Walker lane, Mrs. Walker.
Infirmary, London road.—Consulting Physician, Richard Forester Forester ; Physicians, Thomas Bent, William Baker, James Heygate ; Consulting Surgeon, R. B. Godwin ; Surgeons, John Wright, Douglas Fox, and John Whittaker Johnson ; House Apothecary, Richard Dix ; Chaplain, Rev. Gervase Wright ; Secretary, Samuel Whitaker ; Master and Mistress, Mr. and Mrs. Rimington.
Lancastrian School, Orchard street.—Mr. Britton.
Liberal Operative Association Rooms, Corn market.
Mechanics' Institution, Wardwick.—Joseph Strutt, esq., President ; Richard Stone, Secretary.
National Schools, Curzon street, Master, Mr. Henry Cumming ; Mistress, Miss Warner ; Traffick street, Master, Mr. Pescud.
Nottinghamshire and Derbyshire Fire and Life Assurance Company, Office, St. Alkmund's church yard.—Mr. Smith.
Operative Conservative Association Rooms, George street.
Permit Office, Mrs. Abbott, Cross Keys, Corn market.
Police Office, Town Hall.—Superintendent, Mr. J. A. Thompson.
Post Office, Athenæum Buildings, Corn market, T. P. Bainbrigge, esq.
Savings Bank, Friar gate ; attendance every Monday and Friday, from half-past Eleven to half-past Twelve o'clock.—Actuary, John Watson.
Self-supporting, Charitable, and Parochial Dispensary, Bridge gate.—John Wright Gallimore, Resident Apothecary.
Stamp and Legacy Duty Office, 29, St. Mary's gate.—Valentine Kirk, Distributor.
Theatre, Bold lane.
Town Hall, Market place.
Town Clerk's Office, Town Hall.—B. T. Balguy, esq.
Town and County Museum, Athenæum, Victoria street.
Trinity School, Liversage street.—Master, Mr. Aldridge ; Mistress, Mrs. M. C. Field.
Union Workhouse, Osmaston road.—William Webster, Governor ; Mrs. Webster, Matron.
Vagrant Office, Union Workhouse.—Superintendent, Mr. Webster.
Water Works Company, St. Michael's lane.—David Yates, Manager.
Weights and Measures.—Inspector, Mr. G. Webster, Derby.

POST OFFICE REGULATIONS.

RULES.—All letters to be charged by weight, without reference to the number of enclosures ; and the charge on all letters passing between one part of the United

Kingdom and another, the Channel Islands and Isle of Man inclusive, whether by the General Post, or the London District (the Twopenny and Threepenny) Post, to be one Penny for every single rate as follows :—

	oz.		oz.	Prepaid. s. d.	Unpaid. s. d.
Not exceeding	½			0 1	0 2
Exceeding	...½ and not exceeding	...	1	0 2	0 4
	1		2	0 4	0 8

And Twopence for every additional ounce weight.

ARRIVALS AND DEPARTURES OF THE MAILS.

	ARRIVES.	DEPARTS.
LONDON	5—55 morning	9—30 night
BIRMINGHAM	ditto ditto	9—30 ditto
LEICESTER and RUGBY	ditto ditto	9—30 ditto
SHEFFIELD and YORK	ditto ditto	9—30 ditto
NOTTINGHAM, 1st,	1—30 afternoon	5—0 ditto
Ditto, 2nd,	5—55 ditto	9—30 ditto
MANCHESTER	ditto ditto	9—30 morn.
ASHBOURNE (Gig mail)	4—45 ditto	6—0 ditto
ASHBY ditto	4—10 ditto	6—0 ditto
CASTLE DONINGTON and KEGWORTH	4—30 ditto	7—0 ditto

Box closes for London, Birmingham, Leicester, and Sheffield, at half-past eight o'clock in the evening, and the other mails at half an hour before departure.

LORD LIEUTENANT OF THE COUNTY.

His Grace the Duke of Devonshire.

MEMBERS OF PARLIAMENT FOR THE COUNTY.

For the North, the Hon. G. H. Cavendish, and William Evans, esq.
For the South, E. M. Mundy, esq., and C. R. Colvile, esq.

HIGH SHERIFF, &c.

High Sheriff, Jas. Sutton, esq., Shardlow.
Under Sheriff, J. Barber, esq., Derby.
Clerk of the Peace, John Charge, esq., Chesterfield.
Deputy Clerk of the Peace, John Barber, esq., Derby.
Treasurer, William Leaper Newton, esq., Derby.

CORONERS.

Balguy, B. T., esq., Derby, for the Borough.
Hutchinson, John, esq., Chesterfield, for Scarsdale.
Mander, T., esq., Bakewell, for High Peak.
Mozley, Henry, jun., esq., Derby, for Appletree.
Sale, Joseph, esq., Derby, for Repton and Gresley.
Whiston, W., jun., esq. Derby, for Morleston and Litchurch.

COUNTY MAGISTRATES.

Arkwright, Richard, esq.	Willersley Castle
Arkwright, Robert, esq.	Sutton Hall, near Chesterfield
Arkwright, Charles, esq.	Dunstall Hall, near Burton-on-Trent
Arkwright, Peter, esq.	Rock House, Cromford
Arkwright, George, esq.	Sutton Hall, near Chesterfield
Abney, William Wootten, esq.	Measham, near Ashby-de-la-Zouch
Andrews, G., esq.	Romily, near Stockport
Ashton, Robert, esq.	Hyde, near Stockport
Ashby, William A., esq.	Quenby Hall, Leicestershire
Barton, Henry, esq.	Rangemore House

Blakiston, Sir Matthew, bart. - -	Sandy Brook, near Ashborne
Bagshaw, William John, esq. - -	The Oaks, near Sheffield
Boothby, Sir William, bart. - -	Ashborne Hall
Bilbie, Thomas, esq. - -	Nettleworth, near Mansfield
Burnell, Broughton B. Pegge, esq. -	Beauchief Abbey, near Sheffield
Barker, John Henry, esq. -	The Croft, near Bakewell
Balguy, John, esq. - - -	Duffield, near Derby
Burlington, The Right Hon. Earl of -	Burlington House
Bent, Thomas, esq., M.D. - - -	Derby
Clarke, Hyde John, esq. - -	Hyde, near Stockport
Crompton, John Bell, esq. - -	Milford
Crompton, Gilbert, esq. - -	Chesterfield
Crewe, Sir George, bart. - -	Calke Abbey, near Ashby-de-la-Zouch
Clarke, Charles, esq. - -	Matlock
Clowes, William L., esq. - -	Spondon Hall
Cavendish, The Hon. G. H.; M.P.	Ashford Hall, near Bakewell
Cave, Sir John Robert Browne, bart.	Stretton-en-le-Field
Coke, E. T. esq. - - -	Brimmington Hall, near Chesterfield
Darwin, Sir Francis S., knt. -	Sydnope, near Darley Dale
Davenport, Sir Salisbury, knt. - -	Bamal Hall, near Stockport
Evans, William, esq., M.P. -	Allestree Hall
Forester, Richard Forester, esq., M.D. -	Abbott's Hill, Derby
Fitzherbert, Sir Henry, bart. -	Tissington Hall, near Ashborne
Fox, Samuel, esq. - - -	Late of Osmaston Hall
Goodwin, Francis Green, esq. -	Wigwell, near Wirksworth
Gisborne, Thomas, esq. - -	Horwich House, Chapel-en-le-Frith
Gisborne, Matthew, esq. - -	Walton Hall, near Burton-on-Trent
Gisborne, John Guy, esq. - -	Horwich House, near Stockport
Greaves, William, esq., M. D. -	Mayfield, Staffordshire, and Cheltenham
Hall, Thomas Kirkpatrick, esq. -	Holly Bush, near Lichfield
Hurt, Francis, esq. - - -	Alderwasley
Holden, Robert, esq. - - -	Nuttall Temple, near Nottingham
Heathcote, Cockshutt, esq. - -	Bath
Hurt, Edward Nicholas, esq.	34, Dorset square, London
Harrison, John, esq. - - -	Snelston Hall, near Ashborne
Hurt, Francis, jun., esq. - -	Duffield, near Derby
Holte, Richard Orford, esq. - -	Torkington Lodge, Cheshire
Holden, Edward Anthony, esq. -	Aston Hall, near Derby
Hall, John, esq. - - - -	South Audley street, London
Hall, Lorenzo Kirkpatrick, esq. -	Milford, near Derby
Hadfield, Moses, esq. - - -	Glossop
Heacock, Philip, esq. - - -	Buxton
Hurt, Charles, esq. - - -	Wirksworth
Jebb, Joshua, esq. - - -	Walton Lodge, near Chesterfield
Jessopp, William, esq. - - -	Butterley Hall, near Alfreton
Leigh, Thomas, esq. - - -	Lyme Park, near Dishley, Cheshire
Lockett, William, esq. - - -	Derby
Middleton, Marmaduke M. esq. -	Leam Hall, near Stony Middleton
Moseley, Sir Oswald, bart. - -	Rolleston Hall, near Burton-on-Trent
Meynell, Godfrey, esq. - -	Langley Park
Moseley, Ashton Nicholas Every, esq.	Burnaston Park
Mundy, William, esq. - - -	Markeaton Hall, near Derby
Maynard, Edmund Gilling, esq. -	Chesterfield
Milnes, William, esq. - - -	Stubbin Edge, Ashover
Moseley, Oswald, esq. - - -	Rolleston Hall, Burton-on-Trent
Morewood, William Palmer, esq. -	Alfreton Hall
Mundy, Edward Miller, esq., M.P. -	Shipley Hall
Mundy, Charles Godfrey, esq. -	
Meynell, John, esq. - - -	Tapton Grove, near Chesterfield
Moore, George, esq. - - -	Appleby, near Ashby-de-la-Zouch
Newton, George William, esq. -	Aspinshaw Hall, near Stockport
Norton, William Fletcher Norton, esq.	Elton Manor, Bingham

Newton, James, esq. - - - -	Cheadle Heath, near Stockport
Nightingale, W. E., esq. - - -	Lea Hurst, near Wirksworth
Oakes, James, esq. - - -	Riddings House, near Alfreton
Portland, His Grace the Duke of - -	Welbeck Abbey, Nottinghamshire
Philips, Charles March, esq. - -	Garendon Park, Leicestershire
Peach, Thomas, esq. - - - -	Kirk Langley Hall
Pares, Thomas, esq. - - - -	Hopwell Hall, near Derby
Pye, Henry James, esq. - - -	Clifton Hall, near Tamworth
Pole, Edward Sacheverel Chandos, esq.	Radbourne Hall
Radford, John, esq. - - - -	Smalley, near Derby
Russell, Jesse Watts, esq. - - -	Ilam Hall, near Ashborne
Scott, Hugh, esq. - - - -	Draycott House, near Derby
Simpson, Richard, esq. - - -	Mellor, near Stockport
Sitwell, Sir George, bart. - - -	Renishaw Hall, near Chesterfield
Slacke, Thomas, esq., M.D. - -	Slacke Hall, near Chapel-en-le-Frith
Storey, John, esq. - - - -	Lockington Hall
Stracey, Sir Edward, bart. - - -	The Beach, Macclesfield
Strutt, Edward, esq., M.P. - -	St. Helen's, Derby
Strutt, Jedediah, esq. - - -	Belper
Strutt, Anthony Radford, esq. - -	Makeney
Strutt, John, esq. - - - -	Bridge hill House, Belper
Thornhill, William Pole, esq. -	Stanton by Youlgreave, near Bakewell
Vernon, The Right Hon. Lord -	Sudbury Hall
Waterpark, Rt. Hon. H. M. Lord	Doveridge Hall
Webster, William, esq. - - -	Ashborne
White, John, esq. - - - -	Park Hall, near Chapel-en-le-Frith
Wilmot, Henry Sacheverel, esq.	Chaddesden Hall
Worsley, Thomas Carill, esq. -, -	Winster, near Wirksworth
Walthall, Peter, esq. - - -	Darley Dale

ALPHABETICAL LIST

OF THE

PRINCIPAL SEATS, HALLS, MANSIONS, ETC.

THE RESIDENCES OF THE

NOBILITY, GENTRY, AND CLERGY

OF THE COUNTY OF DERBY.

Abbott's Hill	Derby	Richard Forester Forester, esq.
Aldercar Hall	In the parish of Heanor	Rev. John Smith
Alderwasley Hall	2 miles E of Wirksworth	Francis Hurt, esq.
Alfreton Park	13 miles N of Derby	William Palmer Morewood, esq.
——— Vicarage	... ...	Rev. Richard John Hope
Allestree Hall	2½ miles N of Derby	William Evans, esq. M.P.
Alvaston Hall	3 miles S of Derby	Parker Wheeldon, esq.
Alport	... ...	William Melland, sen., esq.
Appleby	5 miles W of Ashby	Rev. John M. Eschalez
——— Hall	... ...	George Moore, esq.
——— School	... ...	Rev. Charles Mackie
... ...	... ...	Rev. William Homer
——— House	... ...	John Moore, esq.
Ashbourn Hall	13 miles NW of Derby	Sir Wm. Boothby, bart.
——————	... ...	Cecil Brooke Boothby, esq.
———	... ...	Frederick Arkwright, esq.
———	... ...	William Webster, esq.
———	... ...	John Brittlebank, esq.
———	... ...	Peter Bainbridge Le Hunt, esq.
——— School	... ...	Rev. George Edward Gepp
——— School	... ...	Rev. C. W. Kingston, B.A.

Ashbourn Vicarage ...	...	13 miles NW of Derby	...	... Rev. Samuel Shipley
Ashford Hall ...	...	2½ miles N of Bakewell	...	... Duke of Devonshire, occupied by
				The Hon. G. H. Cavendish, M.P.
Ashford Parsonage	...	... ...	...	... Rev. Wm. Galley Giles
Ashgate ...	...	3 miles E of Chesterfield	...	... John Gorrell Barnes, esq.
Ashover, The Butts ...	...	7 miles N of Wirksworth	...	... Charles Milnes, esq.
——— Rectory	...	7 miles N of Wirksworth	...	... Rev. Joseph Nodder
Aspinshaw	...	Thornsett	...	... Rev. Irvinge Carlyle
———— Rectory	...	5 miles S of Derby ...	...	... Edward Anthony Holden, esq.
Aston-upon-Trent Hall				... Rev. N. P. Johnson
Atlow ...	...	5 miles E of Ashbourn	...	... Rev. Robt. E. Atkins
Bakewell ...	...	26 miles N of Derby	...	... Thomas Walthall, esq.
——— ...	...	... ...	...	... Richard Walthall, esq.
——— Eastern Lodge	...	... ...	...	... John Henry Barker, esq.
——— Hill Top	...	... ...	...	... John Barker, esq.
——— Castle hill ...	...	... ...	...	... Captain Underwood
——— Burre house	...	... ...	...	... John Barker, esq.
———	...	... ...	...	... Rev. James Coates
——— Vicarage	...	... ...	...	... Rev. Herbert Kestell Cornish.
Bank Hall ...	...	1 mile W of Chapel-en-le-Frith	...	... Godfrey Webster, esq.
Banner Cross ...	...	10 miles N of Chesterfield	...	... Rev. Wm. Bagshaw, Yorkshire
Barlborough Hall	...	8 miles E of Chesterfield	...	... Rev. C. H. R. Rhodes
——— Rectory	...	7 miles E of Chesterfield ...	...	... Rev. Martyn Stapleton
Barlow ...	...	... ...	...	... Rev. Courtnay Smith.
Barrow Hall ...	...	5 miles S of Derby...	...	... Dowager Lady Scarsdale
——— Vicarage	...	... ...	...	... Rev. Wm. Heacock, occupied by
				Rev. Richard Hollins
Barton Blount Park ...	...	9 miles W of Derby ...	...	... Francis Bradshaw, esq.
——— Rectory	...	... ...	...	... Rev. G. P. Lowther
Baslow ...	...	4 miles E of Bakewell	...	... Rev. A. A. Barker
Beauchief Abbey	...	8 miles N of Chesterfield	...	... B. B. Pegge Burnell, esq.
Beighton ...	...	9 miles NE of Chesterfield ...	...	... Rev. Joseph Dixon
——— Vicarage	...	... ...	...	... Hon. and Rev. Thos. Erskine
Belper Laund Hill	...	8 miles N of Derby ...	...	... John Harrison, gent.
———	...	... ...	...	... Rev. Matthew Tunstall
——— Bridge Hill	...	... ...	...	... Benjamin B. Ward, esq.
——— Green House	...	... ...	...	... John Strutt, esq.
———	...	... ...	...	... Jedediah Strutt, esq.
———	...	... ...	...	... James Swettenham, esq.
———	...	... ...	...	... Thomas Ingle, esq.
Belmont ...	...	2 miles W of Chesterfield	...	... Charles Dakeyne Gladwin, esq.
Birdholme ...	...	3 miles S of Chesterfield	...	... James Hunloke, esq.
Blackwall ...	...	... ...	...	... A. H. Heathcote, esq.
Blackwall ...	...	3 miles SW of Wirksworth ...	...	... Rev. Charles Evans
Blackwell Vicarage	...	3 miles NE of Alfreton	...	... Rev. Thos. Cursham, D.D.
Bladon Wood, or Castle	...	10 miles SW of Derby	...	... G. Kettle, esq.
Blakeley Lodge	...	5 miles W of Derby	...	... Simon Fred. Every, esq., occupied
				by Henry Crask Roper, gent.
Bolsover Castle	...	6 miles SE of Chesterfield	...	... Duke of Portland, occupied by Rev.
				John Hamilton Gray
Borrowash	...	5 miles E of Derby	...	... Bryan Thomas Balguy, esq.
Bonsall Rectory	...	3 miles NW of Wirksworth	...	... Rev. T. S. Basnett
Boulton ...	...	3 miles S of Derby	...	... Rev. Wm. Cantrill
——— ...	...	... ...	...	... Rev. Edward Pool
Bowbridge ...	...	3 miles NW of Derby	...	... Miss Fielding
Bowden Hall ...	...	Near Chapel-en-le-Frith	...	... John Plack, esq.
Boylston Rectory	...	9 miles W of Derby	...	... Rev. R. Bickerstaff
Brackenfield ...	...	... ...	...	... Rev. H. R. Goodwin
Bradbourn Rectory	...	5 miles NE of Ashbourn	...	... Rev. German Buckston
Bradley Hall ...	...	3 miles E of Ashbourn	...	... Capt. Archer
——— Rectory	...	... ...	...	... Rev. William Skinner., occupied by
				Rev. Henry Thomas Buckston.
Brailsford ...	...	7 miles N of Derby ...	...	... Edward Soresby Cox, esq.
——— Rectory	...	... ...	...	... Rev. Walter Shirley
Brampton ...	...	3 miles E of Chesterfield	...	... Rev. Wm. Peach
——— House	...	... ...	...	... John Dixon, esq.
——— Hall	...	3 miles E of Chesterfield	...	... William Melland, esq.
Brassington Hall	...	4 miles W of Wirksworth	...	... William Charlton, esq.
——— ...	...	... ...	...	... Rev. Henry Thomas Buxton.
Breadsall Priory	...	3 miles NE of Derby	...	... Sir Francis Darwin.
——— Rectory	...	3 miles NE of Derby	...	... Rev. H. R. Crewe.
Bretby Hall ...	...	10 miles SW of Derby	...	... Earl of Chesterfield.
Brimington Hall	...	Near Chesterfield	...	... Edward Thos. Coke, esq.
——— Parsonage	...	... ...	...	... Rev. John Kirk Marsh.
Brookfield Hall	...	1½ W. of Hathersage	...	... Mrs. Holworthy.
Brookhill Hall	...	2 miles NE of Alfreton	...	... D'Ewes Coke, esq.
Broughton House	...	7 miles S of Derby ...	...	... Mrs. Sutton
Bubnell Hall ...	...	4 miles E of Bakewell	...	... Miss Barker
———	...	... ...	...	... John Gardom, gent.
Burnaston Park	...	5 miles W of Derby ...	...	... Ashton N. E. Moseley, esq.
Butts, Ashover ...	...	Ashover	...	... Charles Milnes, esq.
Butterley Hall	...	3 miles S. of Alfreton	...	... William Jessop, esq.
Buxton ...	...	38 miles NW of Derby	...	... Philip Heacock, esq.
———	...	... ...	...	... George Goodwin, esq.
Buxton Edge Moor ...	...	31 miles NW of Derby	...	... Rev. George Trevor Spencer

L

Calke Abbey	10 miles S of Derby	Sir George Crewe, bart.
Calwich Abbey ...	3 miles W of Ashbourn ...	Court Granville, esq.
Carnfield Hall ...	1½ mile N of Alfreton ...	Thomas Radford, esq.
Castleton	5 miles E of Chapel-en-le-Frith	Isaac Hall, esq.
———	... ...	Joseph Hall, esq.
——— Vicarage ...	... ...	Rev. Charles Cecil Bates.
Catton Hall	7 miles NW of Burton ...	Sir Robert Wilmot, bart.
Cauldwell Hall ...	6 miles NW of Burton ...	Miss Evans.
Chaddesden Hall ...	½ mile E of Derby ...	Sir Henry Sacheverel Wilmot, bart.
Chapel-en-le-Frith ...	40 miles NW of Derby	Rev. George Hall.
———	... ...	William Bennett, esq.
Chapel Milton ...	2 miles NW of Chapel-en-le-Frith	Rev. E. Glossop.
Chatsworth House ...	3 miles SE of Bakewell ...	Duke of Devonshire.
Chatsworth Gardens ...	3½ miles SE of Bakewell ...	Joseph Paxton, esq.
Cheadle Heath ...	Near Cheadle	James Newton, esq.
Chesterfield Spring Bank	24 miles N of Derby ...	Rev. Robert Wallace.
———	... ...	Bernard Lucas Maynard, esq.
———	... ...	Edward Gilling Maynard, esq.
———	... ...	William Waller, esq.
———	... ...	Gilbert Compton, esq.
———	... ...	Samuel Dutton, esq.
——— Spittle ...	... ...	John Charge, esq.
——— Vicarage ...	... ...	Rev. Thomas Hill.
———	... ...	Peter Lely, esq.
———	... ...	William Thompson, esq.
———	... ...	Godfrey Heathcote, esq.
———	... ...	Rev. Ralph Heathcote.
———	... ...	Edward Heathcote, gent.
Church Broughton ...	... ...	Rev. John William Jones.
Chilwell Hall, Notts.	12 miles E of Derby ...	Thomas Broughton Charlton, esq.
Cliff House	1 mile N of Matlock Bath ...	R. B. Leacroft, esq., occupied by John Greaves, esq.
Clifton Camville ...	Staffordshire	Henry James Pye, esq.
Codnor Castle ...	In ruins (site of) ...	E. L. H. Masters, esq.
Compstall Bridge ...	Near Mellor	G. Andrews, esq.
Coton in the Elms Hall	8 miles SW of Burton ...	Right Hon. R. W. Horton, bart.
Coxbench ...	5 miles N of Derby ...	Mrs. Johnson.
Cressbrook Hall ...	3 miles S of Tideswell ...	Henry M'Connell, esq.
———	... ...	James M'Connell, esq.
Crich Vicarage ...	4 miles E of Wirksworth ...	Rev. Thomas Carson.
Croft	Near Bakewell ...	John Henry Barker, esq.
Crongstone Grange ...	Near Buxton	John B. Cantrell, esq.
Croxall Vicarage ...	9 miles W of Burton ...	Rev. James Gisborne.
Cubley	... ...	Rev. Richard William Vevers.
Cutthorpe Hall ...	2 miles S of Chesterfield ...	
Dalbury Rectory ...	9 miles W of Derby ...	Rev. Charles Evelyn Cotton.
Darley Abbey House ...	1 mile N of Derby ...	Mrs. Evans.
Darley Abbey Hall ...	... ...	Samuel Evans, esq.
Darley Grove House	... ...	Misses Strutt.
Darley Dale ...	... ...	Rev. William W. Fowler.
——— Hackney Lane	... ...	Miss Knowlton.
——— in the Dale Hall	3 miles S of Bakewell ...	Thomas Potter, esq.
——— Toadhole ...	... ...	James Dakeyne, esq.
——— Dale Rectory	... ...	Rev. Richard Lee
——— Hackney Lane	... ...	John Allsop, esq.
———	... ...	Peter Walthall, esq.
———	... ...	Benjamin Broomhead, esq.
———	... ...	Richard Dalton, esq.
Denby Old Hall ...	7 miles NE of Derby ...	John Cooke, esq.
Deptdale, Notts. ...	Near Mansfield ...	Rev. —— Dashwood.
Derby	126 miles NNW of London	John Bingham, esq.
———, Rose Hill ...	... ...	R. F. Forester, esq., M.D.
———, Abbott's Hill ...	... ...	Hon. Admiral H. Curzon.
———, Ashbourn Road	... ...	Rev. James Gawthorne.
———, Becket-well Lane	... ...	Rev. Thomas Sing.
———, Bridge Gate ...	... ...	Thomas P. Bainbrigge, esq.
———, Corn Market	... ...	William Eaton Mousley, esq.
———, Exeter House	... ...	Miss Cox.
———, Friar Gate ...	... ...	Rev. Philip Gell.
——— ...	... ...	William Baker, esq. M.D.
——— ...	... ...	Miss Meynell.
——— ...	... ...	Thomas Bent, esq., M.D.
——— ...	... ...	Major Gell.
——— ...	... ...	John Wright, esq.
——— ...	... ...	Henry Mozley, esq.
———, Friary ...	... ...	Mrs. Mellor.
———, Friar Gate ...	... ...	Rev. Henry Edward Abney.
———, Firs	... ...	John Egerton Killer, esq.
———, Friar Gate ...	... ...	Francis Shaw, gent.
——— ...	... ...	John Baker, gent.
———, Osmaston Road	... ...	Mrs. Bateman.
——— ...	... ...	Alleyne Sacheverel Bateman, esq.
——— ...	... ...	Rev. James Dean.
——— ...	... ...	George Cox, esq.
——— ...	... ...	Thomas Pegg, gent.

Derby, Osmaston road	126 miles NNW of London	Rev. William Fisher.
———— Street	... ...	Richard Beacher Leacroft, esq.
———, Kedleston Road	... ...	Mrs. Poyser.
———, Uttoxeter Road	... ...	Alexander Radford, esq.
———, Victoria Street	... ...	Henry Mozley, jun., esq.
———, Osmaston Street	... ...	William Whiston, jun., esq.
———, Full Street ...	... ...	John Curzon, esq.
...	... ...	Rev. Ley Brookes.
...	... ...	J. H. Stevens, esq.
———, St. Peter's Street	... ...	John Moss, esq.
———, Iron Gate ...	... ...	John Bell Crompton, esq.
———, Park Field ...	... ...	Henry Cox, esq.
———, Park Field	... ...	Rev. Edward Unwin.
———, Ley Lands	... ...	William Leaper Newton, esq.
———, Lodge Lane ...	... ...	Rev. J. G. Howard.
———, London Street	... ...	Mrs. Hope.
...	... ...	Robert Hope, esq.
————	... ...	George Ferguson, esq., M.D.
————	... ...	Robert Bromley, gent.
———, Queen Street	... ...	John Barber, esq.
———, St. Alkmund's Ch. yd.	... ...	John Hill, esq.
———, St. Helen's House	... ...	Edward Strutt, esq., M.P.
———, St. Michael's Ch. yd.	... ...	Richard Wright Haden, esq.
———, St. Peter's Street	... ...	Rev. William Fletcher.
...	... ...	Joseph Strutt, esq.
...	... ...	William Whiston, esq.
———, St. Mary's Gate	... ...	James Simpson, esq.
...	... ...	John Bromley, gent.
———, The Elms ...	... ...	Rev. J. Latham.
———, Wardwick ...	... ...	William Lockett, esq.
————	... ...	Francis Jessopp, esq.
————	... ...	Douglas Fox, esq.
————	... ...	Rev. Roseingrave Macklin.
———, North Parade	... ...	Samuel Fox, jun., esq.
———, Parker Street	... ...	Rev. J. D. G. Pike.
———, Windmill Hill	... ...	Mrs. Crompton.
———, College ...	... ...	James Heygate, esq., M.D.
Derwent Hall ...	In the Parish of Hathersage	John Read, esq.
Doe Hill	Tibshelf	John Robert Sharpe, esq.
Donington Park ...	9 miles S of Derby ...	The Marquis of Hastings.
Dove Cliff	9 miles W of Derby ...	Thomas Thornewill, esq.
Doveridge Hall ...	16 miles NW of Derby ...	Lord Waterpark.
———— Rectory	... ...	Hon. and Rev. Thomas Cavendish.
...	... ...	Hon. H. Manners Cavendish.
Drakelow Hall ...	13 miles SW of Derby ...	Captain de Voeux.
Draycott House ...	6 miles E of Derby ...	Hugh Scott, esq.
Dronfield	6 miles N of Chesterfield	Rev. Thomas Roscrow.
———— Hall ...	... ...	Mrs. Jane Cecil.
———— Greenhill	... ...	William Booker, gent.
————	... ...	Francis Broadhurst, esq.
————	... ...	George Bland, esq.
... ...	... ...	Thomas M. S. Milnes, esq.
———— Vicarage	... ...	Rev. William Spencer.
Duffield	4 miles N of Derby ...	Rev. William Barber.
————	... ...	Francis Hurt, jun., esq.
————	... ...	Rev. Evan Owen Jones.
————	... ...	Rev. Richard Mellor Hope.
———— Hall	... ...	Charles Robert Colvile, esq., M.P. occupied by Col. Colvile.
———— Hill Cottage	... ...	Rev. William Henry Wayne.
———— House ...	4½ miles N of Derby ...	John Balguy, esq.
Dunstall Hall ...	Staffordshire, 3 miles from Burton	Charles Arkwright, esq.
...	2 miles N of Chesterfield	Rev. William Smith.
Durant Hall ...	Near Chesterfield ...	Adam Barker Slater, esq.
Eccles House ...	Near Chapel-en-le-Frith ...	Thomas Goodman, esq.
Earl Sterndale	Near Buxton ...	Rev. William Buckwell.
Ecclesbourne House	3 miles S of Wirksworth ...	Mrs. Statham.
Eckington Rectory ...	7 miles E of Chesterfield ...	Rev. Frederick Rickets, occupied by Rev. A. C. Broomhead.
Edale	Near Castleton	Rev. John Champion.
Edensor Vicarage ...	3 miles E of Bakewell ...	Rev. R. C. Wilmot.
Edge Hill	4 miles N of Derby ...	James Pickering Orde, esq.
Edinghall ...	9 miles SW of Burton ...	Rev. George Evans.
Edlaston Rectory ...	3 miles W of Ashbourn ...	Rev. Thomas Cupiss.
Ednaston Lodge ...	9 miles N of Derby ...	Rev. —— Green.
Egginton Hall ...	8 miles SW of Derby ...	Sir Henry Every, bart.
———— Rectory	... ...	Rev. John Leigh.
Elvaston Castle ...	4 miles SE of Derby ...	Earl of Harrington.
———— Vicarage	... ...	Rev. Frederick Nathan. Highmore.
Etwall	6 miles W of Derby ...	Rev. W. B. Sleath, D.D.
———— Hall ...	... ...	Col. E. Rowland J. Cotton.
————	... ...	William Eaton, Esq.
———— Vicarage	... ...	Rev. William Eaton Mousley.
Elton Manor ...	Bingham, Notts. ...	William Fletcher N. Norton, esq.
Elton	1 mile W of Winster ...	Rev. John Fisher Garrett.
Eyam Hall	5 miles NE of Bakewell ...	Peter Wright, esq.

Eyam Rectory	5 miles NE of Bakewell	Rev. E. B. Bagshawe.
—— Firs	... ...	William John Wright, esq.
——	... ...	James Mower, esq.
Fairfield	1 mile E of Buxton	Rev. George Mounsey.
Farnah Hall	6 miles NW of Derby	Lord Scarsdale.
Fenney Bentley ...	2½ miles N of Ashbourn ...	John Goodwin Johnson, esq.
Ford Hall	6 miles S of Chesterfield ...	Mrs. Mary Holland.
Foremark Hall ...	7 miles SW of Derby ...	Sir Francis Burdett, bart.
Foston Hall	9 miles W of Derby (Ruins of) ...	John Broadhurst, esq.
Garrendon Park ...	Leicestershire	Charles March Philips, esq.
Gatehouse	Wirksworth	Rev. Robert Gell.
Glapwell Hall ...	6 miles E of Chesterfield ...	Thomas Hallowes, esq.
Glossop Hall	12 miles NW of Chapel-en-le-Frith	Duke of Norfolk, in occupation of Thomas Ellison, esq.
Green Bank	Turnditch	William Statham, gent.
Green House	Belper	Jedediah Strutt, esq.
Grove	Near Ashbourn	John Greaves, esq.
Haddon Hall	2½ miles S of Bakewell ...	Duke of Rutland.
Hardwick Hall ...	5 miles SE of Chesterfield ...	Duke of Devonshire.
Hartington Vicarage	6 miles N of Ashbourn ...	Rev. Matthew W. Ward.
Hartshorne	10 miles SW of Derby ...	Thomas Hassall, esq.
——	... ...	John Lester, gent.
——	... ...	Thomas Worthington, esq.
—— Rectory ...	... ...	Rev. W. H. Buckley.
Hasland	1 mile N of Chesterfield ...	Bernard Lucas, esq.
Hassop	3 miles NE of Bakewell ...	Rev. John Jones.
—— House ...	... ...	Richard Stanley, esq.
—— Hall ...	... ...	Earl of Newburgh.
Hathersage	8 miles E of Chapel-en-le-Frith	Rev. George Jinks.
Hathersage Hall ...	... ...	A. A. Shuttleworth, esq.
—— Vicarage ...	... ...	Rev. John Le Cornu.
——	... ...	Rev. John Ross.
Hayfield	5 miles NW of Buxton ...	Rev. Samuel Wass.
Hazlebage Hall ...	... ...	Duke of Rutland, occupied by George Fox, gent.
Heage	... ...	Rev. Henry William Wayne.
Heanor Hall	8 miles NE of Derby ...	John Ray, esq.
——	... ...	George H. Ray, gent.
—— Vicarage ...	... ...	Rev. R. Whinfield.
Heath Rectory ...	5 miles E of Chesterfield ...	Rev. Charles Currey.
Highfields	2 miles N of Chesterfield ...	
Hilcote Hall	3 miles NE of Alfreton ...	John Slater Wilkinson, esq.
Hilton Cottage ...	7 miles W of Derby ...	William Simpson, esq., M.D.
Hognaston Parsonage	... ...	Rev. Augustus Wergman.
Horsley Woodhouse	... ...	Charles John Sitwell, esq.
Horsley	... ...	Rev. Samuel Fox.
Holbrook Hall ...	6 miles N of Derby	Rev. John Edward Carr.
Holme Hall	Bakewell	John Hodgson, esq.
Holmesfield	8 miles N of Chesterfield ...	Rev. William Pashley.
Hope Vicarage ...	6 miles E of Chapel-en-le-Frith	Rev. Francis Orton.
Hopton Hall	2 miles W of Wirksworth ...	Executors of the late Philip Gell, esq.
Hopwell Hall	6 miles E of Derby	Thomas Pares, esq
Hollybush	Abbotts Bromley, Staffordsh. ...	Thomas Kirkpatrick Hall, esq.
Horridge House ...	Near Chapel-en-le-Frith ...	Thomas Gisborne, esq.
——	... ...	Fysh Henry Gisborne, esq.
——	... ...	Rev. Charles Evans.
Hulland	3 miles S of Wirksworth ...	Robert Cresswell, e sq.
Ideridgehay	4 miles N of Ashbourn ...	J. Watts Russell, esq.
Ilam Hall	... ...	J. D. Watts Russell, esq., M.P.
Ilkeston Vicarage ...	9 miles NE of Derby ...	
Kedleston Hall ...	4 miles NW of Derby ...	Lord Scarsdale.
Kilbourn Hall	7 miles N of Derby	Charles Vicars Hunter, esq.
——	... ...	William Hunter Hunter, esq.
King's Newton ...	7 miles S of Derby	Joseph Cantrell, esq.
—— Hall ...	... ...	Lord Melbourne, in occupation of George Vandeleur, esq.
Kirk Hallam Rectory	5 miles NE of Derby ...	Rev. Pelley Parker.
Kirk Hill House ...	Duffield	W. H. Wayne, esq.
Kirk Ireton Rectory	2 miles S of Wirksworth ...	Rev. H. Gordon, occupied by Rev. Robert Gell.
Kirk Langley House	5 miles NW of Derby ...	Thomas Goodall Copestake, esq.
—— Rectory	... ...	Rev. H. J. Fielding.
—— Hall	... ...	Thomas Peach, esq., M. D.
Lea Hall	4½ miles NE of Wirksworth ...	Thomas Hallowes, esq.
Lea Hurst	4 miles E of Wirksworth ...	W. E. Nightingale, esq.
Lea Wood	2 miles NE of Cromford ...	James Milnes, esq.
Leam Hall	2 miles N of Stoney Middleton	M. M. Middleton, esq.
Lees Hall	2½ miles S of Glossop ...	Joseph Hadfield, esq.
Lilies (The)	7 miles NW of Derby ...	Gilbert Crompton, esq., occupied by Thomas Porter, gent.
Litchurch Lodge ...	Near Derby	Rev. Edward M. Wade.
Longstone, Little ...	4 miles NE of Bakewell ...	James Longsdon, esq.
Littleover Hall ...	2 miles W of Derby	Cockshut Heathcote, esq., occupied by Mr. Camp.

Lockington Hall	Leicestershire	John Bainbrigge Storey, esq.
Locko Hall	5 miles E of Derby	Mrs. Drewry Lowe.
Longford Hall ...	9 miles NW of Derby	Earl of Leicester, occupied by Thomas William Coke, esq.
Long Eaton	10 miles SE of Derby ...	Edward William Browne, esq.
Longstone, Great ...	3 miles N of Bakewell ...	—— Longsdon, esq.
—————— Parsonage	... ...	Rev. Malkin Mills.
—————— Hall ...	3 miles NE of Bakewell ...	William Carliel, esq.
Longshaw	Near Hathersage ...	The Duke of Rutland.
Ludworth	In Glossop Dale	John Wright, esq.
Lullington	7 miles SW of Burton ...	Charles Robert Colvile, esq., M.P.
—————— Vicarage ...	... ...	Rev. —— Eschalez.
Lumsdale	... ...	John Garton, gent.
Lyme Hall	Cheshire	Thomas Leigh, esq.
Mackworth Vicarage ...	2½ miles W of Derby ...	Rev. George Pickering.
—————— Castle ...	In Ruins (site of) ...	Lord Scarsdale.
Makeney Cottage ...	2 miles S of Belper ...	Anthony Radford Strutt, esq.
Mappleton	1½ mile N of Ashbourn ...	Francis Goodwin, esq.
Markeaton Hall ...	1 mile W of Derby ...	William Mundy, esq.
Marsh Hall	Chapel-en-le-Frith ...	John Higginbotham, esq.
Marsh Green Hall ...	Near Ashover	Rev. Joseph Nodder.
Marston Montgomery ...	12 miles W of Derby ...	Rev. John Williams.
Mayfield Hall ...	2 miles W of Ashbourn ...	William Greaves, esq., M.D., Bath.
	... ...	Charles Springal Greaves, esq.
Matlock	2 miles N of Cromford ...	George Nuttall, esq.
... ...	... ...	William Melville, esq.
—————— Lumshill ...	... ...	Edward Radford, esq.
—————— Rectory ...	... ...	Rev. Henry Melville
—————— Cottage ...	... ...	Col. Payne.
—————— Bath ...	... ...	Mrs. Woolley.
... ...	... ...	Charles Clarke, esq.
—————— Torr Cottage	... ...	James Sakeld H. Collingwood, esq.
Measham	3 miles W Ashby-de-la-Zouch	Rev. Joseph Christian Moore.
—————— Hall ...	... ...	
—————— Field ...	... ...	William Wootton Abney, esq.
Meersbrook Hall ...	3 miles S of Sheffield ...	
Melbourne Hall ...	8 miles S of Derby ...	Lord Melbourne.
—————— Vicarage ...	... ...	Rev. Joseph Dean.
Mellor	7 miles NW of Buxton ...	Rev. Matthew Freeman.
... ...	... ...	Moses Hadfield, esq.
—————— Hall ...	... ...	Thomas Moult, esq.
—————— Lodge ...	... ...	Richard Simpson, esq.
Meynell Langley Park ...	4 miles NW of Derby ...	Godfrey Meynell, esq.
Mickleover Rectory ...	4 miles W of Derby ...	Hon. and Rev. Frederick Curzon.
Middleton by Youlgrave	4 miles SW of Bakewell ...	Thomas Bateman, esq.
Milford House ...	5 miles N of Derby ...	Occupied by J. B. Crompton, esq. Lorenzo Kirkpatrick Hall, esq.
Morley Rectory ...	5 miles NE of Derby ...	Rev. William Sitwell, occupied by Rev. Samuel Fox.
—————— House ...	... ...	Robert Sacheverel Sitwell, esq.
Morton Rectory ...	4 miles N of Alfreton ...	Rev. Thomas Land.
Mossbrough Hall ...	7 miles NE of Chesterfield	John Smith, esq.
Mugginton Farm ...	5 miles NW of Derby ...	Hon. and Rev. Alfred Curzon.
Netherseal Hall ...	8 miles S Burton on Trent ...	Rev. Sir William Nigel Gresley, bart.
Newbold	Near Chesterfield ...	Godfrey Booker, esq.
Newhall Parsonage ...	4 miles S of Burton ...	Rev. John Henry Moran.
Newton Solney ...	10 miles SW of Derby ...	R. Bardeston Yates, esq
... ...	... ...	Thomas Worthington, esq.
Newton Mount	... ...	Thomas Allsop, esq.
Norbury Vicarage ...	5 miles W of Ashbourn ...	Rev. F. Clement Broughton.
Normanton, South ...	Near Alfreton ...	Rev. Charles Rolfe.
... ...	... ...	Rev. Howard Frizell.
Northwingfield ...	4 miles S of Chesterfield ...	John Wilkinson Clay, esq.
... ...	... ...	William Clay, esq.
—————— Rectory ...	... ...	Rev. Edward Walter Lowe.
Norton	8 miles N of Chesterfield ...	Rev. H. Hunt Piper.
... ...	... ...	William Webster, esq.
—————— Hall ...	... ...	Samuel Offley Shore, esq.
—————— House ...	... ...	Thomas Beard Holy, esq.
—————— Vicarage ...	... ...	Rev. Henry Pearson.
Nunsfield House ...	Alvaston	Charles Holbrook, esq.
Nuttall Temple ...	Nottinghamshire ...	Robert Holden, esq.
Oaks (The)	8 miles N of Chesterfield ...	J. W. Bagshawe, esq.
... ...	... ...	Francis Darling Bagshawe, esq.
Ockbrook Rectory ...	7 miles E of Derby ...	Rev. Samuel Hey.
Oddo	Winster	Lord Searsdale, occupied by William Brittlebank, esq.
Ogston Hall	4 miles NW of Alfreton ...	Mrs. Turbutt.
... ...	... ...	William Turbutt, esq.
Okeover Hall	3 miles N of Ashbourn ...	H. F. Okeover, esq.
Oldercar Hall	Heanor	Rev. Henry Smith.
Ollerenshaw House ...	Chapel-en-le-Frith ...	William Thornhill, esq.
Osmaston Hall ...	1½ mile from Derby ...	Sir Robert Wilmot, bart.
Overton Hall ...	7 miles N of Wirksworth ...	John Bright, esq. M.D.
Packington	... ...	Joseph Lester Hassall, esq.
—————— Vicarage ...	... ...	Rev. Charles Pratt.

Painter's Lane	... ...	3 miles S of Ashbourn ...	... Mrs. Butler.
Park Hall	... ...	7 miles E of Chesterfield	... E. Sacheverel Chandos Pole, esq., occupied by Mrs. Pole.
Park Hall	... ...	1 mile N of Hayfield ...	... John White, esq.
Park Hill	...	6 miles W of Derby	... Ashton Nicholas Every Moseley, esq.
Parwich Hall	...	... ...	... William Evans, esq.
Pastures House		4 miles W of Derby ...	... Sir Seymour Blaine, bart.
Pear Tree House		Near Derby ...	... Thomas Briggs, gent.
Pinxton Rectory		3 miles E of Alfreton	... Rev. Ellis Williams.
Pilsbury House		Near Hartington	... Edmund Gould, esq.
Pleasley	...	4 miles N of Mansfield ...	... Rev. James Robert Holden.
Quorndon Cottage		3 miles NW of Derby	... W. B. Wayne, esq.
Quenby Hall	...	Leicestershire ...	... William A. Ashby, esq.
Radbourn Hall	...	5 miles NW of Derby	... E. S. Chandos Pole, esq.
———— Rectory	...	... ...	... Rev. R. Chandos Pole.
Ravenstone Hall		3 miles S of Ashby-de-la-Zouch	Leonard Fosbrook, esq.
———— House		... ...	... Robert Green Creswell, esq.
		... ...	... Richard Edward Cresswell, esq.
———— Rectory		... ...	... Rev. Giles Prickett.
Renishaw Hall	...	6 miles E of Chesterfield	... Sir George Sitwell, bart.
Repton Park	...	8 miles SW of Derby ...	... Edmund Lewis Crewe, esq.
...	...	... ...	... Charles Hugh Crewe, esq.
————	...	... ...	... Rev. John Smith.
————	...	... ...	... Rev. John Hare.
————	...	... ...	... Rev. John Pattison.
———— Priory		... ...	... Sir Francis Burdett, bart., occupied by Rev. Thomas W. Peile.
	...	... ...	... Rev. William Stoddart.
	...	... ...	... Rev. James Garvey.
	...	... ...	... Francis Holbrook, gent.
Riddings Hall	...	2½ miles E of Alfreton ...	... James Oakes, esq.
———— Parsonage		... ...	... Rev. William Haward.
Ringwood Hall	...	2 miles E of Chesterfield	... George H. Barrow, esq.
Ripley	... ...	10 miles N of Derby	... Robert Wood, esq.
Risley	... ...	7 miles E of Derby ...	... John Michael Fellowes, esq.
————	... ...	... ...	... Henry Banks Hall, gent.
————	...	... ...	... William H. Hall, gent.
————	...	... ...	... Rev. John Hancock Hall, jun.
———— Hall	...	... ...	... Rev. John Hancock Hall.
Rock House	...	2 miles N of Wirksworth	... Peter Arkwright, esq.
————	...	... ...	... James Charles Arkwright, esq.
————	...	... ...	... Ferdinand W. Arkwright, esq.
————	...	... ...	... Edward Arkwright, esq.
Rolleston Hall	...	8½ miles W of Derby ...	... Sir Oswald Mosley, bart.
Romeley	...	In the Parish of Barlborough	... Rev. Thomas Hill.
Rosliston	...	4 miles W of Burton	... Thomas Hamp, esq.
Sandybrook Hall	...	1½ miles N of Ashbourn	... Sir M. Blakiston, bart.
Sawley Vicarage	...	9 miles S of Derby ...	... Rev. James Lowther Senhouse.
Shardlow Hall	...	7 miles S of Derby	... James Sutton, esq.
Shipley Hall	...	8 miles E of Derby	... Edward Miller Mundy, esq.
Shirebrook	...	Near Pleasley	... Reynolds Sutton esq.
Shirland Rectory	...	3 miles N of Alfreton	... Occupied by Rev. William Barlow.
Shirley Vicarage	...	3 miles S of Ashbourn	... Rev. Walter A. Shirley.
			... Rev. Thomas Gibbs.
Smalley	...	6 miles NE of Derby ...	... John Radford, esq.
Slacke Hall	...	Chapel-en-le-Frith	... Thomas Slacke, esq. M.D.
Smisby Hall	...	2½ miles N of Ashby-de-la-Zouch	Sir George Crewe, bart., occupied by Joseph Lester Hassall, esq.
...	...	... ...	... Rev. Marmaduke Vavasour.
Snelston Hall	...	3 miles W of Ashbourn ...	... John Harrison, esq.
Snitterton Hall	...	5 miles N of Wirksworth	... Edmund Turnor, esq., occupied by Robert Sybray, gent.
Somershall Herbert	...	... ...	... Rev. George William Straton.
Somersall Hall	...	1 mile W of Chesterfield ...	... Samuel Johnson, esq.
Southgate House	...	1½ mile E of Barlborough	... John Bruno Bowden, esq.
			Henry Bowden, esq.
South Normanton Vicarage		3 miles NE of Alfreton	... Rev. Frederick Doveton.
South Wingfield	...	2½ miles W of Alfreton	... Thomas Pearson, esq.
———— Manor House		... ...	... Rev. Immanuel Halton.
Spinkhill	... ...	Near Barlborough	... Rev. M. Tristram.
Spondon	... ...	3 miles E of Derby	... James Cade, esq.
	...	... ...	... William Thomas Cox, esq.
———— Hall Dyke House		... ...	... George H. R. Cox, esq.
	...	... ...	... Rev. R. Wilmot.
———— Hall	...	... ...	... Roger Cox, esq.
———— House	...	... ...	... Jacob Osborne esq., occupied by W. L. Clowes, esq.
	...	... ...	... John Dawes Mather, esq.
———— Vicarage	...	... ...	... Rev. Alexander Atkinson Holden.
Stainsby House	...	7 miles NE of Derby	... Edward Degg Sitwell, esq.
	...	... ...	... Charles John Sitwell, esq.
Stanton by Bridge Rectory	...	6 miles S of Derby	... Rev. T. W. Whittaker.
———— Dale		6 miles E of Derby	... Lawrence Hall, gent.
———— Rectory		... ...	... Rev. J. G. Howard.

Stanton House ...	... 2 miles N of Winster ...	... William Pole Thornhill, esq.
———— Woodhouse	... 4 miles S of Bakewell ...	... Duke of Rutland.
Stapenhill ...	... 1 mile S of Burton ...	... Mrs. Allsop.
———— ...	... ...	... Rev. John Clay.
———— ...	... ...	... Nathaniel Nadin, esq.
Staveley Hall ...	... 5 miles E of Chesterfield	... Duke of Devonshire.
———— Rectory ...	... ...	... Rev. Bernard Moore.
Stoke Hall ...	... 1 mile E of Stoney Middleton	... Hon. B. Simpson, Babworth, Notts.
Stonecliff Hall ...	... 5 miles S of Bakewell ...	... A. H. Heathcote, esq.
Stoney Middleton ...	... 5 miles E of Bakewell ...	... Rev. A. B. Greaves.
———— Hall	... ...	... Right Hon. Lord Denman.
Stretton in the Fields Hall ...	3 miles SW of Ashby-de-la-Zouch	Sir Thomas C. Browne Cave, bart.
———— ...	... ...	... Rev. E. S. Brown Cave.
Stretton Rectory ...	... ...	... Rev. John Cave Brown.
Stubbing Edge ...	... 7 miles N of Wirksworth	... William Milnes, esq.
Stubbing Court ...	... 4 miles W of Chesterfield	... C. D. Gladwin, esq., late occupied by Lord Dunfermline.
Sturston House ...	... Near Ashbourn ...	... Rev. Alexander Start.
Sudbury Hall ...	... 15 miles W of Derby ...	... Lord Vernon.
———— Vicarage	... ...	... Hon. and Rev. Frederick Anson.
———— ...	... ...	... Rev. Frederick Anson, jun.
Sutton Hall ...	... 4 miles SE of Chesterfield	... Robert Arkwright, esq.
———— ...	... ...	... George Arkwright, esq., M.P.
———— ...	... ...	... William Arkwright, esq.
———— ...	... ...	... Godfrey Harry Arkwright, esq.
———— Rectory ...	... ...	... Rev. Michael Maughan Humble.
Sutton-on-the-Hill	... ...	... Rev. German Buckstone.
Summershall Herbert	... 3 miles NW of Tutbury	... Henry Vernon, esq.
———— Rectory	... ...	... Rev. George William Straton.
Swanwick Hall ...	... 2 miles S of Alfreton ...	... Rev. John Wood.
———— Grange	... ...	... Cressey Hall, esq.
Swarkeston Lowes	... 5 miles S of Derby ...	... Occupied by William Smith, gent.
Sydnope, near Darley	... ...	... Sir Francis Sacheverel Darwin.
Taddington Parsonage	... 6 miles NW of Bakewell	... Rev. John Henry Coke.
Tapton Grove ...	... 1½ mile S of Chesterfield	... John Meynell, esq.
———— Hall ...	... ...	... George Stephenson, esq.
———— Lane	... ...	... Robert Malkin, esq.
Taxall Lodge ...	... In Cheshire	... William George Newton, esq.
Temple Normanton	... 2 miles E of Chesterfield	... Rev. Robert Bromehead.
Thornhill House ...	... ¾ mile W of Derby ...	... Mrs. Trowell.
Thorne Bridge ...	... In Longstone ...	... Sydney Smithers, esq.
Thorpe	... 3 miles W of Ashbourn	... Rev. B. G. Blackden, M.A.
Thurlston Lodge ...	... 4 miles S of Derby ...	... Earl of Harrington, unoccupied.
Tibshelf	... 5 miles N of Alfreton ...	... John Robert Sharpe, esq.
———— ...	... ...	... Francis William Sharpe, esq.
———— ...	... ...	... John Chambers, esq.
———— Rectory	... ...	... Rev. G. D. Goodyer.
Tideswell Vicarage	... ...	... Rev. H. Barrow, Chinn.
———— Dale Cottage	... ...	... Rev. George Best Brown.
Ticknall Vicarage	... ...	... Rev. Richardson Cox.
Tissington Hall ...	... 3 miles NE of Ashbourn	... Sir H. Fitzherbert, bart.
———— ...	... ...	... Rev. W. Alderson, Aston Rectory, Yorkshire.
Troway ...	... In Eckington	... John Turner, esq.
Twyford Hall ...	... 5 miles SW of Derby ...	... Samuel Ellis Bristow, esq., occupied by Mr. Bromley.
Vernon's Oak ...	... Sudbury	... George Chawner, gent.
Walton Lodge ...	... 3 miles W of Chesterfield	... Joshua Jebb, esq.
———— on Trent Hall	... 4 miles W of Burton on Trent	... Colonel Disbrowe, occupied by Matthew Gisborne, esq.
———— Rectory	... ...	... Rev. Francis Blick, occupied by Rev. Richard Wanstall.
Welbeck Abbey ...	... Near Worksop, Nottinghamshire ...	The Duke of Portland.
Wensley Hall ...	... 5 miles NW of Cromford	... John Allsop, gent.
Weston Underwood	... ...	... Hon. and Rev. Alfred Curzon.
———— on Trent Hall	... 5 miles S of Derby ...	... E. A. Holden, esq. occupied by M. Champion, gent.
———— Rectory	... ...	... Rev. Robert French, occupied by Rev. William Dewe.
Wheatley Hall ...	... 6 miles S of Bakewell ...	... Thomas Potter, esq., occupied by Mr. Bentley.
Wheat Hill ...	... 3 miles N of Derby ...	...
Wheston Hall ...	... Near Tideswell	... John Allen, gent.
West Hallam Rectory	... ...	... Rev. Pelly Parker.
Whitehough Hall	... Chapel-en-le-Frith ...	... ———— Hughes, esq.
Whittington ...	... 3 miles N of Chesterfield	... Robert Edmund Mower.
———— ...	... ...	... R. E. M. Smith, esq.
———— ...	... ...	... Rev. Robert Broomhead.
———— ...	... ...	... Charles Hugh May, esq.
———— Hall	... ...	... Henry Dixon, esq.
———— Rectory	... ...	... Rev. George Gordon, occupied by Rev. R. Robinson.
Whitwell Rectory	... 4 miles NW of Worksop	... Rev. George Mason.
Willersley Castle	... 2 miles N of Wirksworth	... Richard Arkwright, esq.
Wigwell Grange	... ...	... William Henry Goodwin, gent.

Wigwell Grange ...	... 1 mile E of Wirksworth	... Francis Cornelius Goodwin, gent.
————	... ...	... Francis Green Goodwin, esq.
————	... ...	... James Berrisford Goodwin, gent.
Willesley Hall ...	... 1½ mile W of Ashby-de-la-Zouch ...	Sir Charles Abney Hastings, bart.
———— ...	... ...	... Dowager Lady Hastings.
———— Rectory	... ...	... Rev. George Pleywell Lloyd.
Willington Hall ...	... 6 miles SW of Derby	... Sir Francis Burdett, bart., unoc.
———— House	... ...	... Rev. Francis Ward Spilsbury.
Winster ...	... 6 miles N of Wirksworth	... Mrs. Carill Worsley.
———— ...	... ...	... Charles Carill Worsley, esq.
Wirksworth ...	... 13 miles N of Derby	... Charles Hurt, esq.
———— ...	... ...	... Richard Hurt, esq.
———— ...	... ...	... James Hurt, esq.
———— ...	... ...	... Philip Hubbersty, esq.
———— ...	... ...	... Rev. Nathan Hubbersty.
———— Gatehouse	... ...	... Rev. Robert Gell.
———— ...	... ...	... Thomas Poyser, esq.
———— Vicarage	... ...	... Rev. J. Harwood.
———— ...	... ...	... Alfred Arkwright, esq.
———— ...	... ...	... Edward Arkwright, esq.
Wingerworth Hall	... 2½ miles S of Chesterfield	... Sir John Henry Hunloke, bart.
———— Rectory	... ...	... Rev. Samuel Revell.
Wilne ...	... ...	... Rev. Philip Fosbrooke.
Wood End ...	... 2½ miles NE of Wirksworth	... James Milnes, esq.
Wollaton Hall ...	... 13 miles E of Derby	... Lord Middleton.
Wormhill ...	... 2 miles N of Tideswell	... Rev. James Parker.
———— Hall ...	... ...	... William John Bagshawe, esq.
Yolgrave Vicarage ...	... 5 miles SW of Bakewell	... Rev. R. P. Hull.
Yoxall Lodge ...	... ...	... Rev. Thomas Gisborne.
...	... ...	... Walter Gisborne, esq.

CARRIERS BY WATER,

WITH THE DAYS THEY LEAVE DERBY.

MESSRS. J. AND W. SORESBY, SIDDALS LANE.

A Boat every Wednesday and Saturday, for Shardlow, Loughborough, Leicester, Northampton, Market Harborough, Coventry, Nottingham, Newark, Gainsborough, Hull, Bristol, Gloucester, Worcester, Stafford, Wolverhampton, Birmingham, the Staffordshire Potteries, Manchester, Liverpool, and London, both by sea and canal.

Fly Boats daily to London.

PICKFORD AND CO., SIDDALS LANE.

A Fly Boat daily to Birmingham, Leamington, Cheltenham, Gloucester, Wolverhampton, Worcester, Lichfield, Atherstone, Aylesbury, Banbury, Bedford, Bewdley, Bridgenorth, Burton-upon-Trent, Cosgrove, Coventry, Dudley, Tamworth, Fenny Stratford, Oxford, Shardlow, Shrewsbury, Kidderminster, Stourbridge, Stratford-upon-Avon, Tewkesbury, Bristol, Warwick, and Wellingborough.

A Fly Boat daily to London.

A Fly Boat every day, for Manchester, Liverpool, Leek, the Potteries, Macclesfield, Congleton, Stockport, and all places on the line.

A Fly Boat every Tuesday, Thursday, and Saturday, to Gainsborough and Hull.

SUTTON AND CO., COCKPIT HILL.

A Fly Boat, every Tuesday, Thursday, and Saturday evening, for Manchester, and Liverpool.

A Boat every Monday, Tuesday, Thursday, and Saturday, for Shardlow, Loughborough, Leicester, and Coventry.

A Boat for Nottingham, Newark, Gainsborough, and from thence to London by sea, every Monday, Tuesday, Thursday, and Friday Evenings.

A Boat, to Pinxton, Buckland Hollow, and Cromford, every Wednesday at 12 o'clock.

A Boat, to Birmingham, Wolverhampton, &c., every Wednesday evening.

TUNLEY AND HODSON, SIDDALS LANE.

A Fly Boat, every Tuesday, Thursday, and Saturday, to Manchester and Liverpool.

A Fly Boat, every Tuesday, Thursday, and Saturday, to Burton, and the Potteries.

A Fly Boat daily to London.

N.B. Lock-up Boats, for the safe conveyance of Wines, Spirits, Teas, and other valuable Merchandise.

WHEATCROFT AND SON, COCKPIT HILL.

A Fly Boat, every Tuesday, Thursday, and Saturday, for Birmingham, Dudley, Stourbridge, &c.

A Fly Boat, every Monday, Wednesday, and Friday, for Cromford; from thence to Manchester, by the Cromford and High Peak Railway.

MESSRS. CROWLEY, HICKLIN, BATTY, AND CO.;
FROM LISTER'S WHARF, SIDDALS LANE.

A Fly Boat every Tuesday and Friday, to Birmingham, Warwick, Coventry, Banbury, and Oxford.

CARRIERS BY RAILWAY.

PICKFORD AND CO., SIDDALS LANE.

Daily to Chesterfield, Masbro', Sheffield, Barnsley, Wakefield, Leeds, York, Darlington, and a Wagon from Darlington to Newcastle-upon-Tyne.

Daily to Brighouse, Rochdale, Manchester, and Liverpool.

Daily to Birmingham, Gloucester, Cheltenham, and Bristol.

Daily to Loughborough, Leicester, Wolverton, Rugby, and London.

Daily to Nottingham.

A Van daily to Ashbourn, Leek, Macclesfield, and Congleton.

SUTTON AND CO., COCKPIT HILL.

Daily to London, Birmingham, Loughborough, Nottingham, Leicester, Manchester, Wakefield, Sheffield, Barnsley, Leeds, and all parts of Yorkshire.

DEACON, WADE AND CO.

General Carriers by Railway, Park Street.

W. W. WALLIS, SADLER GATE,

AGENT TO THE BIRMINGHAM AND DERBY, JUNCTION RAILWAY COMPANY.

Daily to London, Birmingham, Bristol, Bath, Cheltenham, Liverpool, Manchester, Chester, Nottingham, Newark, Lincoln, Grantham, Hull, Leicester, Huddersfield, Bradford, Leeds, and York, and all parts of the Kingdom.

WHEATCROFT AND SON, COCKPIT HILL.

Daily to Birmingham, Sheffield, Leeds, Wakefield, Barnsley, and London.

LISTER AND CO., SIDDALS LANE.

Daily to Birmingham, Sheffield, Chesterfield, Barnsley, Wakefield, Leeds, York, Hull, Selby, &c.

MAILS AND COACHES,

WITH THE TIME OF THEIR DEPARTURE FROM DERBY.

Mail Gig to Ashbourn, *George M. Calladine, Agard Street.*
———— to Kegworth, *John Prince, Morledge.*
———— to Ashby, *Charles Smith, Corn Market.*
———— to Rugeley and Uttoxeter, *James Alton, King Street.*
———— to Burton, *William Potter, Kensington.*
———— to Nottingham, *Edward Woodhall, Bull's Head.*
Nelson, to Manchester, (through Matlock and Buxton,) every morning at a quarter past eight. Office, Sadler Gate, and Tiger Inn, Corn Market.
Defiance, to Manchester, (through Ashbourn, Leek, and Macclesfield,) every morning at half-past nine, Sundays excepted. Office, Sadler Gate, and Tiger Inn, Corn Market.
Adelaide, to Uttoxeter, Lane End, Stoke, and Newcastle, every Tuesday, Thursday, and Saturday morning, at eleven o'clock, from the Nag's Head, St. Peter's Street, Bell Hotel, and New Inn, *Elijah Roberts.*
Hero, to Uttoxeter, Lane End, Stoke, and Newcastle, every Monday, Wednesday, and Friday morning, at eleven o'clock, from the New Inn, and Bell Hotel, Sadler Gate, *Gregory Dawson.*
Victoria Omnibus, to Ashbourn, every Monday, Wednesday, and Friday afternoon, at four o'clock, from the Nag's Head, *Miers and Mellor.*
Protector Omnibus, to Ashbourn, every Monday, Wednesday, and Friday afternoon, at four o'clock, from the Bell Hotel, Sadler Gate.
Standard Omnibus, every day except Sundays, to Ashby, at one o'clock, and to Nottingham at six o'clock in the afternoon, from the Nag's Head, *William Pegg, Nottingham.*

LIST OF CARRIERS,

With the days they leave Derby, and the Inns they start from.

Alfreton, *Kemp,* from the Angel, Corn Market,
————, *Bacon,* Thorn Tree, St. Peter's Street, Monday, Wednesday, and Friday.
————, *Webster,* Nag's Head, Royal Mail, every day, Sunday excepted.
Allestree, *Pickard,* Saracen's Head, St. James's Lane, Monday, Wednesday, and Friday.
————, *Watson,* Flower Pot, King Street, every day except Sunday.
————, *Beeston,* Dolphin, Queen Street, Monday, Wednesday, and Friday.
Alvaston, *A. Smith,* Thorn Tree, St. Peter's Street, Tuesday and Friday.
————, *Tinkler,* Rose and Crown, Corn Market, Tuesday and Friday.
————, *Fisher,* Rose and Crown, Corn Market, Tuesday and Friday.
Ashbourn, *Johnson,* Telegraph, Morledge, Monday and Friday.
————, *Bridden,* Black Swan, Siddals Lane, Monday, Wednesday, and Friday.
————, *Hardy,* Robin Hood, Iron Gate, Friday.
————, *Frost,* Dog and Partridge, Tenant Street, Tuesday and Friday.
Ambaston, *A. Smith,* Thorn Tree, St. Peter's Street, Tuesday and Friday.
————, *Winfield,* Nag's Head, Friday.
Ashby-de-la-Zouch, *Gilbert,* Thorn Tree, St. Peter's Street, Tuesday and Friday.
———— ————, *Cox,* Thorn Tree, St. Peter's Street, Tuesday and Friday.
———— ————, *Smith,* Corn Market, Mail Gig every morning.
———— ————, *Smith,* Carrier's cart, Corn Market, every day.
Aston, *Young,* Saracen's Head, St. James's Lane, Friday.
Atherstone, *Smith,* Corn Market, daily.
Atlow, *Cooper,* White Hart, Bridge Gate, Friday.
————, *Woodhouse,* Shakspeare, Sadler Gate, Friday.
Bakewell, *Hardy,* Robin Hood, Iron Gate, Friday.

Bakewell, *Weston*, Talbot, Iron Gate, Monday, Wednesday, and Friday.
————, *Frost*, Dog and Partridge, Tenant Street, Tuesday and Friday.
Barrow, *Sharpe*, Nag's Head, St. Peter's Street, Friday.
————, *Bancroft*, Rose and Crown, Corn Market, Friday.
————, *Earp*, Angel, Corn Market, every day except Sunday.
Barton, *Briscoe*, Talbot, Iron Gate, Monday, Wednesday, and Friday.
————, *Salt*, Rose and Crown, Corn Market, Monday, Wednesday, and Friday.
Beeston, *Smith*, Thorn Tree, St. Peter's Street, Tuesday and Friday.
————, *Barnes*, Green Lane, every morning at 4 o'clock, except Sunday.
Belton, *Rowlston*, White Swan, St. Peter's Street, Tuesday and Friday.
Belper, *Webster*, Nag's Head, St. Peter's Street, Friday.
————, *Watson*, Rose and Crown, every day except Sunday.
————, *Brinsley*, Nag's Head, St. Peter's Street, Wednesday.
Blakeley Lodge, *Dicken*, Thorn Tree, St. Peter's Street, Wednesday.
Blythe Marsh, *Dawson*, New Inn, King Street, Monday, Wednesday, and Friday.
————, *Roberts*, New Inn, King Street, Monday, Wednesday, and Friday.
Borrowash, *Barnes*, Green Lane, every morning at four o'clock, except Sunday.
————, *Towle*, Dog and Partridge, Tenant Street, Tuesday and Friday.
————, *Robinson*, Talbot, Iron Gate, Friday.
————, *Cooke*, Dolphin, Queen Street, Friday.
Bonsall, *Allsopp*, Telegraph, Morledge, Friday.
Bradley, *Greaves*, Nag's Head, St. Peter's Street, Monday, Wednesday, & Friday.
Bradbourne, *Woodhouse*, Shakspeare, Sadler Gate, Friday.
Brailsford, *Johnson*, Telegraph, Morledge, Friday.
————, *Bridden*, Black Swan, Siddals Lane, Monday, Wednesday, and Friday.
Branston, *Briscoe*, Talbot, Iron Gate, Monday, Wednesday, and Friday.
Bramcote, *Barnes*, Green Lane, every morning at four o'clock, except Sunday.
Bratby, *Elverson*, Green Man, St. Peter's Street, Tuesday and Friday.
Breadsall, *Booth*, Dolphin, Queen Street, every day except Sunday.
Breaston, *Cooke*, Dolphin, Queen Street, Friday.
————, *Robinson*, Talbot, Iron Gate, Friday.
Breedon, *Rowlson*, White Swan, St. Peter's Street, Tuesday and Friday.
————, *Earp*, Angel, Corn Market, every day except Sunday.
Brindsley, *Searson*, White Swan, St. Peter's Street, Friday.
Bull Bridge, *Bowmer*, Rose and Crown, Corn Market, Friday.
Burnaston, *Dicken*, Thorn Tree, St. Peter's Street, Friday.
————, *Greaves*, Nag's Head, St. Peter's Street, Monday, Wednesday, & Friday.
Burton, *Dicken*, Thorn Tree, St. Peter's Street, Friday.
————, *Gilbert*, Thorn Tree, St. Peter's Street, Tuesday and Friday.
————, *Upton*, Thorn Tree, St. Peter's Street, Tuesday and Friday.
————, *Briscoe*, Talbot, Iron Gate, Monday, Wednesday, and Friday.
————, *Smith*, Corn Market, daily.
————, *Salt*, Rose and Crown, Corn Market, Monday, Wednesday, and Friday.
————, *Potter*, Talbot, Mail Gig, daily.
Butterley, *Kemp*, Angel, Corn Market, Monday, Wednesday, and Friday.
————, *Bacon*, Thorn Tree, Monday, Wednesday, and Friday.
Buxton, *Frost*, Dog and Partridge, Tenant Street, Tuesday and Friday.
Calke, *Earp*, Angel, Corn Market, every day except Sunday.
Castle Donnington, *A. Smith*, Thorn Tree, Tuesday and Friday.
————, *Fisher*, Rose and Crown, Tuesday and Friday.
Cavendish Bridge, *A. Smith*, Thorn Tree, Tuesday and Friday.
Chaddesden, *Barnes' Van*, Warehouse, Green Lane, every morning at four o'clock, except Sunday.
————, *Holden*, Dolphin, Queen Street, every day except Sunday.
————, *Barton*, White Hart, Bridge Gate, Friday.
Chesterfield, *Bacon*, Thorn Tree, St. Peter's Street, Monday, Wednesday & Friday.
————, *Bacon*, Thorn Tree, Tuesday, Thursday, and Saturday.
————, *Kemp*, Angel, Monday, Wednesday, and Friday.
Chilwell, *A. Smith*, Thorn Tree, St. Peter's Street, Monday, Wednesday, & Friday.
Church Broughton, *Cook*, Thorn Tree, St. Peter's Street, Friday.
————, *Adams*, Rose and Crown, Corn Market, Friday.
————, *Turner*, Spotted Horse, Victoria street, Friday.

Church Gresley, *Elverson*, Green Man, St. Peter's Street, Tuesday and Friday.
————————, *Gilbert*, Thorn Tree, Tuesday and Friday.
Claycross, *Bacon*, Thorn Tree, Monday, Wednesday, and Friday.
Clay Mills, *Baldwin*, Saracen's Head, St. James's Lane, Friday.
Codnor, *Eyre*, Dolphin, Queen Street, Friday.
————, *Allen*, Victoria Street, Friday.
Coleorton, *Rowlson*, White Swan, St. Peter's Street, Tuesday and Friday.
Cotmanhay, *Holmes*, Dolphin, Queen Street, Friday.
Coton, *Briscoe*, Talbot, Monday, Wednesday, and Friday.
Cow's Lane, *Frost*, Dog and Partridge, Tuesday and Friday.
Crapper, *Maskery*, Horse and Jockey, Friday.
Chellaston, *Smith*, Saracen's Head, St. James's Lane, Monday, Wednesday, and
        Friday.
————————, *Ward*, Saracen's Head, St. James's Lane, every day except Sunday.
————————, *Toplis*, Angel, Corn Market, Monday, Wednesday, and Friday.
————————, *Earp*, Angel, Corn Market, every day except Sunday.
———— —, *Gilbert*, Thorn Tree, St. Peter's Street, Tuesday and Friday.
————————, *Sharpe*, Nag's Head, St. Peter's Street, Friday.
————————, *Cox*, Thorn Tree, St. Peter's Street, Friday.
————————, *Bates*, Dog and Partridge, Tuesday and Friday.
————————, *Elverson*, Green Man, St. Peter's Street, Tuesday and Friday.
Cheadle, *Upton*, Thorn Tree, St. Peter's Street, Tuesday and Friday.
————, *Coxon*, Saracen's Head, uncertain, but generally Thursday and Saturday.
———, *Atkins*, Spotted Horse, Victoria Street, Friday.
Coventry, *Smith*, Corn Market, daily.
Crich, *Bowmer*, Rose and Crown, Corn Market, Friday.
Cromford, *Allsop*, Telegraph, Morledge, Friday.
————, *Brinsley*, Nag's Head, St. Peter's Street, Wednesday.
————, *Stevenson*, Canal Tavern, every day except Sunday.
————, *Weston*, Talbot, Iron Gate, Monday, Wednesday, and Friday.
————, *Frost*, Dog and Partridge, Tenant Street, Tuesday and Friday.
Coxbench, *Bacon*, Thorn Tree, Monday, Wednesday, and Friday.
————, *Searson*, White Swan, St. Peter's Street, Friday.
————, *Webster*, Nag's Head, every day except Sunday.
————, *Kemp*, Angel, Corn Market, Monday, Wednesday, and Friday.
Cubley, *Roberts*, Rising Sun, Friar Gate, Friday.
————, *Turner*, from Dimmock's, Victoria Street, Monday and Friday.
Dale Abbey, *Barton*, White Hart, Bridge Gate, Friday.
Dalbury Lees, *Shaw*, Thorn Tree, St. Peter's Street, Friday.
————————, *Maskery*, Horse and Jockey, Sadler Gate, Friday.
Denby, *Kemp*, Angel, Corn Market, Monday, Wednesday, and Friday.
————, *Fisher*, Fox and Owl, Bridge Gate, Wednesday and Friday.
Diseworth, *Smith*, Thorn Tree, St. Peter's Street, Tuesday and Friday.
Dishley, *Tinkler*, Rose and Crown, Corn Market, Tuesday and Friday.
Doveridge, *Dawson*, New Inn, King Street, Monday, Wednesday, and Friday.
————, *Roberts*, Nag's Head and New Inn, Tuesday, Thursday, and Saturday.
————, *Upton*, Thorn Tree, St. Peter's Street, Tuesday and Friday.
————, *Coates*, Nag's Head, St. Peter's Street, Tuesday and Friday.
————, *Wilson*, Nag's Head, St. Peter's Street, Thursday and Saturday.
Draycott, *Astle*, Angel, Corn Market, Friday.
————, *Cooke*, Dolphin, Queen Street, Friday.
Duffield, *Brinsley*, Nag's Head, St. Peter's Street, Wednesday.
————, *Beeston*, Dolphin, Queen Street, Monday, Wednesday, and Friday.
————, *Frost*, Dog and Partridge, Tenant Street, Tuesday and Friday.
————, *Batty*, Talbot Inn, Iron Gate, Friday.
————, *Weston*, Talbot Inn, Iron Gate, Monday, Wednesday, and Friday.
————, *Allsop*, Telegraph, Morledge, Friday.
————, *Pickard*, Saracen's Head, St. James's Lane, Monday, Wednesday, and
        Friday.
Duffield, *Watson*, Flower Pot, King Street, every day except Sunday.
Dovecliff, *Coates*, Nag's Head, St. Peter's Street, Tuesday and Friday.
Eastwood, *Holden*, Dolphin, Queen Street, every day except Sunday.

Eastwood, *Searson*, White Swan, St. Peter's Street, Friday.
Egginton, *Dicken*, Thorn Tree, St. Peter's Street, Friday.
—— ——, *Baldwin*, Saracen's Head, St. James's Lane, Friday.
————, *Briscoe*, Talbot, Iron Gate, Monday, Wednesday, and Friday.
————, *Salt*, Rose and Crown, Corn Market, Monday, Wednesday, and Friday.
Elvaston, *Fisher*, Rose and Crown, Corn Market, Monday, Wednesday, and Friday.
———, *Smith*, Thorn Tree, St. Peter's Street, Tuesday and Friday.
Etwall, *Dawson*, New Inn, King Street, Monday, Wednesday, and Friday.
———, *Roberts*, Nag's Head, Tuesday, Thursday, and Saturday.
———, *Hollis*, Saracen's Head, St. James's Lane, Tuesday and Friday.
———, *Coxon*, Saracen's Head, St. James's Lane, Thursday and Saturday.
———, *Cooke*, Thorn Tree, St. Peter's Street, Friday.
———, *Yeomans*, Talbot, Iron Gate, Tuesday and Friday.
———, *Hunt*, Rose and Crown, Corn Market, Monday and Friday.
———, *Upton*, Thorn Tree, St. Peter's Street, Tuesday and Friday.
Findern, *Dicken*, Rose and Crown, Corn Market, Friday.
Foston, *Cooke*, Thorn Tree, St. Peter's Street, Friday.
———, *Upton*, Thorn Tree, St Peter's Street, Friday.
———, *Dawson*, New Inn, King Street, Monday, Wednesday, and Friday.
———, *Roberts*, Nag's Head, and New Inn, Tuesday, Thursday, and Saturday.
Foremark, *Greaves*, Nag's Head, St. Peter's Street, Monday, Wednesday, and Friday.
Fritchley, *Leam*, Rose and Crown, Corn Market, Friday.
Garendon, *Tinkler*, Rose and Crown, Corn Market, Tuesday and Friday.
Hartshorne, *Gilbert*, Thorn Tree, St. Peter's Street, Tuesday and Friday.
————, *Elverson*, Green Man, St. Peter's Street, Tuesday and Friday.
Hatton, *Bates*, Thorn Tree, St. Peter's Street, Friday.
———, *Upton*, Thorn Tree, St. Peter's Street, Tuesday and Friday.
———, *Yeamans*, Talbot, Iron Gate, Tuesday and Friday.
———, *Cooke*, Thorn Tree, St. Peter's Street, Friday.
Hathern, *Tinkler*, Rose and Crown, Corn Market, Tuesday and Friday.
Hathersage, *Frost*, Dog and Partridge, Tenant Street, Tuesday and Friday.
————, *Weston*, Talbot, Iron Gate, Monday, Wednesday, and Friday.
Heage, *Webster*, Nag's Head, St. Peter's Street, every day except Sunday.
Heanor, *Holmes*, Dolphin, Queen Street, Friday.
———, *Holden*, Dolphin, Queen Street, every day except Sunday.
———, *Eyre*, Dolphin, Queen Street, Friday.
———, *Nelson*, Bull's Head, Queen Street, Friday.
———, *Searson*, White Swan, St. Peter's Street, Friday.
Hemington, *A. Smith*, Thorn Tree, St. Peter's Street, Tuesday and Friday.
Higham, *Bacon*, Thorn Tree, St. Peter's Street, Monday, Wednesday, and Friday.
Hilton, *Yeomans*, Talbot, Iron Gate, Tuesday and Friday.
———, *Hunt*, Rose and Crown, Corn Market, Monday and Friday.
———, *Upton*, Thorn Tree, St. Peter's Street, Tuesday and Friday.
———, *Dawson*, New Inn, King Street, Monday, Wednesday, and Friday.
———, *Roberts*, Nag's Head and New Inn, Tuesday, Thursday, and Saturday.
———, *Cooke*, Thorn Tree, St. Peter's Street, Friday.
Hognaston, *Hardy*, Robin Hood, Iron Gate, Friday.
————, *Cooper*, White Hart, Bridge Gate, Friday.
————, *Woodhouse*, Shakspeare, Sadler Gate, Friday.
Horsley, *Fisher*, Fox and Owl, Bridge Gate, Wednesday and Friday.
———, *Searson*, White Swan, St. Peter's Street, Friday.
Horsley Woodhouse, *Searson*, White Swan, St. Peter's Street, Friday.
————————, *Booth*, Dolphin, Queen Street, every day except Sunday.
Holbrooke, *Fisher*, Fox and Owl, Bridge Gate, Wednesday and Friday.
Horninglow, *Salt*, Rose and Crown, Corn Market, Monday, Wednesday, and Friday.
Hulland Ward, *Cooper*, White Hart, Bridge Gate, Tuesday and Friday.
Ideridge Hay, *Pickard*, Saracen's Head, Monday, Wednesday, and Friday.
Ilkeston, *Burrowes*, Bull's Head, Queen Street, Friday.
———, *Holmes*, Dolphin, Queen Street, Friday.
———, *Hunt*, Fox and Owl, Bridge Gate, Friday.
Ingleby, *Smith*, Saracen's Head, St. James's Lane, Wednesday.

Ireton, *Wooton*, Talbot, Iron Gate, Friday.
Kedleston, *Cooper*, White Hart, Bridge Gate, Friday.
———, *Woodhouse*, Shakspeare, Sadler Gate, Friday.
Kegworth, *Tinkler*, Rose and Crown, Corn Market, Tuesday and Friday.
———, *Mee*, Rose and Crown, Friday.
———, *Smith*, Thorn Tree, St. Peter's Street, Tuesday and Friday.
———, *Prince*, Morledge, Mail Gig every morning.
Kilburne, *Fisher*, Fox and Owl, Bridge Gate, Wednesday and Friday.
———, *Bacon*, Thorn Tree, St. Peter's Street, Monday, Wednesday, and Friday.
———, *Kemp*, Angel, Corn Market, Monday, Wednesday, and Friday.
King's Mills, *Fisher*, Rose and Crown, Corn Market, Tuesday and Friday.
King's Newton, *Earp*, Angel, Corn Market, every day except Sunday.
———, *Ward*, Saracen's Head, St. James's Lane, every day except Sunday.
Langley, *Bridden*, Black Swan, Siddals Lane, Monday, Wednesday, and Friday.
Langley Mills, *Atkinson*, Dolphin, Tuesday, Friday, and Saturday.
Lane End, *Dawson*, New Inn, King Street, Monday, Wednesday, and Friday.
———, *Roberts*, New Inn, King Street, Tuesday, Thursday, and Saturday.
Leicester, *Tinkler*, Rose and Crown, Tuesday and Friday.
Lenton, *Barne's Van*, Warehouse, Green Lane, every morning at four o'clock, Sundays excepted.
Lichfield, *Smith*, Rodney yard, daily.
Little Eaton, *Kemp*, Angel, Corn Market, Monday, Wednesday, and Friday.
———, *Fisher*, Fox and Owl, Bridge Gate, Wednesday and Friday.
———, *Bacon*, Thorn Tree, St. Peter's Street, Monday, Wednesday, and Friday.
———, *Searson*, White Swan, St. Peter's Street, Friday.
Littleover, *Greaves*, Nag's Head, St. Peter's Street, Monday, Wednesday, and Friday.
———, *Dicken*, Thorn Tree, St. Peter's Street, Friday.
———, *Salt*, Rose and Crown, Corn Market, Monday, Wednesday, and Friday.
Lockington, *A. Smith*, Thorn Tree, Tuesday and Friday.
Locko, *Cope*, Dog and Partridge, Tenant Street, Tuesday and Friday.
Long Eaton, *Smith*, Thorn Tree, St. Peter's Street, Tuesday and Friday.
———, *Cooke*, Dolphin, Queen Street, Friday.
Longford, *Bull*, Robin Hood, Iron Gate, Friday.
———, *Tipper*, Queen's Head, Victoria Street, Friday.
———, *Millward*, Royal Oak, Market Place, Friday.
Loscoe, *Holden*, Dolphin, Queen Street, every day except Sunday.
———, *Eyre*, Dolphin, Queen Street, Friday.
———, *Nelson*, Dolphin, Queen Street, Friday.
———, *Hogg*, Bull's Head, Queen Street, Friday.
Loughborough, *Tinkler*, Rose and Crown, Corn Market, Tuesday and Friday.
———, *Smith*, Thorn Tree, St. Peter's Street, Tuesday and Friday.
———, *Ward*, Saracen's Head, St. James's Lane, Friday.
Lount, *Earp*, Angel, every day except Sunday.
Lullington, *Briscoe*, Talbot, Monday, Wednesday, and Friday.
Mackworth, *Bridden*, Black Swan, Siddals Lane, Monday, Wednesday, and Friday.
Mansfield, *Bacon*, Thorn Tree, St. Peter's Street, Monday, Wednesday, and Friday.
———, *Barnes*, Green Lane, every morning at four o'clock, Sundays excepted.
Manchester, *Pickford and Co's.* Van, from Siddals Lane, daily.
Mapperley, *Hunt*, Fox and Owl, Bridge Gate, Friday.
———, *Holden*, Dolphin, Queen Street, every day except Sunday.
Marlpool, *Holden*, Dolphin, Queen Street, every day except Sunday.
Matlock, *Brinsley*, Nag's Head, St. Peter's Street, Wednesday.
———, *Stevenson*, Canal Tavern, Cockpit Hill, every day except Sunday.
———, *Paling*, Saracen's Head, Friday.
———, *Frost*, Dog and Partridge, Tenant Street, Tuesday and Friday.
———, *Weston*, Talbot, Iron Gate, Monday, Wednesday, and Friday.
———, *Allsop*, Telegraph, Morledge, Friday.
Melbourne, *Earp*, Angel, Corn Market, every day except Sunday.
———, *Ward*, Saracen's Head, Monday, Wednesday, and Friday.
———, *Smith*, Rodney Yard, daily.

Melbourne, *Rowlson*, White Swan, St. Peter's Street, Tuesday and Friday.
Mickleover, *Yeomans*, Talbot, Iron Gate, Tuesday and Friday.
———— ——, *Upton*, Thorn Tree, St. Peter's Street, Tuesday and Friday.
———— ——, *Hunt*, Rose and Crown, Corn Market, Monday and Friday.
———— ——, *Dawson*, New Inn, King Street, Monday, Wednesday, and Friday.
———— ——, *Roberts*, Nag's Head and New Inn, Tuesday, Thursday, and Saturday.
—— ——, *Hollis*, Saracen's Head, St. James's Lane, Monday and Friday.
———— ——, *Coxon*, Saracen's Head, St. James's Lane, uncertain, but generally
Thursday and Saturday.
———— ——, *Cooke*, Thorn Tree, St. Peter's Street, Friday.
Middleton, *Allsop*, Telegraph, Morledge, Friday.
Milford, *Watson*, Flower Pot, King Street, every day except Sunday.
——, *Webster*, Thorn Tree, St. Peter's Street, every day except Sunday.
Milton, *Greaves*, Nag's Head, St. Peter's Street, Monday, Wednesday, and Friday.
Morley, *Eyre*, Dolphin, Queen Street, Friday.
——, *Booth*, Dolphin, Queen Street, every day except Sunday.
——, *Nelson*, Bull's Head, Queen Street, Friday.
——, *Hogg*, Bull's Head, Queen Street, Friday.
——, *Holmes*, Dolphin, Queen Street, Friday.
Mugginton, *Hardy*, Robin Hood, Iron Gate, Friday.
——— ——, *Cooper*, White Hart, Bridge Gate, Friday.
Newbold, *Rowlson*, White Swan, St. Peter's Street, Tuesday and Friday.
——— ——, *Earp*, Angel, Corn Market, every day except Sunday.
Newhall, *Elverson*, Green Man, St. Peter's Street, Tuesday and Friday.
—— ——, *Gilbert*, Thorn Tree, St. Peter's Street, Tuesday and Friday.
Newcastle, *Roberts*, New Inn, King Street, Tuesday, Thursday, and Saturday.
Nottingham, *Barnes*' *Van*, Warehouse, Green Lane, every morning at four o'clock,
Sundays excepted.
Normanton, *Stevenson*, Green Man, Friday.
Ockbrook, *Cope*, Dog and Partridge, Tenant Street, Tuesday and Friday.
Pastures, *Salt*, Rose and Crown, Corn Market, Monday, Wednesday, and Friday.
Painter's Lane, *Bridden*, Black Swan, Siddals Lane, Monday, Wednesday, & Friday.
Priory, *Booth*, Dolphin, Queen Street, every day except Sunday.
Quorndon, *Clifford*, Robin Hood, Iron Gate, every day except Sunday.
——— ——, *Cooper*, White Hart, Bridge Gate, Friday.
Radbourne, *Shaw*, Thorn Tree, St. Peter's Street, Friday.
Repton, *Greaves*, Nag's Head, St. Peter's Street, Monday, Wednesday, and Friday.
Riddings, *Bacon*, Thorn Tree, St. Peter's Street, Monday, Wednesday, and Friday.
Ripley, *Bacon*, Thorn Tree, St. Peter's Street, Monday, Wednesday, and Friday.
——, *Kemp*, Angel, Corn Market, Monday, Wednesday, and Friday.
——— ——, *Whysall*, Nag's Head, Tuesday and Friday.
Risley, *Barnes*' *Van*, Green Lane, every morning at four o'clock, except Sunday.
Rosliston, *Briscoe*, Talbot, Iron Gate, Monday, Wednesday, and Friday.
Roston, *Froggatt*, Rising Sun, Friday.
Rowlson, *Coates*, Nag's Head, St. Peter's Street, Tuesday and Friday.
Sandiacre, *Barnes*' *Van*, Green Lane, every morning at four o'clock except Sunday.
——, *Barton*, White Hart, Bridge Gate, Friday.
Sawley, *Cook*, Dolphin, Queen Street, Friday.
——, *A. Smith*, Thorn Tree, St. Peter's Street, Tuesday and Friday.
Scropton, *Cook*, Thorn Tree, St. Peter's Street, Friday.
Shardlow, *A. Smith*, Thorn Tree, St. Peter's Street, Tuesday and Friday.
——, *Fisher*, Rose and Crown, Corn Market, Tuesday and Friday.
Sheffield, *Bacon*, Thorn Tree, Monday, Wednesday, and Friday.
Shipley, *Holden*, Dolphin, Queen Street, daily.
Shirland, *Bacon*, Thorn Tree, Monday, Wednesday, and Friday.
Shirley, *Bridden*, Black Swan, Siddals Lane, Monday, Wednesday, and Friday.
Shottle, *Weston*, Talbot, Iron Gate, Monday, Wednesday, and Friday.
Smalley, *Booth*, Dolphin, Queen Street, every day except Sunday.
——, *Eyre*, Dolphin, Queen Street, Friday.
——, *Nelson*, Bull's Head, Queen Street, Friday.
——, *Cook*, Dolphin, Queen Street, Friday.

Smalley, *Holmes*, Dolphin, Queen Street, Friday.
Smisby, *Cox*, Thorn Tree, St. Peter's Street, Friday.
———, *Smith*, Corn Market, daily.
———, *Pegg*, Nag's head, every day except Sunday.
Sommershall, *Upton*, Thorn Tree, St. Peter's Street, Tuesday and Friday.
Spath, *Maskery*, Horse and Jockey, Sadler Gate, Friday.
Spondon, *Joyce*, Royal Oak, Market Place, Friday.
———, *Cope*, Dog and Partridge, Tenant Street, Tuesday and Friday.
———, *Robinson*, Talbot, Iron Gate, Friday.
———, *Burrowes*, Dolphin, Queen Street, Friday.
Stafford, *Upton*, Thorn Tree, St Peter's Street, Tuesday and Friday.
Staffordshire Potteries, *Upton*, Thorn Tree, St. Peter's Street, Tuesday and Friday.
Stanley, *Holden*, Dolphin, Queen Street, every day except Sunday.
———, *Hunt*, Fox and Owl, Bridge Gate, Friday.
Stanton-by-Bridge, *Earp*, Angel, Corn Market, every day except Sunday.
———, *Ward*, Saracen's Head, St. James's Lane, every day except Sunday.
———, *Elverson*, Green Man, St. Peter's Street, Tuesday and Friday.
———, *Toplis*, Angel, Corn Market, Monday, Wednesday, and Friday.
Stanton-by-Dale, *Hunt*, Fox and Owl, Bridge Gate, Friday.
Stapenhill, *Briscoe*, Talbot, Iron Gate, Monday, Wednesday, and Friday.
Stapleford, *Barnes' Van*, Green Lane, every morning at four o'clock, except Sunday.
Staunton-Harold, *Earp*, Angel, Corn Market, every day except Sunday.
Stoke, *Dawson*, New Inn, King Street, Monday, Wednesday, and Friday.
———, *Roberts*, Nag's Head, and New Inn, Tuesday, Thursday, and Saturday.
Stretton, *Dicken*, Thorn Tree, St. Peter's Street, Friday.
———, *Salt*, Rose and Crown, Corn Market, Monday, Wednesday, and Friday.
———, *Briscoe*, Talbot, Iron Gate, Monday, Wednesday, and Friday.
Sudbury, *Coates*, Nag's Head, St. Peter's Street, Tuesday and Friday.
———, *Upton*, Thorn Tree, St. Peter's Street, Tuesday and Friday.
———, *Cook*, Thorn Tree, St. Peter's Street, Friday.
———, *Dawson*, New Inn, King Street, Monday, Wednesday, and Friday.
———, *Roberts*, New Inn, King Street, Tuesday, Thursday, and Saturday.
———, *Coxon*, Saracen's Head, uncertain, but generally Thursday and Saturday.
Sutton-on-the-Hill, *Shaw*, Thorn Tree, St. Peter's Street, Friday.
———, *Allen*, Shakspeare, Sadler Gate, Monday, Wednesday, & Friday.
———, *Maskery*, Horse and Jockey, Sadler Gate, Friday.
Swadlincote, *Elverson*, Green Man, St. Peter's Street, Tuesday and Friday.
———, *Gilbert*, Thorn Tree, Tuesday and Friday.
Swanwick, *Kemp*, Angel, Corn Market, Monday, Wednesday, and Friday.
———, *Bacon*, Thorn Tree, St. Peter's Street, Monday, Wednesday, & Friday.
Swarkeston, *Smith*, Saracen's Head, St. James's Lane, Monday, Wednesday, and
    Friday.
———, *Pegg*, Nag's Head, every day except Sunday.
———, *Earp*, Angel, Corn Market, every day except Sunday.
———, *Ward*, Saracen's Head, St. James's Lane, every day except Sunday.
———, *Toplis*, Angel, Corn Market, Monday, Wednesday, and Friday.
———. *Gilbert*, Thorn Tree, St. Peter's Street, Tuesday and Friday.
———, *Elverson*, Green Man, St. Peter's Street, Tuesday and Friday.
———, *Sharpe*, Nag's Head, St. Peter's Street, Tuesday and Friday.
———, *Bates*, Dog and Partridge, Tuesday and Friday.
———, *Smith*, Corn Market, daily.
Tean, *Dawson*, New Inn, King Street, Monday, Wednesday, and Friday.
———, *Roberts*, Nag's Head and New Inn, Tuesday, Thursday, and Saturday.
Thringstone, *Rowlson*, White Swan, St. Peter's Street, Tuesday and Friday.
Thulston, *Fisher*, Rose and Crown, Tuesday and Friday.
———, *A. Smith*, Thorn Tree, St. Peter's Street, Tuesday and Friday.
Ticknall, *Smith*, Saracen's Head, St. James's Lane, Monday, Wednesday, and
    Friday.
———, *Gilbert*, Thorn Tree, St. Peter's Street, Tuesday and Friday.
———, *Cox*, Thorn Tree, St. Peter's Street, Tuesday and Friday.
———, *Elverson*, Green Man, St. Peter's Street, Tuesday and Friday.
———, *Toplis*, Angel, Corn Market, Monday, Wednesday, and Friday.

Ticknall, *Cox*, Thorn Tree, St. Peter's Street, Friday.
————, *Smith*, *Charles*, Corn Market, daily.
Tutbury, *Coates*, Nag's Head, St. Peter's Street, Tuesday and Friday.
————, *Upton*, Thorn Tree, St. Peter's Street, Tuesday and Friday.
————, *Yeamans*, Talbot, Iron Gate, Tuesday and Friday.
Trowel, *Hunt*, Fox and Owl, Bridge Gate, Friday.
Trusley, *Shaw*, Thorn Tree, St. Peter's Street, Friday.
————, *Maskery*, Horse and Jockey, Friday.
Uttoxeter, *Coxon*, Saracen's Head, St. James's Lane, Thursday and Saturday.
————, *Cook*, Thorn Tree, St. Peter's Street, Friday.
————, *Coates*, Nag's Head, St. Peter's Street, Tuesday and Friday.
————, *Dawson*, New Inn, King Street, Monday, Wednesday, and Friday.
————, *Upton*, Thorn Tree, St. Peter's Street, Tuesday and Friday.
————, *Roberts*, Nag's Head, Tuesday, Thursday, and Saturday.
Walton, *Briscoe*, Talbot, Iron Gate, Monday, Wednesday. and Friday.
Whatton House, *Tinkler*, Rose and Crown, Corn Market, Tuesday and Friday.
Weston Underwood, *Woodhouse*, Shakspeare, Sadler Gate, Friday.
West Hallam, *Holden*, Dolphin, Queen Street, every day except Sunday.
————————, *Hunt*, Fox and Owl, Bridge Gate, Friday.
Willington, *Greaves*, Nag's Head, St. Peter's Street, Monday, Wednesday, and Friday.
————————, *Dicken*, Thorn Tree, St. Peter's Street, Friday.
Wilson, *Earp*, Angel, Corn Market, every day except Sunday.
————, *Rowlson*, White Swan, St. Peter's Street, Tuesday and Friday.
Windley, *Pickard*, Saracen's Head, St. James's Lane, Monday, Wednesday, and Friday.
Wirksworth, *Pickard*, Saracen's Head, St. James's Lane, Monday, Wednesday, and Friday.
————, *Weston*, Talbot, Iron Gate, Monday, Wednesday, and Friday.
————, *Stevenson*, Canal Tavern, Cockpit Hill, every day except Sunday.
————, *Allsopp*, Telegraph, Morledge, Friday.
————, *Frost*, Dog and Partridge, Tenant Street, Tuesday and Friday.
Wittick, *Rowlson*, White Swan, St. Peter's Street, Tuesday and Friday.
Wooden-Box, *Gilbert*, Thorn Tree, St. Peter's Street, Tuesday and Friday.
————, *Elverson*, Green Man, St. Peter's Street, Tuesday and Friday.
Woollaston, *Hunt*, Fox and Owl, Bridge Gate, Friday.
Watstandwell Bridge, *Brinsley*, Nag's Head, St. Peter's Street, Wednesday.
Worthington, *Rowlson*, White Swan, St. Peter's Street, Tuesday and Friday.

Derbyshire is 56 miles in length, 34 in breadth, and 130 in circumference ; contains 1,026 square miles ; 656,640 statute acres ; it is divided into 6 hundreds, 116 parishes, and 10 market towns.

INDEX OF DISTANCES FROM TOWNS IN THE COUNTY OF DERBY.

The names of the respective Towns are on the top and side, and the squares where both meet give the distance.

		Distance from London
	Alfreton, FRI.	140
Ashbourn	17 Ashbourn, SAT.	139
Bakewell	15 16 Bakewell, FRI.	153
Belper	8 12 18 Belper, SAT.	134
Bolsover	11 24 18 16 Bolsover	145
Buxton	25 20 12 28 29 Buxton, SAT.	160
Castleton	24 28 12 28 26 10 Castleton	164
Chapel-en-le-Frith	28 26 14 30 29 6 7 Chapel-en-le-Frith, THURS.	167
Chesterfield	10 22 12 16 6 24 17 23 Chesterfield, SAT.	150
DERBY**	14 13 26 8 24 33 38 40 24 DERBY, TUES. and FRI.	126
Dronfield	15 27 11 22 9 23 14 20 6 29 Dronfield	156
Matlock Bath	11 14 10 8 12 22 22 24 12 16 18 Matlock Bath......	143
Tideswell	23 19 7 23 23 6 5 7 16 32 15 15 Tideswell, WED.	160
Winster	12 10 6 11 17 15 16 18 13 22 16 4 12 Winster, SAT.	145
Wirksworth	9 9 11 6 16 20 21 23 14 14 17 16 3 17 5 Wirks. TUES.	139

The Asterisks (*) attached to the name of the Town denote the number of Representatives returned to Parliament, and the Small Capital Letters signify the Market Days.

Burgesses not included in the first Alphabetical arrangement, and additions during the time the work has been in the press.

Abbot, John	Draper	Sadler gate	
Adams, James	Overlooker at Bridgett's Mill	Mansfield road	B
Adams, Charles	Framework-knitter	Normanton road	B
Allen, Joseph	Manager at Frost and Stevenson's	6, Darwin terrace	B
Allen, William	Fitter-up	Mansfield road	B
Allcock, Thomas	Bricklayer	William street	B
Allsebrook, Joseph	Huckster	Brook street	B
Allport, James J. esq.	Agent to the Birmingham Railway Co.	Derby station	
Akers, William	Lacehand	4, Goodwin street	B
Appleby, John	Labourer	16, Bloom street	
Armstrong, George	Shopkeeper	10, Walker lane	
Ashmore, Jeremiah	Servant	Osmaston street	
Ault, Samuel	Labourer	5, Bridge gate	
Allkin, William	Painter	Castle street	
Bagley, Thomas	Smith at railway	Sitwell street	
Ball, Matthew	Labourer	St. James's lane	
Barnsby, William	Compositor	Wilmot street	B
Barson, William	Huckster	8, Sadler gate	
Banser, William	Brickmaker	Court, Darley lane	
Bettison, Joseph Widnall	Beerseller	Canal street	B
Biddle, John	Weaver	28, Full street	
Bingham, Joseph	Warehouseman	12, St. Mary's gate	B
Birkin, Richard	Shoemaker	38, Darley lane	
Blackwall, John	works at Lead mill	Leonard street	
Blackwall, Thomas	works at Foundry	Exeter place	
Blood, Thomas	Breeches maker	Wardwick	B
Bonnington, James	Lace hand	17, Fowler street	
Bolsover, Samuel	Pawnbroker	Queen street	B
Botham, James	Cooper	5, Erasmus street	
Bonam, William	Collector of debts	St. Peter's church yard	
Bowler, William	Gardener	Sacheverel street	
Brown, Edward	Horsebreaker	Siddals lane	
Brentnall, James	Confectioner	St. Peter's street	B
Briggs, George, and George	Drapers	St. Peter's bridge	
Briggs, Mary & Sarah	Grocers and tea-dealers	Traffic street	
Bromley, Robert	Land agent and surveyor, and agent to the Atlas Insurance Co.	London street	
Budworth, Thomas	Shoemaker	Siddals lane	
Budworth, James	Tobacconist	London road	
Bullock, John	Huckster	Brook street	
Burke, Frederick	Victualler	St. Peter's street	
Burrows, William	Framework-knitter	Court 3, Hill street	
Butler, William	Butcher	New market	B

Burnett, James	Corn miller	Nuns' street	
Buxton, Anthony	Joiner	Mansfield road	B
Carrington, James	Tailor	35, Agard street	
Carwithin, John	Tailor	19, Orchard street	B
Cay, Joseph	Jeweller	Traffic street	
Cheetham, John	Joiner	Mansfield road	B
Chester, Richard	Fitter-up	Canal street	
Cholerton, Matthew	Upholsterer	Queen street	
Clarke, Joseph	Porter at Station	Traffic street	B
Clarke, Frederick	Joiner	Hill street	B
Clulow, John	Shopkeeper	Osmaston street	B
Collumbell, William	Tailor	Goodwin street	B
Collumbell, Edward	Basket maker	King street	
Cooke, Thomas	Gentleman	Park street	
Cockayne, William	Butcher	New market	
Cook, Thomas	Grocer	Parker street	B
Cooke, Isaac	Shoemaker	Traffic street	
Cook, Henry	Traveller	Normanton road	B
Cooke, James	Hatter	Forester street	B
Corden, John	Stamp distributor	Osmaston road	
Cowlishaw, James	Builder and Surveyor	London road	B
Cowlishaw, Jas. & John	Wheelwrights	London road	
Cox, Mrs. John		Friar gate	
Cox, Miss		Friar gate	
Cross, Frederick	Joiner	George street	B
Crown, Daniel	Silkweaver	Green lane	B
Crooks, Paul	Moulder	32, Erasmus street	
Cresswell, William	Blacksmith	Darley lane	
Cuppleditch, William	Overlooker	2, Bridge street	
Dawson, Gregory	Beerseller	John street	B
Dewick, William	Shopkeeper	Sacheverel street	B
Doe, Joseph	Dyer	Nun's street	
Draper, William	Tailor	Darley lane	
Drewry, Mrs.		Tenant street	
Dyson, James Thomas	Bookkeeper	Normanton road	B
Eaton, George	Gentleman	Park street	
Eccleshaw, Edward	Strawbonnet maker	12, Brook street	
Eggleston, Joseph	Gardener	Normanton road	B
Eccleshaw, William	Framework knitter	Agard street	
Eld, Mrs.		Friar gate	
Ellis, John		Chaddesden hill	
Elliott, William	Works at Lead mill	Normanton road	B
Elliott, William	Coachman	Green lane	
Eyre, Samuel	Gentleman	54, Sadler gate	B
Eyre, James	Silk hand	Full street	
Elwall, Thomas	J. joiner	4, Nun's street	
Eley, Samuel	Labourer	7, Ford street	
Faulkner, John	Victualler, Seven Stars	Nottingham road	
Farrel, Roger	Lodging house	Bag lane	
Fearn, William	Works at railway	Traffic street	
Fearn, Robert	China Painter	Upper Brook street	
Fearn, Richard	Fitter-up	Mansfield road	

Flavell, William	Shoemaker	80, Bridge street	
Ford, William	Gardener	Friar gate	B
Ford, Matthew	Shoemaker	Darley lane	
Frost, Thomas	Moulder	Hope street	
Furniss, William	Grocer	Nun's street	
Freake, J. F.	Auctioneer & appraiser	St. Mary's gate	B
Gilman, George	Labourer	Waterloo street	
Gilbert, Edward	Moulder	Duke street	
Glazebrook, John	J. joiner	Traffic street	
Glover, Stephen & Son	Printers, publishers, auctioneers, valuers, accountants, general agents, landlord's bailiffs and messengers in Bankruptcies	Devonshire street	
Gill, Thomas	Clothier	Bold lane	
Haden, Richard W. esq.	Magistrate	Market place	
Hamilton, John	Surgeon	St. Mary's gate	B
Hanson, William, esq.	Superintendent North Midland Railway Station		
Hardy, William	Policeman	Sacheverel street	B
Hardy, Samuel	Policeman	Silk mill lane	
Hanson, Richard	Policeman	34, Bridge gate	
Hawkesworth, Samuel	Gardener	St. Alkmund's ch. yard	
Hardy, George	Engineer	10, Bath street	
Harvey, James	Framework-knitter	3, Nun's street	
Haynes, John	Shopkeeper	Wright street	
Hartmann, Charles	Pork butcher	Sadler gate	
Haskew, James	Draper	2, Iron gate	B
Hawkesworth Samuel	Framework-knitter	22, Rivett street	
Hawkridge, Thomas	Tailor and draper	King street	
Hardy, William	Silkhand	Mill street	
Hart, John	Gentleman	3, St. John's terrace	B
Heald, George	Gentleman	St. Helen's street	B
Hind, Charles	Horse dealer	Hope street	B
Hithersay, John	Dealer in lace and haberdasher	Iron gate	B
Hodgkinson, Henry	Fitter-up	Chester place	B
Holbrook, John	Modeller	Gisbourne street	
Holme, Daniel	Shoe warehouse	Corn market	B
Holmes, Brammel	Colour manufacturer	North parade	B
Hollins, Thomas	Brass founder	Devonshire street	
Howell, Richard	Engine driver	John street	
Hopkinson, James	Fitter-up	Burton road	B
Hill, John	General dealer	Willow row	
Hornshaw, Lewis	Whitesmith	Brook street	
Hobson, Isaac	Bookbinder	Cavendish street	
Hood, Henry	Gentleman	15, Osmaston street	B
Horton, David	Fitter-up	Bath street	
Hunt, John	Lock and whitesmith	St. Mary's gate	
Hunt, Edward	Baker	Market place	B
Hughes, Thomas	Tailor	Nun's street	

Humpstone, Joseph	Butcher	New market	B
Inott, Robert Cox	Hairdresser & perfumer	Rotten row	B
Ironmonger, Eli	Auctioneer	1, Friar gate	B
Jackson, John	Framework-knitter	Bridge street	
James, James	J. coach builder	35, Grove street	
Jankinson, Charles	J. joiner	Green street	
Johnson, William	Weaver	11, Fowler street	
Johnson, John	Overlooker	12, Parker street	B
Johnson, Charles		Canal side	
Keeling, John	Architect and building surveyor	Ashbourn road, office Iron gate	B
Kay, Robert Stanley	Brushmaker	Brook street	B
Kenny, Henry	Gentleman's servant	39, Full street	B
Kent, Charles	Draper	2, Iron gate	B
Kershaw, Robert V.	Stonemason	Duke street	B
Knight, Rhodas	Broker	12, Nun's street	
Knight, William Yates	Clerk at Station	London road	B
Kirby, John	Plasterer	Drewry lane	
Lee, John	J. joiner	34, Agard street	
Lakin, Robert	Shoemaker	Court 2, Hill street	
Large, John	Silkhand	Silk mill lane	
Littlewood, William	Joiner	Mansfield road	B
Lambert, Richard	Labourer	John street	
Langham, John	Smith at foundry	34, Devonshire street	
Lomas, George	Weaver	Castle place	
Loughenbury, Hugh	Moulder	Court 2, Bridge gate	
Longden, William	Baker	Short street	B
Lucey, Bartholomew C.	Gentleman	Park street	
Macklaier, George	Sadler	Queen street	B
Mason, John	Colourman	Ashbourne road	B
Marriott, Robert	Manager at Mr. Moss's	Osmaston street	B
Mason, John	Lodging house	Walker lane	
Marriott, James	Butcher	Upper Brook street	
Meynell, Thomas	Shopkeeper	Upper Brook street	
Miers, John	Joiner	24, Bridge street	B
Minion, Walker	Framework knitter	Court 9, Bridge gate	
Moseley, Joseph	Weaver	William street	
Morley, John	Works at China factory	Traffick street	
Neal, William	Fitter-up	John street	
Newbold and Egan	Surveyors, accountants, law stationers, estate and general agents	Iron gate	
Oakley, William	Timber merchant	Siddals lane	B
Oakes, George	Works at mill	Nun's street	
Otterwell, John	Cooper	6, Amen alley	
Odery, James	Tailor	Ford street	B
Ordish, Thomas	Labourer	Exeter street	
Orme, Joseph		2, River street	B
Owen, James	Baker	Traffick street	
Parkins, James	Tailor and draper	31, Exeter street	
Parker, George	Framework knitter	Drewry lane	
Partridge, Robert	Ticket collector	Siddals lane	

Peach, William James	J. Stonemason	Old Uttoxeter road	
Pearson, Thomas	Baker	Nun's street	
Pearson, Thomas	Bone cutter	30, Burton road	B
Perfect, George	Carver and gilder	10, Osmaston street	
Phillips, John	Clerk at station	Park street	
Pike, Isaac, jun.	Plasterer	15, Parker street	B
Poole, Edwin	Stonemason	Baker's lane	B
Potter, George	Butcher	New market	
Porter, James	J. joiner	Nottingham road	
Poulton, Thomas	Cross Keys Com. Inn	Corn market	
Pratt, John	Watchman	Bridge street	
Prince, Paul	Smith	Chester place	
Reedman, Wm. & Sons	Coal dealers	Ford street	
Richardson, Thomas	Shoemaker	2, Goodwin street	
Ride, Thomas	Shopkeeper	33, Agard street	B
Riley, Henry	Overlooker at silk mill	Agard street	
Robinson, Luke	Lace maker	St. Werburgh's ch. yd.	B
Robinson, John	Joiner	Wilmot street	
Robinson, Isaac	Framework knitter	Court 1, Burton road	
Robotham, John	Book-keeper	Morledge	
Roome, Joseph	Labourer	Searl street	B
Rowbotham, William	Attorney at law	College place	
Salt, John	Bricklayer	St. Helen's street	
Sandars, Francis	Land agent & surveyor	Full street	B
Sansom, William	Moulder	6, Erasmus street	
Severne, Mrs.		Osmaston road	
Sewell, William	Framework knitter	17, Bloom street	
Shaw, Samuel	Butcher	Sacheverel street	
Slater, John	Butcher	Brook street	
Sharpe, Edward	Joiner	Old Uttoxeter road	B
Sherlock, Thomas	Brickmaker	Ashbourn road	
Shilcock, Joseph	Draper	Iron gate	B
Shipley, Mary	Confectioner	Queen street	
Slack, Samuel	Milkseller	Bridge street	
Slater, John	Higgler	Wright street	
Slater, Thomas		43, Devonshire street	
Simmons, Samuel	Blacksmith	Walker lane	
Sims, James	Builder	Traffick street	B
Sims, James	Deputy governor of county gaol	Old Uttoxeter road	
Sims, William	Butcher	Burton road	
Simpson, Edward	Gentleman	31, Bridge gate	B
Simpson, George	Shoemaker	Castle street	
Simpson, George	Gentleman	Sadler gate	B
Smith, John	Victualler, Old Boat	Morledge	
Smith, Christopher	Framework-knitter	Court 9, Bridge gate	
Smith, Edmund	Broker	Bold lane	B
Smith, Charles	Mail gig contractor, and carrier to Melbourn, Ticknall, Smisby, and Ashby	Corn market	
Smith, Andrew	Engineer	Canal street	B

Smith, John	Traveller	7, Darwin terrace	B
Smith, Thomas	J. watchmaker	Hope street	
Smith, William	Nailmaker	9, Devonshire street	
Smith, John	Bookseller	Liversage street	
Smith, John	Watchmaker	Traffic street	
Simpson, Henry	Hairdresser	London road	
Sproat, Robert	Tea dealer	Wilmot street	B
Smithard, Edward	Pork butcher	Corn market	
Smithard, Henry	Draper	Corn market	
Slater, William	Builder	Canal street	
Soresby, Wm. Charles	General carrier	Morledge	B
Spalton, William	Grocer and tea dealer	34, Corn market	
Stanley, Thomas	Gardener	25, Bridge gate	B
Stevenson, George	Shoemaker	10, Bold lane	
Stevens, Henry	Bricklayer	Back Sitwell street	
Stain, Thomas	Moulder	Chester place	
Sutton, Joseph	Labourer	6, Ford street	
Stretton, Thomas	Weaver	11, Bath street	
Taft, Henry	Higgler	Lodge lane	
Talbot, Joseph	Clerk at Station	Park street	B
Tait, John	Bricklayer	William street	
Taylor, William	Keeps a mangle	Leonard street	
Taylor, Thomas	Pipe maker	42, Nun's street	B
Taylor, James	Framework-knitter	4, St. Alkmund's ch. yd.	
Tateham, Joseph	Groom	Court, Darley lane	
Thompson, Samuel	Butcher	New market	
Thompson, Samuel	Builder	Liversage street	
Thompson, Joseph	Builder	52, Devonshire street	
Tomlinson, George	Joiner	Erasmus street	
Tompson, George	Carpenter and builder	Exeter street,	B
Topham, Thomas, jun.	Butcher	Old shambles	B
Tomlinson, Robert	Dyer	Court, St. Mary's gate	
Turner, John	Gentleman	Ashbourn road	
Twigg, Samuel	Works at Darley mill	Bath street	
Twigg, John	Joiner	Court, Darley lane	
Tyrell, Abijah	Framework knitter	Bridge gate	
Unwin, Edward	Butcher	Sadler gate	
Vadey, Louis	Music & dancing master	Baker's lane	
Ward, John Dewick	Tailor	Traffic street	
Walker, Richard	Weaver	Bridge street	
Webster, Isaac	Brewer	Upper Brook street	
Wetton, John	Blacksmith	Willow row	B
Whitaker, William	Porter at station	Hope street	B
Whittaker, John	China painter	26, Erasmus street	
Whitaker, John	Draper	Friar gate	
White, George	Book-keeper	George street	
White, Jeremiah	Hosier	7, Devonshire street	
Whitworth, Joseph	Joiner	Siddals lane	B
Wheeldon, Thomas	Moulder	Parker street	
Wigley, William	Dyer	Court 3, Brook street	
Whitehurst, James	Tin plate worker	Court Wright street	
Wilders, John & Henry	Burton ale & porter stores	Full street	

Winfield, Thomas	Baker	Market place	B
Woodward, William	Engineer	28, Burton road	B
Woolhouse, John	Plaster manufacturer	Duke street	B
Woolley, John	Tailor	34, Leonard street	B
Whitworth, John	Shoemaker	6, Eagle street	
Whitworth, Joseph	Joiner	Siddals lane	
Wright, Joseph	Gilder and painter	79, Devonshire street	
Wright, William		Ashbourn road	
Yeomans, John	Framework-knitter	Burton road	B
Yeomans, William	Draper	Green lane hill	

Country Butchers who regularly attend the Market and have shops in the New Market.

Ashby, Thomas, Spondon.
Banks, George, Findern.
Belfield, Thomas, Duffield.
Brown, Thos., Horsley Woodhouse.
Butler, William, Belper.
Cockayne, William, Quorndon.
Coxon, Thomas, Hollington.
Eley, John, Horsley Woodhouse.
Goodwin, Samuel, Chaddesden.
Haynes, Henry, Duffield.
Haynes, Thomas, Willington.
Hicking, Samuel, Twyford.
Horrobin, William, Willington.
Humpstone, Joseph, Breadsall.
Holbrook, Henry, Spondon.
Holmes, James, Alvaston.
Johnson, William, Mercaston.
Leedham, William, Shirley.
Maddox, Joseph, Mackworth.
Meakin, George, Repton.
Mills, Robert, West Hallam.
Morley, Robert, Ednaston.
Peat, Joseph, Duffield.
Peat, John, Spondon.
Potter, Joseph, Smalley.
Plackett, William, Breaston.
Potter, Thomas, Stanley.
Poyser, Joseph, Langley.
Roome, Samuel, Mickleover.
Simpson, James, Kirk Ireton.
Smith, Samuel, Quorndon.
Thorpe, William, Repton.
Thorpe, Henry, Repton.
Thompson, Samuel, Langley.
Turner, John, Duffield.
Watson, John, Mickleover.
Watson, Benjamin, Findern.
Winterton, William, Borrowash.

PRIVATE ESTABLISHMENT for the INSANE, Green-Hill House, Derby, by MR. FISHER, Surgeon.

This House and Premises are delightfully situated on rising ground, the apartments are numerous, spacious, and lofty. The lawn, pleasure-grounds and gardens, are three acres in extent, surrounded by a wall, and entirely secluded from public view ; into which are introduced various objects of attraction, thus admitting space, and holding out inducements to take air, exercise, and healthful recreations, and avoiding as much as possible every appearance of restraint. An extensive library and other sources of amusement have also been provided, to divert the mind, and employ the time of the Patient as may be most agreeable and beneficial.

Mr. and Mrs. Fisher have dedicated more than twenty years to the care and management of the Insane, and have witnessed the happy results arising from a proper system of medical treatment, combined with kindness and attention ; and as they reside in the house, under no circumstance will patients be left exclusively to the care of servants.

A limited number of both sexes are received on terms not exorbitant, but such as will insure the respectability of persons admitted, and the most liberal treatment.

J. WATSON, INDIA BEER, PORTER, and PALE ALE BREWER, Derby, will be happy to supply a small quantity of his *Pale Ales* and *Table Beer* upon trial, which will be found the same in every respect as *home-brewed ;* and of his *Porter,* which he is happy to say is generally approved of.

Reference can be given, if required, to many of the most respectable Families in Derby and its Vicinity.

J. W. also humbly solicits attention to his *India Beer,* which he can with confidence recommend. Testimony as to its uniform excellence of quality for six successive years in India can be produced.

HENRY HUNT, ALE and PORTER BREWER, Navigation Brewery, Nottingham Road, Derby. Ale and Porter stores, St. Peter's street, opposite the Nag's Head Inn. Dealer in CIDER.

H. CANTRILL, Nag's Head Commercial Inn, St. Peter's Street, Derby. Excellent Beds, Good Stabling, Wines and Spirits of superior quality. Post Horses, Gigs, Flies, &c.

FRANCIS HUGGINS, Royal Hotel and Commercial Inn, Derby. Private Rooms for Families, Superior Stabling, and Lock-up Coach Houses. Wines and Spirits of the finest quality.

HOLME and SMITHARD, WATCH and CLOCK MAKERS, JEWELLERS and SILVERSMITHS, Corn market, Derby, and Repton. Wedding Rings, &c.

M. EGGLESTON, 33, Iron-gate, CONFECTIONARY and ITALIAN WAREHOUSE. Jellies, Bride Cakes, and Funeral Biscuits on the shortest notice. Sole agent for Captain Pidding's Howqua's Teas, as supplied to the Royal Table. British Wines in every variety.

COX, HADEN, and POUNTAIN, IMPORTERS of WINES and BRANDY, 16, Market Place, Derby.

EDWARDS and HALLAM, WINE and SPIRIT MERCHANTS, Derby. N.B. Perry, Cider, and London and Dublin Brown Stout.

BENJAMIN POUNTAIN, Wholesale and Retail WINE and SPIRIT MERCHANT, No. 6, Rotten Row, Derby. N.B. Cider, Perry, London and Dublin Brown Stout.

JONES'S COMMERCIAL LODGING and BOARDING HOUSE, No. 12, Union Passage, New Street, Birmingham.

GEORGE HUNT, BRAZIER, IRON and TIN PLATE worker, Market Place, Chesterfield.

JOHN WHITEHURST, No. 1, Cherry Street, Derby, Manufacturer of Church, Turret, House, and Cottage CLOCKS, Alarums, &c. Gold and Silver Watches of every description; self-illuminating and extinguishing Dials for Church Clocks and other Public Buildings; Sun, Wind, and Miners' Dials; Weather Vanes; Spirit Levels, Barometers, Thermometers, Philosophical and Mathematical Instruments; improved Roasting Jacks, with single or double spits; Church, Turret, and Dinner Bells, or old Bells recast; Brass founder, &c. Original manufacturer of the Watchman's Clock, for protection from fire or robbery; these Clocks are extensively used in London, Manchester, Liverpool, and most of the large towns in the United Kingdom, in the establishments of many noblemen and gentlemen, in Mills, Manufactories, Wharfs, Docks, &c. The nightly watchmen of the town of Derby are regulated by these clocks, upon the Derby system, particulars of which may be known at the Manufactory.

Wm. Hunt Navigation Brewery, Derby.

THE BRUNSWICK Railway and Commercial INN, Railway Terrace, adjoining the Station, Derby.

H. LANE begs to inform the Travelling Community, that this House is now open for the reception of Families and Commercial Gentlemen. The Charges are framed with a view to the strictest economy consistent with the best quality of articles.

H. L. begs to assure all those who may favour him with their patronage, that the Wines and Spirits have been selected with the greatest care, and that no expense has been spared to render every appointment in this Establishment both comfortable and convenient to its Visitors.

TERMS:

Breakfast, plain, ...	1s. 6d.
Ditto, with Meat, &c., ...	2s. 0d.
Dinner, ...	2s. 0d.
Tea, ...	1s. 6d.
Supper, ...	1s. 6d.
Beds, ...	2s. 0d.
Wine, ...	5s. per Bottle.

No fees are allowed to be taken by any servant in the Establishment. Horses and Carriages let to Hire.—H. LANE, Proprietor.

TRYPHENA TAYLOR, TIGER Commercial INN, Corn Market, Derby.—Excellent accommodation for Commercial Gentlemen, good stabling, Lock-up Gig-houses.—Flies & Gigs at the shortest notice.—Railway and Coach Office.—The Omnibus calls to and from the Station, on the arrival and departure of every Train.

THOMAS WARD, SARACEN'S HEAD, COMMERCIAL INN, St. James's Lane, Corn Market, Derby, respectfully informs his Friends that this old established Inn, from its central situation, affords excellent accommodation to commercial gentlemen, farmers, and dealers attending the market, and to carriers. An Ordinary every Friday. Fine old wines and spirits, of the best quality, good beds and stabling.

THOMAS GREEN, QUEEN'S HEAD INN, Victoria Street, opposite the Royal Hotel, Derby, most respectfully informs his Friends and the Public, that he has made it his study to fit up and furnish the above Inn, so as to afford every accommodation and comfort to all who may honour him with their custom. The house being situate in the very centre of the Borough, will be found exceedingly convenient to strangers, commercial gentlemen, agriculturists, and carriers who attend the markets.

WILLIAM SWAIN, Hosier and Haberdasher, No. 14, Rotten Row, Derby, returns his sincere thanks to his Friends and the Public, for the encouragement he received during many years' residence in Grove street, and begs most respectfully to inform them, that he has removed to a more central situation, where he hopes to receive that patronage and continued support it will ever be his study to merit.

GEORGE B. GREAVES, DISPENSING CHEMIST, Ashbourn. Physicians' Prescriptions carefully prepared. Horse and Cattle Medicines. Patent Medicine Warehouse. Family Medicines. Wax, Composition, Kensington, and Spermaceti Candles.

THOMAS CRUMP, ENGINEER, PLUMBER, &c., Friar-gate, opposite George-street, Derby, Manufacturer of Water Closets, Force Pumps, Fire Engines, Improved Portable Fire and Garden Engines, Copper-rivetted Leather Hose Pipes, Suction Pipes, Leather Buckets, and every apparatus connected with Fire Engines.

Gas Fittings of every description ; Plans furnished and works erected complete. Hot Houses, Shops, Dwellings, and Factories heated with Hot Water, or Steam. Brass Work, Smiths' Work, and Machinery in general.

Fire Engines constructed on Improved Principles, calculated for Gentlemen's Residences, Parishes, or Towns, constructed to discharge water in two streams at the same time, the carriages fitted up with strong springs, driving seat, and equipped complete for travelling. Improved Portable Fire Engines of various sizes, adapted also for Garden Engines, simple in their construction, can be kept filled with water, and ready at all times for action in cases of fire. These Engines occupy but trifling space, and can readily be carried up stairs, or removed at pleasure ; the capabilities of these Engines, and advantages possessed from their portability, contribute to render them of great utility for Shipping, Warehouses, Workshops, Private Houses, &c.

Agent for Vaucher's Patent Woven Hose, without seam, for conveying Fluids under pressure any distance, when applied to Force Pumps, Fire and Garden Engines, Breweries, &c.

JOHN HARRISON, ENGINEER, Nos. 46 and 47, Bridge-gate, and $1\frac{1}{2}$, Mansfield-road, Derby. Manufacturer of all kinds of wrought iron Steam Engine Boilers, for high or low pressure. Gas and Water Tanks, Gas-Holders. Iron Pleasure and Canal Boats, Barges, Flats and Ferry-boats. Wrought iron Roofs for Buildings, Brewing and Bleaching Pans, or any kind of vessel that can be manufactured of wrought iron.

Gas Works erected complete. All kinds of Cooking Apparatus for large or small establishments, adapted to any situation, for roasting, steaming, stewing, &c. Water and Smoke Jacks. Baths constructed of copper, enamelled, and other materials, and heated on the most approved principles : also every other description of Bath furnished. Hot Air Stoves, Cockles, Hot Water and Steam Apparatus for heating dwelling houses, churches, chapels, manufactories, and forcing houses of every description.

Weighing Machines for road carriages, or small ones for warehouses. Freezing Machines, to freeze from one to three ice creams at the same time. Washing and Squeezing Machines. Apparatus for cutting chaff for cattle, to be worked by horse power or otherwise. Steam Boilers and Cisterns, with all their apparatus for cooking food for cattle. Thrashing Machines, to be worked by hand, capable of thrashing one hundred strikes per day (and they can also be applied to horse power.) Vineries, Peach Houses, Pine Pits, Conservatories, and Green Houses, erected of iron, and heated on the best known principle. All kinds of elastic wire and permanent Fencing, Hurdles, &c. Inventor and manufacturer of the Iron Easy Chair.

Bell-hanging, and every kind of Lock and Smiths' work.

JOHN KNIGHT, Fox and Hounds Inn, Syston. Excellent Wines and Liquors. Comfortable Conveyances to and from the Railway Station.

CUFF'S MIDLAND HOTEL, Railway Station, Derby. The following charges include attendance of every description.

	s.	d.
Bed	4	0
Double Bed, 1s. extra		
Servant's Bed	2	0
Sitting Room	5	0
„ „ Fire	2	0
„ „ „ Evening only	1	0
Wax Lights	2	0
Bed Room Fire	1	0
Breakfast, with Cold Meat or Eggs	2	6
„ with Chops and Eggs	3	0
Tea, with Meat and Eggs	3	0
Plain Tea ...	2	0

Dinners and Wines as per Bill of Fare
Post Horses and Carriages.

GEORGE MOSELEY, Royal Oak Commercial Inn, Bakewell. Well-aired Beds, Good Stabling, and Lock-up Coach Houses. Wines and Spirits of the best quality. N.B. To Let out to hire, Post and Saddle Horses, Phætons, &c. &c.

H. GOODALL, Dispensing CHEMIST and DRUGGIST, (Formerly Apprentice with Mr. STEVENSON, Corn Market,) respectfully announces to the Nobility, Gentry, and the Inhabitants of Derby and its vicinity, that he has taken a House and Shop, in St. Peter's Street, opposite the Nag's Head Inn, for the dispensing of Physicians' and Surgeons' Prescriptions, Family Recipes, and for the sale of pure Drugs and Chemicals.

H. G. having had considerable experience in some of the first houses in London and Manchester, he trusts he will be able to give satisfaction to those who may favour him with their support ; in Dispensing, so much depending on the purity of the Medicines used, he begs to add it is his intention to keep only drugs of the finest quality, and having had opportunities of making himself acquainted with the best Markets, his charges will at all times be found as reasonable as any other house in the trade.

H. G. begs to inform his friends and the public generally, that by his personal management and superintendence of every department, and by strict attention and accuracy, he hopes to merit their preference and support. N. B. Dealer in genuine Patent Medicines, Lemonade and Soda Water, Horse and Cattle Medicines, Fish and other Sauces, with every other article connected with the trade.

JOSEPH BALDWIN George Hotel, Commercial Inn and Posting House, Burton-upon-Trent. J. B. begs to express his gratitude for all favours received, and to assure Commercial Gentlemen and his friends generally, that no exertion shall be spared to secure their patronage and support.

Neat Post Chaises, Hearses, and Mourning Coaches. Lock-up Coach Houses. Conveyance to and from the Railway Station. Excellent well-aired Beds. Genuine Wines and Spirits.

ROWLAND AMCOTTS BREAREY, AGENT to the Church of England INSURANCE OFFICE. Land and General Agency Offices, Corn Market, Derby.

GREGORY'S Foreign Lace, Fancy Drapery, Embroidered Muslins, Scotch, British, and French Muslins, Stays, Gloves, Baby Linen, Scotch Ginghams, and Haberdashery. MRS. GREGORY, Milliner. Opposite the Royal Hotel, Derby.

TERMS of Mr. HUDSON'S ESTABLISHMENT, Full-street, Derby. Board and Instruction, including English Grammar, History, Geography, and use of the Globes, the Mathematics, Natural and Experimental Philosophy. For young Gentlemen,

Under Fourteen years of Age	30 guineas.
Above Fourteen years of Age	35 guineas.
The Latin and Greek Classics, each	2 guineas.
Washing	2 guineas.
ENTRANCE TO THE HOUSE	1 guinea.
Day Boarders	15 guineas.
Day Pupils, for an English Education	8 guineas.

French, Italian, Music, and Drawing, on the Terms of the respective Masters.

Each Boarder is required to bring a pair of Sheets, six Towels, and a Silver Spoon, which will be returned when he leaves the School. Three months' notice, or a quarter's board, is required previously to the removal of a Pupil.

AT the ACADEMY, Osmaston-street, Derby, conducted by J. MATHER, young Gentlemen are liberally boarded, kindly treated, and carefully instructed in the English, Latin, and Greek Languages ; Penmanship, Stenography, Arithmetic, Book-keeping, Mensuration, Practical Surveying, Algebra, Euclid's Elements, with Geometrical Deductions, and Trigonometry ; Ancient and Modern History, Geography, with the Construction of Maps, and the Use of the Globes. Pupils intended for the Medical Profession are prepared in Celsus and Gregory's Conspectus.

TERMS :—23 guineas per annum. Day Pupils, 6 guineas per annum. French, Drawing, Music, and Dancing, on the Terms of the respective Masters.

A select Juvenile Library is attached to the School ; and great attention is paid to Composition, and to the exciting of a taste for Literature. A quarter's notice will be expected previous to the removal of a Pupil. Parents desirous of realizing for their Children a polite and useful Education on reasonable terms, will find this School particularly eligible ; there being no extra charges, except for Washing and Stationery.

JOHN ALLEN, George Commercial Inn and Posting House, Alfreton. Superior Old Wines and Foreign Spirits. Neat Chaises, Single and Double Flies.

G. BULLOCK, Manufacturer and Importer of TOBACCO, SNUFF, and CIGARS, Full Street and Irongate, Derby. Fancy Pipes and Snuff-Boxes of all descriptions. Wholesale and Retail.

JOHN CHATTERTON, Jun., PLUMBER and GLAZIER, Wholesale and Retail, Manufacturer of Sheet Lead, Patent Lead and Tin Pipe, and Authorized Gas Fitter, Morledge, Derby. N.B. Agent to the Manchester and Liverpool Plate Glass Company.

FRANCIS WAIT, ENGLISH AND FOREIGN TIMBER MERCHANT, City Road, near St. Mary's Bridge, Derby, most respectfully returns his sincere thanks to his numerous Friends in the Building and Turning department, and the trade generally, for the very liberal encouragement and extensive patronage he has experienced since his commencement in business; and begs to assure them that no exertion shall be wanting on his part, to execute the orders he may be entrusted with, punctually, and on such terms as will ensure their future favours. The following, and every other article in the trade may be had on the shortest notice, at his Raff Yard, City Road, on the lowest terms. Ceiling and Tiling Laths, Dry Boards, Planks, and Scantlings. Mahogany, Oak, Pine, Birch, red and white Deal, Bed Rounds, Coffin Boards, Pipe Staves, &c. Nails, and every other article in the trade. Fire Bricks, Newcastle Tiles and Quarries, Reeds, &c., wholesale and retail. N.B. Timber cut to order at his Circular Saw Mills, City Road.

ROE and OAKLEY, TIMBER MERCHANTS, Siddals-lane Circular and Reciprocating SAW MILLS, English and Foreign Timber and Raff Yards, Derby, most respectfully return their sincere acknowledgements to their numerous Friends in the Building and Turning department, and the Trade generally, for the very liberal encouragement and extensive patronage they have experienced since they commenced business, and beg to assure them that no attention or exertion on their part shall be wanting to execute all orders they may be entrusted with, punctually, and on such Terms as will ensure their future favours. They beg to assure their Friends that they keep an extensive Stock of the following and every other article in the Building Trade, of the best quality.

Planks and Scantlings, Dry Boards, Veneers, Ceiling and Tiling Laths, Mahogany, Oak, Pine, Birch, Red and White Deal. Pipe Staves, Bed Rounds, Coffin Boards, and Ladder Poles. Newcastle Tiles, Blue and Red Paving Squares or Quarries, Barn Floor and Fire Bricks, Floor Plaster, Roman Cement, Reeds, Holland Rushes, Nails, &c. &c.

N.B. Timber Cut to Order on the shortest notice.

WILLIAM JACKSON, FISHMONGER and Dealer in GAME, WILD FOWL, &c., 45, Full-street, Derby, respectfully informs his Friends and the Public that he has removed to the above commodious premises, in the centre of the Borough, where he carries on the Fish Trade in all its branches, and having fitted up his Oyster Rooms suitable for the accommodation of Gentlemen and Strangers visiting the Town, solicits a continuance of that patronage and support already so liberally bestowed upon him; assuring the Nobility, Gentry, Clergy, and the Public that no exertion in his power shall be wanting to merit it. The best Native Oysters, in barrels, and by the score, with Fish, viz. Cod, Skate, Haddock, and Salmon, fresh from London every morning during the season. Supplied to Families in the Town and County on the shortest notice, and at the lowest prices.

REPTON SCHOOL. Head Master, Rev. THOMAS WILLIAM-SON PEILE, M.A., late Fellow of Trinity College, Cambridge. First Usher, Rev. WILLIAM STODDART, M.A. Second Usher, JAMES GARVEY, Esq., B.A.

The Head Master's Terms for Boarders are 50 guineas; Tuition, Classical and Mathematical, 10 guineas; extra expenses, 5 guineas per annum.

The Under Masters also receive a limited number of Boarders; Terms (including all expenses) 50 guineas per annum.

TERMS of Mr. T. RUSSELL'S BOARDING SCHOOL, Mackworth, near Derby.

Board, and Instruction in the Mathematics, History, Geography, Astronomy, Composition, Book-keeping, Land-surveying, Penmanship, Stenography, &c., 26 guineas per annum.

For Pupils under 12 years of age, 24 guineas per annum.

Board, and Instruction in the Latin, Greek, and French Languages, in addition to the above named branches of education, 28 guineas per ann.

For Pupils under 12 years of age, 26 guineas per annum.

Washing, 2 guineas per ann. Music and Drawing on the usual terms.

Every Pupil to bring a pair of Sheets, three Napkins, and a Silver Spoon; which will be returned on his leaving School. A quarter's notice to be given previously to the removal of a Pupil. Bills to be paid half-yearly.

SAMUEL WATSON, CHEMIST and DRUGGIST, St. Peter's Street, Derby.

S. WATSON, WINE and SPIRIT MERCHANT, respectfully invites the attention of the Public to his extensive Stock of Prime Old Port. S. W. has always on hand a choice Assortment of Prime Sherry, Bucellas, Moselle, Champagne, Burgundy, Claret, and Hock. Also a regular supply of Bottled Ale, India Beer, London and Dublin Bottled Porter.

N.B. London and Dublin Porter in Kilderkins.

JOSIAH NORTON, Professor of Music and Piano-forte tuner, No. 1, Darwin Terrace, Derby.

ANN and WILLIAM GREAVES, Rutland Arms Family Hotel, and Commercial Inn, General Post and Coach Office, and Bridge House Family Board and Lodging House, Bakewell, have the privilege of granting tickets to Fishing Parties, and have excellent accommodation for Families attending the Baths, or for Tourists or Gentlemen visiting this interesting town, for the purpose of enjoying the Scenery and Fishery of the beautiful Trout Streams of the neighbourhood, viz. the Wye, the Lathkill, and the Derwent. Chatsworth—the Palace of the Peak—the seat of His Grace the Duke of Devonshire, being within 3½ miles, and Haddon Hall, the most perfect ancient Baronial residence in the kingdom, the property of His Grace the Duke of Rutland, being within 1½ mile of this superior Inn.

J. SMITH, PLUMBER, GLAZIER, PAINTER, &c., Belper, Imitator of Woods and Marbles, Gilding and Bronzing. Paper hanging neatly executed on the shortest notice. Water Closets, Beer Engines, &c.

NOTTINGHAM BATHING ESTABLISHMENT, 34, Pelham Street. Mrs. Myers returns her most grateful acknowledgements for the kind support bestowed on her late husband, and earnestly solicits a continuance of the same; assuring her Friends and the Public, that no exertions on her part shall be wanting to render the Baths in all respects worthy their patronage.

M. Myers begs to state that she has made accommodation for the use of the celebrated Mineral Waters of Bareges; also Chlorine, Iodine and Artificial Sea Water Baths, with an extensive range of Cold, Warm, Tepid, Vapour, Shower, and Swimming Baths, together with Portable Vapour Baths, and an Upright Bath.

The Cold and Tepid Baths are open from Six in the Morning; and the Hot and Mineral Baths from Seven in the Morning until Eight in the Evening.

The Swimming Bath is open (for Ladies only) from Eleven to One o'clock each Day: its temperature is at present 80° Farenheit.

The terms of Subscription for a Year, or for any number of times, or for a Single Bath, may be known on application at the Establishment.

☞ Distilled Water may be had at the Establishment, at $1\frac{1}{2}d.$ per Gallon. Also Gold and Silver Fish.

SAMUEL KIRK, ANIMAL PAINTER, Derby, under the immediate Patronage of the Right Hon. Earl Howe, and Painter to the Farmer's Magazine, most respectfully informs the Nobility, Gentry, and the Public, that he has commenced in the above department of the arts, and, in soliciting encouragement, begs to assure them it will be his study to produce faithful likenesses, and to finish the paintings in a style that will give satisfaction to those who may honour him with their patronage.

MR. FREAKE, AUCTIONEER, APPRAISER, and GENERAL AGENT, 11, St. Mary's Gate, Derby.

Mr. Freake continues to supply those Friends who may honour him with their commands, with Piano Fortes, of the best manufacture and brilliancy of tone, on the lowest terms possible; having made arrangements with a professional Gentleman in the Metropolis for his personal selection.

WILLIAM HUTCHINSON, takes this opportunity of returning thanks to his numerous friends, for the support they have afforded him since his engagement with Allsopp and Sons, Brewers, Burton-on-Trent, as their Agent for Derby and its vicinity, and wishes to inform them and the public in general, that he is appointed Agent to Mr. Hunt, Navigation Brewery, Nottingham Road, Derby, and that nothing shall be wanted on his part to insure a continuance of their patronage.

W. H. has constantly on hand a large supply of mild, strong, and East India pale Ales, likewise London Porter, in casks and bottles, at his vaults, St. Peter's street, opposite the Nag's Head Inn.

Residence, Old Uttoxeter Road, Derby.

EDMUND WRIGHT, AUCTIONEER, APPRAISER, and GENERAL AGENT, St. Helen's Street, Derby.

SAMUEL EYRE, Auctioneer, Valuer, Accountant, and Agent, No. 15, Full-street, Derby. Collections of Pictures described and arranged.

DERBY PLATE GLASS WAREHOUSE, Wholesale, Retail, and for Exportation. The Glass is delivered here at the same price to the Public, and with the same allowances to the Trade, as at the Manufactory, saving thereby the risk and expense of Carriage. No charge for packing cases. Silvering done when required.

Life Policies effected on the lowest terms consistent with mutual security.

AGENT TO THE

YORK AND LONDON LIFE ASSURANCE COMPANY,

Chairman, George Frederick Young, Esq.; and to

THE IMPERIAL FIRE ASSURANCE COMPANY;

Subscribed and Invested Capital,

ONE MILLION FIVE HUNDRED THOUSAND POUNDS.

Chairman, Robert Barclay, Esq.

ROBERT WALLIS, GREEN MAN, and BLACK'S HEAD, Royal Family Hotel, Commercial Inn, Posting House, and General Coach Office, Ashbourn. The Defiance, London and Manchester Coach, to and from this Inn daily. Hearse and Mourning Coaches on the shortest notice.

R. W. having purchased, enlarged, and much improved the above old established and commodious Inn, assures those Families and Commercial Gentlemen who have for many years honoured him with their patronage, that it will be his constant study to do every thing in his power to accommodate his Friends, and to promote their comfort and convenience.

This Inn is within three miles of Dovedale.

S. JOHNSON, jun., SADLER, Cap, Whip, Collar, and Harness Maker, Ashbourn.

RICHARD FRITH, George and Dragon Commercial Inn, Market-place, Ashbourn.

JOHN MIERS, Wheat Sheaf Commercial Inn, Church-street, Ashbourn, takes this opportunity of expressing his gratitude to the Commercial gentlemen, and his Friends generally, for the distinguished patronage received since he entered on the above establishment, and begs to assure them that no exertion shall be wanting on his part to merit their future favours, or afford every possible comfort to his Friends who may give his house the preference.

Flies and Post Horses on the shortest notice. The Omnibus leaves the Wheat Sheaf Inn, on Mondays, Wednesdays, and Fridays, at $\frac{1}{2}$ past 8 o'clock in the morning for Derby, to meet the Trains to London, and all parts; and leaves the Nag's Head Inn, St. Peter's-street, Derby, for Ashbourn, at 4 o'clock in the afternoon of the same days.

WILLIAM BURN, ANGEL COMMERCIAL INN and POSTING House, Alfreton. Every accommodation for Families and Commercial Gentlemen.

M R. IRONMONGER, AUCTIONEER, APPRAISER, and Agent, No. 1, Friar gate, Derby.

W JEPSON, CHATSWORTH INN, EDENSOR, begs to inform Visitors to Chatsworth and the Romantic Scenery of Derbyshire, that the Inn is an easy walk from Chatsworth House. The numerous walks about the Domain, which are very extensive and beautiful, are open to the Public; parties wishing to remain a few days at the Inn, w:: .neet with every possible attention.

Chatsworth Inn, Edensor, is now conducted by Mr. and Mrs. Jepson, who have in the most spirited ma:.ner, beautified, refitted and furnished the Inn, (the only one in this Division of the County, belonging to His Grace the Duke of Devonshire,) with a view to the comfort and superior accommodation of the numerous Visitors who repair to witness the beauties this splendid Mansion, justly termed the Palace of the Peak, affords to Strangers. This Inn, is adjoining the Park Lodge, within a few minutes' walk of Chatsworth, surrounded by Grounds of extraordinary beauty, and close to the newly erected and interesting Village of Edensor, which contains sixty-one houses, and every house is characterised as being different to each other, and no Village in England can boast of such a varied style of Architecture.

Chatsworth Inn, is 14 miles from Buxton, 10 from Matlock, 10 from Chesterfield, 14 from Sheffield, and 18 from Castleton.

J and R. DYCHE, WHOLESALE and RETAIL, ENGLISH and FOREIGN TIMBER MERCHANTS, Cockpit Hill, Derby, most respectfully return their acknowledgements to their numerous Friends in the Building and Turning department, and the Trade generally, for the distinguished preference and extensive patronage they have experienced since their commencement in Business; and in soliciting a continuance of the same, beg to assure them, that no exertion shall be wanting on their part, to execute all orders they may be entrusted with, punctually and on such terms as will ensure their future favours. The following, and every other article in the trade, may be had on the shortest notice at their Raff Yard, Cockpit Hill, on the lowest terms, viz. Wheelwright's Ware, Laths, Dry Boards, Planks and Scantlings, Mahogany, Veneers, Oak, Pine, Birch, Deal Planks, Bed Rounds, Coffin Boards, Pipe Staves, Nails, Fire Bricks, Newcastle Tiles, Quarries, Barn Floor Bricks, Water Pipes, Coping for Walls, Chimney Pipes, Floor Plaster, Fine Plaster, Roman Cement, Bilston Grind Stones, Reeds, and Holland Rushes. N. B.—Timber cut to order.

N EWBOLD and EGAN, Surveyors, Accountants, and Law Stationers, Estate and General Agents, No. 14, Iron gate, (opposite Messrs. Crompton and Co's. Bank,) Derby. Office for Patents of Invention and Registration of Designs.

ANDREW SMITH, MILLWRIGHT, Engineer, &c., (late of Belper), begs to inform the Millowners, Manufacturers, &c., of Derby and its vicinity, that he has recently removed his establishment, to his newly erected manufactory, in Liversage-street, London-road, Derby. He is conscious of possessing the means of giving entire satisfaction in all branches connected with Mill or Engine Work; and begs to assure those who may intrust him with any portion of their work, of meeting with all that a thorough practical knowledge, connected with the strictest punctuality and despatch, can supply. During the period that A. S. has been engaged in business, he has supplied Planing Machines, Slide Lathes, and Machinery of the finest descriptions, requiring the utmost nicety in fitting, to most parts of this Kingdom, as also to the Colonies, and to the United States.

Inventor and Manufacturer of the Patent Locomotive Cylinder Printing Machine, which requires no more time in preparation and obtaining register, than the common Press, while the speed is of the double action, from 25 to 31 impressions per minute, and of the single action, from 14 to 17. The Demy and Double Crown single action Machines, may be worked by two hands. Prices at the manufactory (exclusive of roller moulds) single action, Demy, £60. Double Crown, £80. Double Royal, £110. Largest sized News, £170. Double action Demy, £80. Double Crown, £130. Double Royal, £150. Largest sized news, £190. Terms of payment, Bill at three months, on delivery.

N. B. Liversage-street is within a very short distance of the Railway Station.

GEORGE BODEN, Ladies' and Gentlemen's Fashionable HAIR CUTTER and DRESSER, Ornamental Hair Manufacturer, Peruke Maker, and Perfumer. Dressing Rooms, 43, Corn-market, Derby. Late Assistant to Mr. MORGAN, St. James's-street, London, Hair Dresser and Perfumer to the Royal Family.

G. B., impressed with a deep sense of gratitude to the Nobility, Gentry, and the Inhabitants of the Borough and County of Derby, for the very flattering encouragement he has experienced since his commencement in business, begs most respectfully to assure them, that it will be his constant study to give satisfaction to those Families who favour him with their commands. G. B. has constantly on sale a well selected Stock of Foreign and British Perfumery, Hair, Tooth, and Nail Brushes, Tortoise-shell, Ivory, and Horn Combs, and a great variety of Miscellaneous Articles connected with the Trade. Sole Agent for Devereux's Macassar Pommade, and the Italian Hair Dye, which latter article will change Red or Grey Hair to a beautiful Brown or Black on one application.

MR. H. W. JAMES, Agard street, Derby, PROFESSOR of MUSIC, Teacher of Piano Forte, Guitar, Violin, Violoncello, &c. Terms, One Guinea per quarter. Piano Fortes procured from any of the London Houses, and guaranteed at the Maker's prices.

MRS. BARROW, the old established Flying-Horse Inn and Posting House, Kegworth, Leicestershire. Mrs. B. begs most respectfully to return her sincere acknowledgements for the extensive support her late husband experienced from a numerous and long tried circle of Friends, for a series of years, and assures them that the same attention and exertion will be observed to afford her guests every accommodation and comfort that such an establishment is capable of.

DR. CAMM'S MEDICINES.—UNRIVALLED REMEDIES for SCROFULA and SCORBUTIC ERUPTIONS.

MR. EARP, Osmaston Street, Derby, the Proprietor, respectfully solicits the attention of the Public to the INIMITABLE EFFICACY of CAMM'S MEDICINES for Scrofulous and Scorbutic Diseases; being convinced, from experience deduced from numerous facts, that they are the only remedies known that will effect a cure in the most desperate and inveterate cases.

The Medicines adapted for Fits, Indigestion, Bilious, Liver, Stomach, and Spinal complaints, are equally efficacious. The beneficial results of the above valuable Medicines may be seen by reference to the Case Papers, containing forty-two extraordinary cures within a few miles of the towns of Derby, Nottingham, Leicester, Loughborough, Chesterfield, Mansfield, &c., which may be had *gratis*, by applying to MR. EARP, Osmaston Street, Derby, or any of his Agents, personally, or by letter, post paid.

HANNAH SPENCER, NEW INN, King Street, Derby, FAMILY and COMMERCIAL INN, and Posting House, begs to inform the Public, that her house affords superior accommodation to Families, and Commercial Gentlemen, whether travelling by Railway, Coach, or in their own Carriages. Neat Post Chaises, good horses, and steady drivers are in constant readiness to forward Families. Coaches to Manchester, Nottingham, Newcastle, &c., every day. The Omnibus runs from her house to meet every train. Good Stabling, Lock-up Coach-houses, and every convenience attached to her establishment.

ROSE TAVERN, BRIDLESMITH GATE, NOTTINGHAM, William Tinley, most respectfully returns his grateful thanks to his numerous Friends, who honoured him with their support during his residence at the Fox and Hounds, Carter Gate, and begs to assure them that they will find every accommodation and attention at his new establishment in Bridlesmith Gate. This house being in the most central part of Nottingham, is particularly convenient for Railway and other travellers.

N. B. Travellers by Coach or Railway during the night, will at all times be admitted.

MILTON'S HEAD COMMERCIAL INN, Milton Street, Nottingham. Edward Smith, begs most respectfully to return his grateful acknowledgements to his numerous Friends, Commercial Gentlemen, and the Public generally, for the support he has received since he entered on the above establishment, and assures them that no exertion shall be wanting to secure a continuation of their favours, and in every way add to the comfort of his guests. Well aired Beds, excellent Stabling, loose Boxes, Gigs, Flys, &c., always ready.

SAMUEL SEVERN, PEACOCK INN, Rowsley. This commodious and excellent Inn, is delightfully situate, near the Junction of the Derwent and the Wye, and is much resorted to by Families and fishing parties, being distant from Stanton Woodhouse, 1 mile, Haddon Hall, 1½ mile, Bakewell, 3 miles, Chatsworth, 3 miles, Matlock Bath, 7 miles, Buxton, 15 miles, Chesterfield, 13 miles, Sheffield, 17 miles, and Derby, 23 miles.

JAMES SUTHERLAND, CARVER and GILDER, Picture-frame, Looking-glass, Barometer, and Thermometer manufacturer; Spectacles made and repaired; Superior self-registering and pine bed Thermometers may be had at his establishment, 20, Friar Gate, Derby, residence, York Street.

SAMUEL CHARLES ROBERTS, HATTER and FURRIER, Market Head, Market Place, Derby, returns thanks to the Inhabitants of Derby and its Vicinity for the liberal encouragement he has received since his commencement in business, and begs to assure his Friends and the Public, that it will be his constant study to have a supply of Hats, Furs, and every article connected with the trade, of the best quality, and at such prices as will insure their future favours. Furs altered and cleaned on the premises.

WILLIAM HASLAM, St. Helen's, street, Derby, (near the New Inn,) BELL HANGER and SMITH, successor to the late Mr. Hartley. Brass Plates, Rods, Tubes, and Castings to order; Chandeliers, Lamps, old brass works of all descriptions, repaired, re-polished, lackered, or bronzed. Smoke Jacks, wrought iron Gates, Palisades, &c. Balustrades for staircases, in wrought iron and brass. Locks and Keys, and all descriptions of fastenings for doors and windows, and alarm bells of various constructions. Bell hanging on the most approved principles, with the recent improvements, and a variety of original inventions.

G. PERFECT, CARVER, GILDER, AND MODELLER, No. 10, Osmaston Street, Derby, respectfully announces to the Nobility, Gentry, and Inhabitants of Derby and the Vicinity, that he has commenced Business in the above situation; and presumes, from his long and recent experience at the Seat of His Grace the Duke of Devonshire, at Chatsworth, and from the very extensive Collection of Gothic, Grecian, French, and Elizabethan designs in his possession, procured from the principal establishments in London, to be enabled to execute all Orders with which he may be favoured, to the entire satisfaction of those who honour him with their patronage.

Orders in the following Departments completed in the most masterly style: Candelabras, Girandoles, Glass Frames of every description, Tables, Tripods, Pedestals and Brackets, Pole and Hand Screens, Window, and Bed Cornices. Old Carving repaired so as not to be perceptible, however ancient. Noblemen's Arms and Crests carved, giving spirited expression to the animals. Ornamental Models for Founders, in Wood, Clay, or Plaster. Cabinet Carving executed in the clearest manner, with attention to Beauty in Design. Old Pictures cleaned, re-lined, and restored to their pristine state. Glasses re-silvered. Picture, Pier, Chimney and Mirror Frames, Ornamental Signs, &c. Noblemen and Gentlemen's Houses attended.

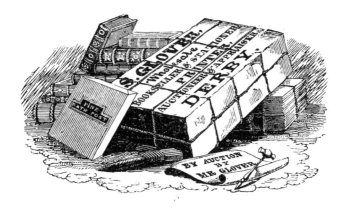

STEPHEN GLOVER and SON, AUCTIONEERS, VALUERS, and ACCOUNTANTS; HOUSE, LAND, and COMMISSION AGENTS; LANDLORDS' BAILIFFS and MESSENGERS IN BANKRUPTCIES; DEVONSHIRE STREET, LONDON STREET, DERBY—respectfully inform the Nobility, Gentry, Clergy, Professional Gentlemen, and other Inhabitants of the Town and County of Derby, and the Midland Counties generally, that they have lately removed to the above residence, where they will be happy to receive the communications of their friends, with reference to employment in the above professions.

In soliciting the continued favors of Public Patronage, S. G. trusts that the experience of twenty-five years, with a particular attention to the nature and value of property, in the several counties of Derby, Nottingham, Leicester, and Stafford, will be deemed an essential qualification, that will not fail to have its due weight as a recommendation to their confidence.

S. G. and Son, pledge themselves to a strict and assiduous attention to the interests of their employers, and to an invariable punctuality in the immediate settlement of all accounts. Bankruptcy accounts arranged with care and accuracy; Valuations of property, for the purpose of administration, on the Probate of Wills; and Appraisements between Incoming and Outgoing Tenants, undertaken on moderate terms. Libraries of Books catalogued, and Collections of Pictures, Prints, and Works of Art, described and arranged.

S. G. and Son, will undertake Sales of every description, on moderate terms.

When the amount of Sale,

Is under £10.   charge, 10 shillings.   £25 to £50.   20 shillings.
    £15.   ditto   15 ditto.   £50. to £75.   30 shillings.
        £75. to £100. ... and upwards   £2.

or five per cent. on all Household Furniture and Stock in Trade Sales, including Advertisements, Catalogues, &c. Farming Stock Sales, charged according to the amount.

Printed by Henry Mozley and Sons, Derby.